100 MATHS LESSONS

YEAR 4

Published by Scholastic Ltd,
Villiers House,
Clarendon Avenue,
Leamington Spa,
Warwickshire CV32 5PR

456789   23456789

SERIES CONSULTANT
Ann Montague-Smith

AUTHORS
John Davis and Sonia Tibbatts

EDITOR
Angela Dewsbury

ASSISTANT EDITOR
Roanne Davis

SERIES DESIGNER
Joy White

DESIGNER
Rachel Warner

COVER PHOTOGRAPH
Kim Oliver

ILLUSTRATIONS
Ray and Corinne Burrows

British Library Cataloguing-in-Publication Data
A catalogue record for this book is available from the British Library.

ISBN 0-439-01696-7

ACKNOWLEDGEMENTS

The publishers wish to thank:
The National Numeracy Strategy: Framework for Teaching Mathematics © Crown Copyright. Reproduced under the terms of HMSO Guidance Note 8.
Galt Educational and NES Arnold Educational Supplies for kindly loaning the equipment used on the front cover.

CONTENTS

INTRODUCTION

ABOUT THE SERIES

100 Maths Lessons is a series of year-specific teachers' resource books, for Reception to Year 6, that provide a core of support material for the teaching of mathematics within the National Numeracy Strategy *Framework for Teaching Mathematics* (March 1999) and within the structure of the 'dedicated mathematics lesson'. Each book offers three terms of medium-term planning grids, teaching objectives and lesson plans. At least 100 maths lessons are given in detail, with outlines for all the others needed to provide support for teachers for a whole year of maths teaching. Photocopiable activity pages and resources are included to support the learning. Regular assessment is built into the structure of the book, with assessment activity pages which can be kept as evidence of attainment.
The activities in this book are designed to encourage pupils to develop mental strategies, to use paper and pencil methods appropriately, and to use and apply their mathematics in realistic tasks. There is a strong emphasis upon encouraging pupils to explain to each other the mathematics that they have used, the strategies that they employed and to compare these with each other to determine efficiency of method.

Each *100 Maths Lessons* book provides support across all the mathematics topics and learning objectives specified for a particular year group. However, the pages of the books have been hole-punched and perforated, so that they can be removed and placed in teachers' own resource files, where they can be interleaved with complementary materials from the school's existing schemes.

These books are intended as a support for the dedicated mathematics lesson for the school mathematics coordinator, teachers and trainee teachers. The series of books can be used as the basis of planning, teaching and assessment for the whole school, from Reception to Year 6. These resources can be adapted for use by the whole school for single-aged classes, mixed-age classes, single- and mixed-ability groups, and for team planning across a year or a key stage. There is sufficient detail in the differentiated group activities within the 100 lesson plans to help classroom assistants working with a group

The content of these activities is appropriate for and adaptable to the requirements of Primary 4-5 in Scottish schools. In schools which decide not to adopt the National Numeracy Strategy, choose activities to match your planning.

During Year Four, there will be the opportunity initially to revise some of the topics from Year Three especially during the oral and mental starter section of the lesson. But the aim now, as children enter the next phase of Key Stage Two, is to cover new ground and lay the foundations for what follows in Years Five and Six. The progression during Years Four, Five and Six is clearly laid out in the double page spread format of the Framework document.

There are also a number of significant changes to the key objectives for Year Four. Children need, for example, to be able to work with larger numbers and have the ability to round off. More formal methods of recording, especially in addition and subtraction where numbers are set in columns, are introduced. Fractions are condidered in more detail, particularly the question of equivalence, and decimal numbers are introduced.

USING THIS BOOK

THE MATERIALS

This book provides at least 100 maths lesson plans for Year 4, and further activity ideas to support all other dedicated maths lessons required during the year. Each maths lesson plan contains ideas for developing pupils' oral and mental maths, a detailed explanation of the main part of the lesson, ideas for differentiated activities, and suggestions for the plenary session. The book follows the Year 4 planning grid given in the National Numeracy Strategy *Framework for Teaching Mathematics* and so for each teaching section, whether one, two or three units of work, there are some detailed lessons plans and objectives and outline content for the other lessons. These materials should be regarded as a core for developing your own personalised folder for the year. More detail on planning and managing all aspects of the National Numeracy Strategy can be found in the *Framework for Teaching Mathematics*.

ADAPTING AND PERSONALISING THE MATERIALS

The materials are based upon the 'Teaching programme and planning grid' for Year 4 from the National Numeracy Strategy *Framework for Teaching Mathematics*. What follows is a suggested method of using this book to its full potential, but bear in mind that you may need to make adjustments to these materials in order to meet the learning needs of the pupils in your class.
● Separate the pages of the book and place them in an A4 ring binder.
● Check that the activities are of a suitable level for your pupils and agree with colleagues who teach higher and lower years that the entry level is a good match. If not, you can use materials from the **100 Maths Lessons** books for the previous or subsequent year, as appropriate.
● Add your own favourite materials in the relevant places.
● If your school uses a published scheme, insert suitable teacher and pupil resources into your file to supplement these materials.

PREPARING A SCHEME OF WORK

All schools are required to write detailed schemes of work, and this series has been designed to facilitate this process. The termly 'Planning grids' given in these books (see page 18 for example) are provided at the beginning of the work for each term and list all the objectives.

ORGANISATION

The organisation chart outlines the key objectives for each part of each maths lesson and can be used as a weekly plan.

LESSON PLANS

After the Organisation chart comes a short section detailing which lessons are shown as full lesson plans and which are extensions of what has already been taught in a previous lesson. Some of these will be shown in grid form.

	LEARNING OUTCOMES	ORAL AND MENTAL STARTER	MAIN TEACHING ACTIVITY	PLENARY
LESSON 1	● Read and write whole numbers to at least 10 000 in figures and words, and know what each digit represents. ● Partition numbers into thousands, hundreds, tens and ones.	PUT UP THE NUMBER: hold up the digits to show a given number.	UP TO 9999: Write three- and four-digit numbers in figures and words and show on an abacus.	Partition numbers into thousands, hundreds, tens and ones.
LESSON 2	● Add/subtract 1, 10, 100 or 1000 to/from any integer, and count on or back in tens, hundreds or thousands from any whole number up to 10 000. ● **Round any positive integer less than 1000 to the nearest 10 or 100.**	STEPPING STONES: Adding 1, 10 and 100 to two- and three-digit numbers.	ADD AND SUBTRACT: Adding and subtracting ones, tens and hundreds then thousands to a number and rounding to the nearest ten, then hundred.	Check adding on and rounding.
LESSON 3	● Record readings from scales to a suitable degree of accuracy. ● **Round any positive integer less than 1000 to the nearest 10 or 100.**	TOP TWENTY: Quick-fire questions on addition and subtraction using numbers up to 20.	READING SCALES: Choose suitable measuring devices. Round to the nearest 1 and 100 and mark distances/amounts on scales.	Check answers and add on 1, 10 or 1000 to each measure.

ORAL AND MENTAL SKILLS Read and write whole numbers to at least 1000 in figures and words. Count on in repeated steps of 1, 10 or 100. (Y3 revision.) Consolidate knowing by heart addition and subtraction facts for all numbers to 20.

DETAILED LESSON PLANS

Each detailed lesson plan is written to the following headings:

Resources

Provides a list of what you need for that lesson.

Preparation

Outlines any advance preparation needed before the lesson begins, such as making resources or photocopying worksheets.

Learning outcomes

These are based upon the objectives in the 'Teaching programme: Year 4' from the *Framework for Teaching Mathematics*. All the objectives are covered at least once in this book. Key objectives for Year 4 are highlighted in bold. as they are in the *Framework for Teaching Mathematics*. If a lesson does not cover an objective in its entirety, then only the portion which is intended to be covered is listed in the 'Learning outcomes' (or any of the grids provided). The specific objectives for the **Oral and mental starter** and **Main teaching activity** are listed separately.

Vocabulary

The National Numeracy Strategy *Mathematical Vocabulary* booklet has been used to provide the vocabulary lists. New or specific vocabulary to be used during the lesson is listed. Use this vocabulary with the whole class so that all the children have a chance to hear it and begin to understand it. Encourage pupils to use the vocabulary orally, when asking or answering questions, so that they develop understanding of its mathematical meaning. Flashcards can be made by printing out onto card the appropriate sections from the CD-ROM which should have accompanied your school's copy of the Framework for Teaching Mathematics.

Oral and mental starter

This is designed to occupy the first 5–10 minutes of the lesson, but the duration of the work is not critical. This section contains activity suggestions to develop oral and mental work to be used with the whole class and is based on what has already been taught. Some suggestions for differentiated questioning are included to show how all the children can benefit. The detail in the lesson plan will help you to: provide a variety of sequentially planned, short oral and mental activities throughout the week; use a good range of open and closed questions; encourage all children to take part; target differentiated questions to individuals, pairs or small groups.

Main teaching activity

This sets out what to do in the whole class teaching session and should last for about 30 minutes. In some lessons much of the time will be spent in whole-class, interactive teaching. In others, the whole-class session will be shorter, with differentiated activities for groups, pairs or individuals. The detailed lesson plan will help you to organise this part of the lesson appropriately.

Differentiation

This section suggests activities for differentiated group, paired or individual work, for the more able and less able children within the class. These activities will take the form of reinforcement, enrichment or extension, and many will provide challenges to encourage pupils to use and apply their mathematics.

Plenary

This session is a chance to bring the children together again for a 10-minute whole-class session. This offers opportunities to: assess pupils' progress; summarise key facts learned; compare strategies used; make links to other topics and to plan for the next topic. Groups of children will often be expected to present the results of their work to the rest of the class as a point of discussion.

EXTENSION LESSON PLANS

These provide activities which extend those already covered. They are less detailed, as they are based on one of the previous lessons for that week.

OUTLINE LESSON PLANS

These contain brief descriptions, as grids, of further lessons. These extend the scope of the book to give sufficient material for a year's work. Since they develop work already introduced, there are no vocabulary suggestions as the same range of words will be needed as in the previous, related lesson(s). For example:

RESOURCES	Range of different measuring instruments including weighing devices, measuring cylinders, measuring sticks, tapes and rulers; photocopiable page 22 ('Reading scales'), one of each per child.
LEARNING OUTCOMES	**ORAL AND MENTAL STARTER** ● Consolidate knowing by heart addition and subtraction facts for all numbers to 20. **MAIN TEACHING ACTIVITY** ● Record readings from scales to a suitable degree of accuracy. ● **Round any positive integer less than 1000 to the nearest 10 or 100.**
ORAL AND MENTAL STARTER	TOP TWENTY: Ask quick-fire questions on addition and subtraction using numbers up to 20, eg *Make pairs of numbers that total 14* (0 + 14, 1 + 13, 2 + 12 and so on). Then start at 14 for subtraction eg 14 − 3 = 11; 14 − 4 = 10; 14 − 5 = 9 and so on. Then look at patterns of similar calculations, eg *9 + 0, 8 + 1 and 7 + 2 total 9, what about 5 + 4? If 12 − 0 = 12, 12 − 1 = 11 and 12 − 2 = 10, what does 12 − 5 equal?*
MAIN TEACHING ACTIVITY	READING SCALES: Display the various measuring instruments and explain to the children that they are to choose suitable measuring equipment for given tasks, eg *What would you use to measure your pencil? The length of the room? A full teapot? A bag of potatoes?* Revise the work done in Lesson 2 on rounding to the nearest 10 and 100. The children then work individually to complete 'Reading scales' (photocopiable page 22).
DIFFERENTIATION	More able: provide scales without numbers for the children to label. Less able: provide blank number lines and count the number of steps between different hundreds numbers.
PLENARY	Review answers to the photocopiable activity and then consider adding on 1 or 10 or 1000 to each measure. *If the measures were 1000 times bigger, would you still use the same measuring devices and units?*

USING THE LESSON PLANS

The plans are designed so that you can work through them in order, if you wish. However, you may prefer to choose the lessons that are appropriate for your pupils, and combine these with your favourite activities from other sources. By placing the pages of this book into a ring binder you can easily incorporate your own supplementary materials.

WEEKLY PLANNING

If you wish to use the ready-prepared plans, follow the Organisation chart which appears at the beginning of each unit or block of units of work. If you prefer to plan your week using some of the lesson plans in the book, and some activities you have chosen yourself, then make some photocopies of the blank 'Weekly planning chart' on page 12 of this book. These can then be completed with details of all the activities which you intend to use, those chosen from this book and those which you have taken from other sources.

MIXED-AGE CLASSES

If you have a mixed-age class, you will probably need to use the materials from more than one book in this series. You will find the blank 'Weekly planning chart' on page 12 a useful planning tool, as you can combine planning from two books onto this chart.

BLANK WEEKLY PLANNING CHART

Make photocopies of this chart, complete a copy on a weekly basis and keep this in your planning file. You may prefer to enlarge the chart to A3.

Week beginning: *7 September*

Learning objectives for oral and mental skills	Read and write whole numbers to at least 1000 in figures and words Count on in repeated steps of 1, 10 or 100 Consolidate knowing by heart + and − facts for all numbers to 20. Use patterns of similar calculations			
	Oral and mental starter	Main teaching activity	Differentiation	Plenary	Resources
M o n d a y	Read and write whole numbers to 1000 in figures and words	Read and write whole numbers to 10 000 and know what eaach digit represents	Less able: use equipment More able: rearrange four digit numbers	Look at expanded and compact numbers	Number fans, abacus diagrams, multibase equipment, digit cards

CLASSROOM ORGANISATION

WHOLE-CLASS TEACHING

During a whole-class session it is important that all the children can see you, the board or flip chart and their table top. In many classrooms space is at a premium, so it is worth spending time considering how the furniture can best be arranged. If you have a carpeted area for whole-class work, think about whether the lesson you are planning to teach would work well with the children seated on the carpet, or whether they would be better placed at their tables, especially if you want them to manipulate apparatus, such as interlocking cubes, or they need to spread out numeral cards in front of them.

GROUP WORK

Again, it is important that the pupils sit so that they can see you, and the board or flip chart if necessary. While they are working in groups you may wish to ask whole-class questions, or remind pupils of how much time is left to complete their task, so eye contact will help to ensure that everyone is listening.

WORKING WITH OTHER ADULTS

If you have classroom helpers, brief them before the lesson starts on which group you would like them to work with; the purpose of the task; the vocabulary they should be helping to develop; and give some examples of the type of questions they should be asking. Check that all the resources needed are available or, if not, that the helper knows where to find them. You may want to ask a classroom helper to work with just one or two pupils; perhaps they are finding the work difficult, or have been absent and this is an opportunity to catch up on missed work. Whatever the reason, always ensure that the helper is well briefed before the lesson starts, and allow a few minutes after the lesson has finished to discuss any specific observations which the helper would like to make.

CHILDREN WITH SPECIAL EDUCATIONAL NEEDS

Include children with special educational needs in the whole class work. If you have a classroom helper or support assistant ask him or her to sit beside the pupils with special needs to provide support. This could include repeating the questions quietly or encouraging them to use individual resources (such as counting apparatus, a number line or number cards) to find the answer. During differentiated questioning, ensure that some questions are specifically focused for these pupils and encourage them to answer appropriately.

To assist all pupils in reading new vocabulary, and to help those with reading difficulties, make flash cards for the specific mathematics vocabulary, or prepare a word bank which will be used in a series of lessons and encourage the children to read these.

Pupils who are partially sighted or deaf will need to sit close to you, so take this into account when considering the layout of the classroom for maths lessons. Those with emotional or behaviour difficulties will benefit from the structure and routines of the daily maths lesson and, where possible, from the support of a helper who can encourage on-task working. For children who are learning English as an additional language, speak more slowly, repeat instructions, and provide visual clues on worksheets or puzzle cards. For pupils who have an Individual Education Plan (IEP) which includes mathematics as an area of learning difficulty, use other books from this series to find activities of an appropriate level which can be linked to the work of the rest of the class.

HOMEWORK

For Year 4 pupils it is recommended that homework is given regularly on a weekly basis. This could be activities designed to be shared with a parent or carer, or could include independent work such as time-constrained exercises, mental calculation practices or puzzles. A homework diary, which is completed by home and school, is a useful tool for logging what the homework is and how the pupil responded. Use a range of different types of tasks for homework:

● suitable shared homework activities may be found in *IMPACT Maths Homework* (Key Stage Two titles) and *Mental Maths Homework for 8/9 year olds* all written by The IMPACT Project (published by Scholastic).

● suggest a game to be played at home which will help the children to learn some number facts and times tables and shape recognition.

● suggest activities that children can become involved with at home to develop their use of mathematics in real life situations. For example, shopping, cooking, use of time-tables, TV programmes and various measuring activities,

RESOURCES

PHOTOCOPIABLE SHEETS

These support the work and can be resource sheets or activity sheets. They are marked with the photocopiable symbol. Some sheets have many applications and are used throughout the book: these appear at the end of this 'Introduction' on pages 14–16. Others can be found at the end of the relevant unit(s).

Resource sheets

These include blank number lines, 1–100 squares and times tables squares. It is a good idea to make enough of these at the start of the year for each pupil to have at least one (set). You may wish to ask for help from parents and friends of the school to make these resources. Photocopy the pages onto card, then cut out and laminate as required.

For the numeral cards, consider whether to use different coloured card so that the children can put them away more easily, using the colour of their set as an aid. These cards can be stored in small polythene bags or tins so that the pupils can keep their resources in their own desks or trays. Alternatively, store these with a rubber band around each set and give them out at the beginning of the lesson. Store class sets of number fans and similar resources in marked boxes.

Activity sheets

These are located at the end of the relevant unit(s) and relate to specific activities. They may offer practical activities, more traditional worksheets or games. Photocopy the pages onto A4 paper for the pupils, some activities may ask for an extra A3 enlargement for whole-class use.

CLASSROOM EQUIPMENT

All the equipment used in this book will normally be found within any primary school. The following list shows what will be needed on a regular basis. Alternatives are suggested where they would be equally appropriate instead. It is important that you create a mathematically-stimulating environment for the children, where they regularly encounter numbers. It is therefore assumed that all classrooms will have a variety of long class number lines with big numerals and a large 100 square. Ideally the children should be able to read all the numbers easily from their seats. A whiteboard or flip chart and marker pens, are essential for interactive whole-class sessions. You will also need:

● Cuisenaire or rods made from interlocking cubes, one colour for each 'number'.

● Counting stick: a metre length of wood or plastic, divided into ten alternately coloured sections. (Some metre rulers are marked in this way)

● Number tracks and lines for individual and whole class use including 0 to 100 in single digits, multiplication squares up to 10x10, 1-9 in single digits, zero to 100 in tens, zero to 1000 in hundreds and zero to 10 000 in thousands

● Measuring apparatus for length, mass and capacity and time including rulers, metre sticks and tape measures marked with centimetres and millimetres, bathroom scales, balance scales, kitchen scales and spring balances showing kilograms and grams in either 100s and 50s, measuring cylinders displaying millilitres in either 100s, 50s, analogue and digital clocks, timers and calendars.

● Shape apparatus: a comprehensive range of 2-D and 3-D shapes.
● Base 10 apparatus like Big Base and Multibase.
● Coins: a full range of up to date plastic coins including £2 pieces.
● Dice: a range of dice, including blanks both six sided and ten sided, number spinners.
● Roamer or PIP and access to a computer system.
● Dominoes, including fraction and decimal dominoes. These can either be made by the teacher or obtained from educational suppliers.
● Lots of interlocking cubes, such as Multilink and Unifix.
● Blank playing cards.
● A variety of commercially produced mathematical games.
● Straws including plastic drinking straws and larger artstraws.

USING INFORMATION COMMUNICATIONS TECHNOLOGY

Make use of your favourite mathematical games software as a paired or small group activity. Some of the activities in this book use a programmable toy such as Roamer or PIP. Pupils can use data-handling software to prepare graphs as part of the activity.
Useful software programs include: *All About Shape and Space*; *Number Shark*; *Superlogo*; *Talking Write Away* (good for making word walls with mathematical vocabulary); *Information Workshop*; *Number Box*; *Maths Mania*; *Counter*.

PUBLICATIONS

Do use your favourite mathematical stories, poems and rhymes as well as the published material available in school The following Scholastic publications contain some useful ideas:

Oral and mental starter
Developing Mental Maths with 7–9/9–11 year olds

Homework
IMPACT Maths Homework (Key Stage Two)
Mental Maths Homework for 8/9 year olds
Quick Mental Maths for 8/9 year olds

Main teaching activity
Maths Focus Kit 3
Practising Mental Maths with 8/9 year olds
Quick Mental Maths for 8/9 year olds

Assessment
Maths Focus Kit 3
Scholastic Portfolio
Assessment: Maths KS2

ASSESSMENT

During the week at the end of each half term, an assessment period of two lessons is built into the planning. This gives you the opportunity to make medium-term assessments of the key objectives for Year 4, listed in the National Numeracy Strategy. The aim of these assessments is to:

● Find out what progress each pupil has made, what he or she knows, understands and can do, whether he or she can apply and use their mathematics in context, and whether he or she has any weaknesses.
● Give you information on which to base feedback to pupils and their parents or carers. It will also help you to plan work for the next few weeks.

ASSESSMENT ADVICE

This is placed just before the assessment activity photocopiable sheets. Here you will find information on the aspects of mathematics which are to be assessed; some assessment activities for oral and mental starters which can be used with the whole class, others which can be used with groups, pairs and individuals; and advice on using the photocopiable assessment tasks provided.

ASSESSMENT ACTIVITIES

These activities have been designed so that you can observe pupils at work, and ask questions. Explain the purpose of the activity to them before they begin, as this will help them to demonstrate to you the things that you want to observe, such as clear recording, discussion of which strategy they used, why they used it, and so on. Target small groups for a specific activity and period of time, and work with them, observing how individuals respond to the activity. You may find it useful to have a notebook handy to make informal notes on observations and discussions.

If you have a classroom helper, he or she can also be involved in the assessment process. Explain the purpose of the assessment, what to do, and what to look for.

After the lesson has finished make time to discuss observations and keep notes on individual pupils' achievements and weaknesses.

ASSESSMENT PHOTOCOPIABLE SHEETS

There are two photocopiable sheets for each half term assessment period. Each sheet has specific assessment criteria written at the bottom. Photocopy the pages for individual pupils to complete while you observe others undertaking the assessment activities. Mark the completed sheets, then give pupils feedback on their strengths, and set targets for improvement in their areas of weaknesses. The sheets can be kept in a portfolio as part of the evidence of the children's achievement.

CLASS ASSESSMENT RECORDING SHEET

This will be found on page 13. It lists the key objectives for Year 4 from the National Numeracy Strategy *Framework for Teaching Mathematics*. Photocopy the sheet, enlarge it to A3, and record individuals' progress on it. By the end of the year, after six assessment sessions, you will have a wealth of assessment evidence to pass on to the children's next teacher.

Each half term assessment offers opportunities to assess all the relevant key objectives that have been taught. Some key objectives re-occur in later assessments. It is not necessary to assess every child each time. Use your assessment records to decide whether to re-assess a child or whether it is appropriate to leave a specific assessment objective which covers content that has already been learned and assessed.

Year Four comes at exactly the midway point between statutory Standard Assessment Tests (SATs) at Year Two and Year Six. Teachers in Year Four are therefore strongly advised to take advantage of the optional QCA tests in mathematics which are available for their age group as it will help to monitor and track the children's progress as they move through Key Stage Two. The QCA tests provide both age related standardised scores and levels that are based on nationally agreed data. Unlike half termly class tests that are narrowly focused to reflect teaching objectives for the half term, the QCA tests provide a broad picture of the child's understanding of a wide range of mathematical topics. They help teachers to highlight specific areas that need attention and reinforcement in the whole year group as well as pointing up strengths and weaknesses in individual children.

The preparation and administration of these QCA tests should be planned and organised in accordance with your school policy. They could be carried out during the two half-termly sessions that are allocated for assessment in the planning framework or they could be used within the dedicated maths lesson itself. Alternatively, they could take place at other times. The Framework does not allocate lessons for every single day of the school year. So, abandoning the National Numeracy Strategy for a week and using some of the 'spare days' for the tests is another possible option.

Weekly planning chart

(Photo-enlarge to A3.)

Week beginning:

Learning objectives
for oral and mental
skills:

	Oral and mental starter	Main teaching activity	Differentiation	Plenary	Resources
Monday					
Tuesday					
Wednesday					
Thursday					
Friday					

Year 4: Class assessment record sheet

Name	Use symbols correctly <, >, =	Round any positive integer less than 1000 to the nearest 10 or 100	Recognise simple fractions that are several parts of a whole, and mixed numbers; recognise the equivalence of simple fractions	Use known number facts and place value to add or subtract mentally, including any pair of two digit whole numbers	Carry out column addition and subtraction of two integers less than 1000, and column addition of more than two such integers	Know by heart facts for the 2,3,4,5 and 10 multiplication tables	Derive quickly division facts corresponding to the 2,3,4,5, and 10 multiplication tables	Find remainders after division	Know and use the relationship between familiar units of length, mass and capacity	Classify polygons, using criteria such as number of right angles, whether or not they are regular and symmetry properties	Choose and use appropriate number operations and ways of calculating (mental, mental with jottings, pencil and paper) to solve problems	Other
Key objectives: Year 4												

Photocopiable resource sheet A – Blank number lines

Photocopiable resource sheet B – 1–100 square

1	2	3	4	5	6	7	8	9	10
11	12	13	14	15	16	17	18	19	20
21	22	23	24	25	26	27	28	29	30
31	32	33	34	35	36	37	38	39	40
41	42	43	44	45	46	47	48	49	50
51	52	53	54	55	56	57	58	59	60
61	62	63	64	65	66	67	68	69	70
71	72	73	74	75	76	77	78	79	80
81	82	83	84	85	86	87	88	89	90
91	92	93	94	95	96	97	98	99	100

Photocopiable resource sheet C – Times tables square

X	2	3	4	5	6	7	8	9	10
2	4	6	8	10	12	14	16	18	20
3	6	9	12	15	18	21	24	27	30
4	8	12	16	20	24	28	32	36	40
5	10	15	20	25	30	35	40	45	50
6	12	18	24	30	36	42	48	54	60
7	14	21	28	35	42	49	56	63	70
8	16	24	32	40	48	56	64	72	80
9	18	27	36	45	54	63	72	81	90
10	20	30	40	50	60	70	80	90	100

TERM 1

Term 1 builds on Year 3 work, developing children's ability to read and write numbers up to 10000. It develops their knowledge of the value of each digit in four-digit numbers and of rounding to the nearest 10 or 100. Mental strategies for adding and subtracting are introduced and the children are taught multiplication and division. Through real-life situations, they make decisions about which number operations to use and how to check results. The children are taught how to choose suitable equipment and units for measuring, learn how to tell the time using analogue and digital locks and extend their knowledge of 2-D and 3-D shapes. Children use fraction notation, relating fractions to division, and find simple fractions of quantities. In data handling, they collect, classify and interpret information, especially using tally charts and pictograms.

ENLARGE THIS SHEET TO A3 AND USE IT AS YOUR MEDIUM-TERM PLANNING GRID.

TERM 1 PLANNING GRID

Oral and mental: Read and write whole numbers to at least 1000 in figures and words. Count on in repeated steps of 1, 10 or 100. (Y3 revision.) Consolidate knowing by heart addition and subtraction facts for all numbers to 20. Add three or four small numbers, finding pairs totalling 10, 9 or 11. Understand the principle of the commutative law as it applies to addition. Find a small difference by counting up. Partition into tens and units, adding the tens first. Partition numbers into hundreds, tens and ones (when adding). Add or subtract 10, then adjust. Identify near doubles, using known doubles. Use the relationship between addition and subtraction. Derive quickly all number pairs that total 100; all pairs of multiples of 50 with a total of 1000. Count on or back in repeated steps of 10, 100 or 1000.

UNIT	TOPIC	OBJECTIVES: CHILDREN WILL BE TAUGHT TO...
1	Place value, ordering and rounding Reading numbers from scales	● Read and write whole numbers to at least 10000 in figures and words, and know what each digit represents. Partition numbers into thousands, hundreds, tens and ones. ● Add/subtract 1, 10, 100 or 1000 to/from any integer, and count on or back in tens, hundreds or thousands from any whole number up to 10000. ● **Round any positive integer less than 1000 to the nearest 10 or 100.** ● Record readings from scales to a suitable degree of accuracy.
2–3	Understanding + and – Mental calculation strategies (+ and –) Pencil and paper procedures (+ and –) Money and 'real life' problems Making decisions and checking results	● Understand the principle of the commutative law as it applies or not to addition and subtraction. ● Count on or back in hundreds or thousands. ● Find a small difference by counting up. ● Partition numbers into hundreds, tens and ones. ● Add or subtract the nearest multiple of 10, then adjust. ● Identify near doubles, using known doubles. ● Consolidate knowing by heart addition and subtraction facts for all numbers to 20. ● Use addition and subtraction to solve word problems involving numbers in 'real life', including money. ● Recognise the outcome of sums or differences of pairs of odd/even numbers. ● Check with the inverse operation. ● Check the sum of several numbers by adding in reverse order.
4–6	Measures, including problems Shape and space Reasoning about shapes	● Derive quickly all number pairs that total 100, all pairs of multiples of 50 with a total of 1000. ● Use, read and write standard metric units of length including their abbreviations. ● **Know and use the relationships between familiar units of length.** ● Know the equivalent of one-half, one-quarter, three-quarters and one-tenth of 1km and 1m. Convert up to 1000 centimetres to metres, and vice versa. ● Suggest suitable units and measuring equipment to estimate or measure length. Record estimates and readings from scales to a suitable degree of accuracy. ● Calculate the perimeter and area of simple shapes, using counting methods and standard units. ● Use addition and subtraction to solve word problems, using one or more steps. ● Describe and visualise 3-D and 2-D shapes. ● **Classify polygons.** ● Make shapes and discuss properties. ● Make and investigate a general statement about familiar shapes by finding examples that satisfy it.
7	Assess and review	See the key objectives listed on the relevant pages.

Oral and mental: Add or subtract the nearest multiple of 10 then adjust. Derive quickly doubles of all whole numbers to 50 and the corresponding halves. **Know by heart multiplication facts for 2, 3, 4, 5 and 10 times tables. Derive quickly division facts corresponding to 2, 3, 4, 5 and 10 times tables.** Use known number facts and place value to multiply and divide integers by 10. Derive quickly all number pairs that total 100; all pairs of multiples of 50 with a total of 1000. Partition into hundreds, tens and ones, adding the hundreds first. Find a small difference by counting up. Consolidate knowing by heart addition and subtraction facts for all numbers to 20. Add three or four small numbers, finding pairs totalling 10. Identify near doubles, using known doubles.

UNIT	TOPIC	OBJECTIVES: CHILDREN WILL BE TAUGHT TO...
8	Properties of numbers Reasoning about numbers	● Derive quickly doubles of all whole numbers to 50 and their corresponding halves. ● **Know by heart multiplication facts for 3 and 4 times tables.** ● Recognise odd and even numbers up to 1000 and some of their properties. ● Make and investigate a general statement about familiar numbers.
9–10	Understanding × and ÷ Mental calculation strategies (× and ÷) Pencil and paper procedures (× and ÷) Money and 'real life' problems Making decisions and checking results	● Extend understanding of the operations of × and ÷ and their relationship to + and –. ● **Find remainders after division.** Round up or down after division, depending on the context. ● Use doubling or halving, starting from known facts. ● Use known number facts and place value to multiply and divide integers by 10. ● Approximate first. Use informal pencil and paper methods to support, record or explain multiplications and divisions. ● Use all four operations to solve word problems involving numbers in 'real life', including money. ● Check with an equivalent calculation.
11	Fractions and decimals	● Use fraction notation. **Recognise simple fractions that are several parts of a whole.** ● Begin to relate fractions to division and find simple fractions of numbers and quantities.
12	Understanding × and ÷ Mental calculation strategies (× and ÷) Pencil and paper procedures (× and ÷) Time, including problems	● Consolidate understanding of relationship between + and –. ● Check with the inverse operation. ● Partition into hundreds, tens and units (when subtracting). ● Use informal pencil and paper methods to support, record or explain additions/subtractions. ● Use, read and write the vocabulary related to time. Read the time from an analogue clock to the nearest minute and from a 12-hour digital clock.
13	Handling data	● Solve a problem by collecting, organising, representing and interpreting data in charts and pictograms.
14	Assess and review	See the key objectives listed on the relevant pages.

UNIT 1

ORGANISATION (3 LESSONS)

	LEARNING OUTCOMES	ORAL AND MENTAL STARTER	MAIN TEACHING ACTIVITY	PLENARY
LESSON 1	● Read and write whole numbers to at least 10000 in figures and words, and know what each digit represents. ● Partition numbers into thousands, hundreds, tens and ones.	PUT UP THE NUMBER: hold up the digits to show a given number.	UP TO 9999: Write three- and four-digit numbers in figures and words and show on an abacus.	Partition numbers into thousands, hundreds, tens and ones.
LESSON 2	● Add/subtract 1, 10, 100 or 1000 to/from any integer, and count on or back in tens, hundreds or thousands from any whole number up to 10000. ● **Round any positive integer less than 1000 to the nearest 10 or 100.**	STEPPING STONES: Adding 1, 10 and 100 to two- and three-digit numbers.	ADD AND SUBTRACT: Adding and subtracting ones, tens and hundreds then thousands to a number and rounding to the nearest ten, then hundred.	Check adding on and rounding.
LESSON 3	● Record readings from scales to a suitable degree of accuracy. ● **Round any positive integer less than 1000 to the nearest 10 or 100.**	TOP TWENTY: Quick-fire questions on addition and subtraction using numbers up to 20.	READING SCALES: Choose suitable measuring devices. Round to the nearest 1 and 100 and mark distances/amounts on scales.	Check answers and add on 1, 10 or 1000 to each measure.

ORAL AND MENTAL SKILLS Read and write whole numbers to at least 1000 in figures and words. Count on in repeated steps of 1, 10 or 100. (Y3 revision.) Consolidate knowing by heart addition and subtraction facts for all numbers to 20.

Lessons 1 and 2 are shown in full. Lesson 3 is an extension of what has already been taught so is shown in outline.

RESOURCES
Prepared number fans; blank abacus diagrams; Multibase equipment; packs of digit cards; pencils.

PREPARATION
Prepare ThHTU number fans, one per child, by attaching four sets of 0–9 number cards together at the corner with a paper fastener. Provide one per child. Draw several blank abacus diagrams on a piece of A4 paper then photocopy, one sheet per child: Provide one pack of 0–9 digit cards per pair and Multibase sets for some groups.

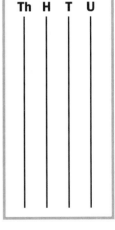

LEARNING OUTCOMES

ORAL AND MENTAL STARTER
● Read and write whole numbers to at least 1000 in figures and words.

MAIN TEACHING ACTIVITY:
● Read and write whole numbers to at least 10000 in figures and words, and know what each digit represents.
● Partition numbers into thousands, hundreds, tens and ones.

VOCABULARY

Units; ones; tens; hundreds; thousands; ten thousands; place value; abacus; digit; number; numeral.

ORAL AND MENTAL STARTER

PUT UP THE NUMBER: Say a number and ask the children to show this number by holding up the correct digits on their fans. Start with two-digit numbers, progress to three-digit numbers then four-digit numbers. Repeat, but this time write the numbers on the board.

MAIN TEACHING ACTIVITY

UP TO 9999: Write some three-digit numbers on the board. Ask the children to say the number in words so you can write this alongside. Repeat but starting from numbers written in words and they give you the digits. Repeat both tasks with four-digit numbers. Write up a wordbank of key words especially 'hundred' and 'thousand' and others from the tens family. In pairs, the children select three or four numeral cards from their set to create a number. They record this at the bottom of one of the abacus diagrams on their sheet. Once each diagram has a number underneath, they go back to the beginning of the sheet and take turns to either record the number in words or to draw in the beads to show it on the abacus. You may want to do one together as an example before the children begin.

DIFFERENTIATION

More able: select four cards to create a four-digit number, such as 5278, then rearrange the digits to make the largest number (8752), smallest number (2578), smallest odd number (2587), nearest number to 3000 (2875), and so on.
Less able: use mathematical equipment such as Multibase to show numbers before writing them in words.

PLENARY

Write a four-digit number on the board. Ask a child to come out and write the value of each digit, for example 4319 written as 4000 + 300 + 10 + 9. Try some more. Then write on the board 6000 + 700 + 90 + 5 for a child to write it as it is normally shown (6795). Try some more of these.

RESOURCES:

Photocopiable resource sheet A ('Blank number lines'); dice, one per pair; pencils; paper.

PREPARATION:

Prepare the number lines from resource sheet A to show the tens going up to 100, hundreds going up to 1000 and thousands going up to 10000, then copy one per child.

LEARNING OUTCOMES:

ORAL AND MENTAL STARTER
● Count on in repeated steps of 1, 10 or 100.

MAIN TEACHING ACTIVITY
● Add/subtract 1, 10, 100 or 1000 to/from any integer, and count on or back in tens, hundreds or thousands from any whole number up to 10000.
● **Round any positive integer less than 1000 to the nearest 10 or 100.**

VOCABULARY

Ones; tens; hundreds; thousands; add on; take away; before; after; count on; count back; more; less.

ORAL AND MENTAL STARTER

STEPPING STONES: Together count in tens from 0 to 100 then in hundreds from 0 to 1000. Then call out two-digit numbers for the children to add 1 to. Repeat for adding 10, then adding 100, eg 63 ⌒ 163. Repeat for three-digit numbers.

MAIN TEACHING ACTIVITY

ADD AND SUBTRACT: Revise adding and subtracting ones, tens and hundreds. *What is one more than 59, 427, 3569, 4399? What is one less than 80, 400, 5500, 6630 and 7000?*

Then ask them to tell you what is 10 or 100 more or less than the numbers given. *What will 1000 more or less be?* Count on from a start number in steps of 1000, eg 2356, 3356, 4356 and so on. Explain that when rounding a number to the nearest 10, if it is less than halfway it moves us back to the previous ten and if it is exactly halfway or more it moves us on to the next ten. So 34 is rounded to 30 while 78 is rounded to 80 and 55 is rounded to 60. The same applies to rounding to the nearest 100 with 50 as the halfway point. So 136 rounds to 100, 382 rounds to 400 and 350 rounds to 400. Work through similar examples. In pairs, the children take turns to roll the dice twice to make a two-digit number, to which they add one thousand, recording both numbers. After 10 goes they repeat for three-digit numbers. They then round the numbers to the nearest ten and then to the nearest hundred, recording their results on the same sheet.

DIFFERENTIATION

More able: set them word problems to check their understanding of using higher numbers, eg *What is ten more than three thousand two hundred and seventeen?*
Less able: use structured sequence questions for the children to fill in the number in the gap, eg 112 ... 114; 120 ... 140; 1234 ... 1434.

PLENARY

Invite children to write their recorded answers on the board. Ask questions to reinforce what they have done, eg *What is one more than 399? What is ten more than 795? What is one hundred more than 2916? What is one thousand more than 6594?* Also check their rounding, eg *Round to the nearest 10: 74, 139, 657, 1345; Round to the nearest 100: 274, 605, 1378, 4643.*

LESSON 3

RESOURCES	Range of different measuring instruments including weighing devices, measuring cylinders, measuring sticks, tapes and rulers; photocopiable page 22 ('Reading scales'), one of each per child.
LEARNING OUTCOMES	**ORAL AND MENTAL STARTER** ● Consolidate knowing by heart addition and subtraction facts for all numbers to 20. **MAIN TEACHING ACTIVITY** ● Record readings from scales to a suitable degree of accuracy. ● **Round any positive integer less than 1000 to the nearest 10 or 100.**
ORAL AND MENTAL STARTER	TOP TWENTY: Ask quick-fire questions on addition and subtraction using numbers up to 20, eg *Make pairs of numbers that total 14* (0 + 14, 1 + 13, 2 + 12 and so on). Then start at 14 for subtraction eg 14 − 3 = 11; 14 − 4 = 10; 14 − 5 = 9 and so on. Then look at patterns of similar calculations, eg *9 + 0, 8 + 1 and 7 + 2 total 9, what about 5 + 4? If 12 − 0 = 12, 12 − 1 = 11 and 12 − 2 = 10, what does 12 − 5 equal?*
MAIN TEACHING ACTIVITY	READING SCALES: Display the various measuring instruments and explain to the children that they are to choose suitable measuring equipment for given tasks, eg *What would you use to measure your pencil? The length of the room? A full teapot? A bag of potatoes?* Revise the work done in Lesson 2 on rounding to the nearest 10 and 100. The children then work individually to complete 'Reading scales' (photocopiable page 22).
DIFFERENTIATION	More able: provide scales without numbers for the children to label. Less able: provide blank number lines and count the number of steps between different hundreds numbers.
PLENARY	Review answers to the photocopiable activity and then consider adding on 1 or 10 or 1000 to each measure. *If the measures were 1000 times bigger, would you still use the same measuring devices and units?*

Reading scales

Write these answers on a separate piece of paper.

1. Length: Give the lengths shown to the nearest centimetre.

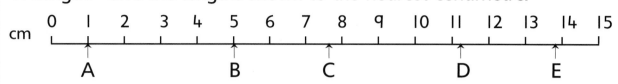

2. Mass: give the weights shown to the nearest 100g.

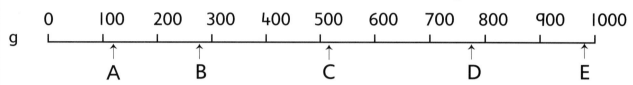

3. Capacity: Give the amounts shown to the nearest 100ml.

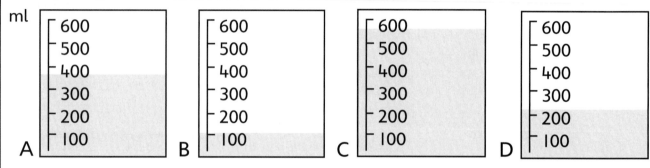

4. Length: Use an arrow to show these lengths on this ruler:

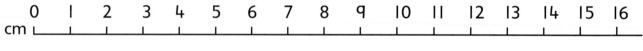

A. 12cm;   B. 3cm;   C. 7cm;   D. $5\frac{1}{2}$ cm;   E. $14\frac{1}{2}$ cm

5. Mass: Use an arrow to show these weights on the scale:

| 0 | 100 | 200 | 300 | 400 | 500 | 600 |

g

A. 200g;   B. 500g;   C. 100g;   D. 350g;   E. 50g

6. Draw a line to show these amounts on the measuring cylinder

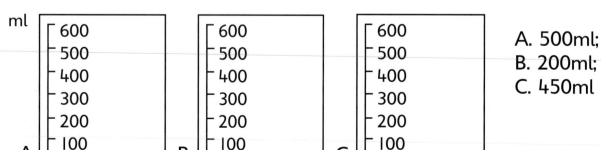

A. 500ml;
B. 200ml;
C. 450ml

ORGANISATION (10 LESSONS)

	LEARNING OUTCOMES	ORAL AND MENTAL STARTER	MAIN TEACHING ACTIVITY	PLENARY
LESSON 1	● Understand the principle (not the name) of the commutative law as it applies or not to addition and subtraction.	MAKE TEN: Use pairs that total 10, 9 or 11 to add three or four single-digit numbers.	IN ANY ORDER: Change the order of the two numbers in a sum and compare results.	Find missing numbers in addition questions.
LESSON 2	● Count on or back in hundreds or thousands.	THINK BIG: Add two numbers by starting from the biggest number and counting on.	COUNTING STEPS: Count on/back in 100s and then 1000s. Find the difference between two numbers.	Children invent their own counting sequences.
LESSON 3	● Find a small difference by counting up (through the next multiple of 10, 100 or 1000).	COUNT UP: Find the difference by counting up from the smaller to the larger number.	IT'S CLOSE: Find differences by counting up.	Use number fans to show correct differences.
LESSON 4	● Partition numbers into hundreds, tens and ones (when adding).	NUMBER SPLITS 1: Add two numbers by adding the tens first.	NUMBER SPLITS 2: Practise informal written methods of adding numbers.	Recap main points and check through examples.
LESSON 5	● Add or subtract the nearest multiple of 10, then adjust.	ADD 10 AND ADJUST: Add 9 or 11 by adding 10 then adjusting by 1.	CLEVER ONE: Add/subtract numbers close to multiples of ten.	Establish rules for adding certain numbers.
LESSON 6	● Identify near doubles, using known doubles.	NEAR DOUBLES: Use near doubles to add two two-digit numbers.	DOUBLE UP: Use near doubles to help with addition.	Use doubles to answer addition questions.
LESSON 7	● Consolidate knowing by heart addition and subtraction facts for all numbers to 20.	TOP TWENTY: Answer quick-fire questions on addition and subtraction using numbers up to 20.	UP TO 20: Make questions to practise addition and subtraction facts to 20.	Find the number from the clues.
LESSON 8	● Use addition and subtraction to solve word problems involving money using one or more steps.	TOP TWENTY: Answer quick-fire questions involving money.	MONEY PROBLEMS: Solve money problems written in words.	Work through children's own money word problems.
LESSON 9	● Recognise the outcome of sums or differences of pairs of odd/even numbers. ● Check with the inverse operation.	IN THE FAMILY: Correspond addition and subtraction facts.	ODDS AND EVENS: Investigate rules for adding/subtracting odd/even numbers and check with inverse operation.	Check on rules.
LESSON 10	● Use addition to solve word problems involving numbers in 'real life'. ● Check the sum of several numbers by adding in reverse order.	MAKE TEN: Add sets of numbers put in different orders.	CHANGE THE ORDER: Change the order of the numbers in addition sums to check the answers.	Test that different orders produce the same answers.

ORAL AND MENTAL SKILLS Add three or four small numbers, finding pairs totalling 10, or 9 or 11. Understand the principle (not the name) of the commutative law as it applies to addition. Find a small difference by counting up. Partition into tens and units, adding the tens first. Partition numbers into hundreds, tens and ones (when adding). Add or subtract 10, then adjust. Identify near doubles, using known doubles. Consolidate knowing by heart addition and subtraction facts for all numbers to 20. Use the relationship between addition and subtraction.

Lessons 1, 2, 4, 7, 8 and 9 are shown in full. Lessons 3, 5, 6 and 10 are an extension of what has already been taught so are shown in outline.

RESOURCES

Dice; pencils and paper.

PREPARATION

Pairs of children will need dice or digit cards to generate numbers.

LEARNING OUTCOMES

ORAL AND MENTAL STARTER:

● Add three or four small numbers, finding pairs totalling 10, or 9 or 11.

MAIN TEACHING ACTIVITY:

● Understand the principle (not the name) of the commutative law as it applies or not to addition and subtraction.

<table>
<tr><td>

VOCABULARY

More; add; sum; total; altogether; increase; plus (+); equals (=); take away; subtract; difference between; decrease; minus (−).

</td></tr>
</table>

ORAL AND MENTAL STARTER

MAKE TEN: Give the children sets of three single-digit numbers to add. Tell them to look for pairs that make 10, eg 3 + 5 + 7 becomes 3 + 7 + 5 to total 15. Then tell them to make 10 first to find the missing number in the next examples. Give examples of the type *If three numbers total 16 and two of them are 2 and 8 what is the third number?* Then give them examples where they must look for pairs of numbers that make 9 and 11 so they can add 10 to the total and adjust by 1, eg 3 + 9 + 8 = 9 + 10 + 1 = 20.

MAIN TEACHING ACTIVITY

IN ANY ORDER: Put simple examples up on the board to explain the commutative law – that addition can be done with the numbers in any order. Ask: *If 9 + 6 = 15, what does 6 + 9 add up to?* Extend to two-digit numbers. Tell the children that this does not work for subtraction. Work through examples on the board to demonstrate, eg 7 − 3 does not equal 3 − 7 and 64 − 39 does not equal 39 − 64. In pairs, children use a dice to generate two two-digit numbers for addition sums. They work out the answers on their own, and for each sum change the order of the two numbers and add them again, to produce the same answer. They then repeat for sums involving a three-digit and a two-digit number, and then for two three-digit numbers. They check each other's results.

DIFFERENTIATION:

More able: try sums with three numbers, changing positions to produce the same answer. Less able: ensure confidence with TU + TU before moving on to HTU + TU.

PLENARY

Put up examples on the board and get children to come out and complete them, eg 25 + 27 = ? + ?. Repeat for other examples with numbers missing, eg 73 + 19 = ? + 73 = ?. Then let children bring out their own examples to write on the board for others to complete. Discuss the strategies used to find the missing numbers.

RESOURCES

Resource sheet A ('Blank number lines'); number line questions; pencils and paper.

PREPARATION

On a blank sheet of A4, draw five number lines marked in 100s from 0 to 1000 and five lines marked in 1000s from 0 to 10000. Photocopy resource sheet A for the more able.

LEARNING OUTCOMES

ORAL AND MENTAL STARTER
● Understand the principle (not the name) of the commutative law as it applies to addition.

MAIN TEACHING ACTIVITY
● Count on or back in hundreds or thousands.

VOCABULARY
Ones; tens; hundreds; thousands; add on; take away; before; after; count on; count back; more; less.

ORAL AND MENTAL STARTER

THINK BIG: Tell the children to work out the addition questions you are going to ask them by putting the larger number first, eg 9 + 24 changes to '24 count on 9'. Now try examples involving tens, eg 20 + 35 becomes '35 and count on two tens'.

MAIN TEACHING ACTIVITY

COUNTING STEPS: Play 'Clap counter'. Start at zero and count on in hundreds. When you clap your hands the children count back from the number, reversing the direction of the count on each clap. Repeat with thousands, eg 0, 1000, 2000, 3000. Try different starting numbers, eg *Count on from 156 in hundreds; Count on from 2378 in thousands*. Then tell the children a start and finish number with the size of step and ask them to work out the difference, eg *Count from 649 to 249 in hundreds, clap each time a hundred is said. How many hundreds?* In pairs, they complete the number lines you have prepared.

DIFFERENTIATION

More able: use the blank number lines to devise questions for a partner to answer.
Less able: limit them to questions that stay with multiples of 100 or 1000.

PLENARY

Invite children to give the rest of the class two numbers andthe size of the steps to be taken between them. Then play 'Clap counter'.

LESSON 3

RESOURCES	Number fans prepared for Lesson 1, Unit 1, one per child; prepare about 15 find the difference questions that involve bridging 10s, 100s or 1000s, eg 58⁀63, 194⁀202, 2,995⁀3,001, and photocopy one per child; pencils.
LEARNING OUTCOMES	**ORAL AND MENTAL STARTER** ● Find a small difference by counting up. **MAIN TEACHING ACTIVITY** ● Find a small difference by counting up (through the next multiple of 10, 100 or 1000).
ORAL AND MENTAL STARTER	COUNT UP: Tell the children they are going to practise finding the difference between two numbers close together by counting up from the smaller to the larger. Start with some two-digit numbers, eg *Count up from 48 to 53*. Quickly move on to three-digit numbers, eg 197 and 201.
MAIN TEACHING ACTIVITY	IT'S CLOSE: Write pairs of three-digit numbers on the board and ask the children to count up with you to find the difference between each pair, eg 896 to 902 … 897, 898, 899, 900, 901, 902 so the difference is six. Then give other examples for the children to show the difference on their number fans. Repeat for four-digit numbers. Gradually increase the size of the difference. The children then work individually to complete the find the difference questions, counting up to work out the differences. They then write similar questions for their partner to answer.
DIFFERENTIATION	More able: try counting back instead; which of the two strategies do they find easiest? Less able: check they are confident counting up through the next multiple of 10 and 100 before moving on to 1000s.
PLENARY	Write up other pairs of numbers on the board and ask children to show on their number fans what the difference is. Check around the class to see how many are responding correctly. Ask the more able group to report back to the others on their attempts to count back instead.

RESOURCES

Sets of dominoes; squared paper.

PREPARATION

Remove the dominoes where the spots sum more than 9 and provide one set per pair.

LEARNING OUTCOMES

ORAL AND MENTAL STARTER
● Partition into tens and units, adding the tens first.

MAIN TEACHING ACTIVITY
● Partition numbers into hundreds, tens and ones (when adding).

VOCABULARY
Units; ones; tens; hundreds; thousands; partition; split; add; addition; more; plus; increase; sum; total; altogether.

ORAL AND MENTAL STARTER

NUMBER SPLITS 1: Practise adding two-digit numbers by adding the ten first, then the units before finally adding the two parts together, eg 25 + 37 split into 20 + 30 and 5 + 7 to make 50 + 12 = 62. Try other examples with the children providing just the answer, eg 36 + 45, 49 + 61, 52 + 77 and 63 + 29.

MAIN TEACHING ACTIVITY

NUMBER SPLITS 2: Extend the activity to introduce adding hundreds, tens and units in the same way. Start with HTU + TU. Put up some examples on the board and talk through the process, eg 115 + 23 would partition into 100 + (10 + 20) + (5 + 3) = 100 + 30 + 8 = 138. Try some examples of HTU + HTU, eg 147 + 216 partitions into (100 + 200) + (40 + 10) + (7 + 6) = 300 + 50 + 13 = 363. Show how the partition method can be written down vertically as well as horizontally as this will help with more formal methods of column addition later.

$$
\begin{array}{r}
312 \\
+\ \ 76 \\
\hline
300 \\
80 \\
8 \\
\hline
388 \\
\hline
\end{array}
\qquad
\begin{array}{r}
215 \\
+\ 364 \\
\hline
500 \\
70 \\
9 \\
\hline
579 \\
\hline
\end{array}
$$

In pairs, children place their dominoes face down and take turns to select first five (then later six) to create two- and three-digit numbers they can use in addition examples of their own. Each domino creates one digit of the number, by summing the spots shown. They should start with HTU + TU and then move to HTU + HTU. Recording on squared paper will help them to set out the sum.

DIFFERENTIATION

More able: encourage them to use the vertical method of setting down; challenge them to try the partition methods when subtracting, eg 56 – 22 = 56 – 20 – 2 = 24.
Less able: work with this group to ensure they are comfortable with TU + TU before moving on to include hundreds.

PLENARY

Emphasise how splitting numbers into hundreds, tens and units makes them easier to add, especially mentally. Remind them that once the number has been partitioned it then has to be recombined to find the total. Invite children to work through their own examples on the board. Ask the more able to show how the recording can be done vertically.

LESSON 5

RESOURCES	Copies of photocopiable page 31 ('Clever one'), one per child; pencils.
LEARNING OUTCOMES	**ORAL AND MENTAL STARTER** ● Add or subtract 10, then adjust. **MAIN TEACHING ACTIVITY** ● Add or subtract the nearest multiple of 10, then adjust.
ORAL AND MENTAL STARTER	ADD 10 AND ADJUST: Revise and practise adding 9 or 11 to two- and three-digit numbers by adding 10 and then subtracting or adding one, eg 27 + 9 would be 27 + 10 – 1 = 36. Repeat for subtraction sums, eg 572 – 11 would be 572 – 10 – 1 = 561.
MAIN TEACHING ACTIVITY	CLEVER ONE: Explain to the children that they are going to add and subtract other numbers close to multiples of 10 such as 19, 29, 39 and 21, 31, 41. Work through some addition examples on the board, eg 37 + 19 would become 37 + 20 – 1 = 56; 237 + 31 would become 237 + 30 + 1 = 268. Then try some subtraction examples, eg 457 – 29 would become 457 – 30 + 1 = 428; 59 – 21 would become 59 – 20 – 1 = 38. Children then work on their own to complete 'Clever one' (page 31).
DIFFERENTIATION	More able: go on to examples where they have to adjust by 2 or more, eg 78 + 8 would become 78 + 10 – 2 = 86 and 94 – 12 would become 94 – 10 – 2 = 82. Less able: consolidate work on adding and subtracting 9 and 11 before progressing to adding and subtracting 19 and 21.
PLENARY	Go through the photocopiable questions. Formulate rules which the children can say together, eg to add 9, add 10 and take away 1; to take away 31, subtract 30 and take away 1 more, and so on.

LESSON 6

RESOURCES	Prepare near doubles questions, ten of the type 14 + 15, 73 + 64, 180 + 190, 710 + 720 plus about five of the type *If double 80 is 160 what is 75 + 78?*, then photocopy, one per child; pencils.
LEARNING OUTCOMES	**ORAL AND MENTAL STARTER** and **MAIN TEACHING ACTIVITY** ● Identify near doubles, using known doubles.
ORAL AND MENTAL STARTER	NEAR DOUBLES: Revise and practise adding two-digit numbers where identifying near doubles can help find the answer: 26 + 25 is double 25 + 1 = 51; 40 + 50 can be found by doubling 40 and adding 10 or doubling 50 and taking away 10; 28 + 26 can be found by doubling 30 then taking away two and then four to get the answer 54. Encourage the children to use different strategies to answer these questions: 46 + 45; 33 + 34; 20 + 30; 50 + 60; 49 + 37; 68 + 66.
MAIN TEACHING ACTIVITY	DOUBLE UP: Explain to the children that they are going to use the strategy of near doubles for adding three-digit numbers. Work through examples on the board, eg 140 + 150, which could be double 100, add 40 and 50; double 140, add 10; double 150, take away 10. Investigate 290 + 290, which could be double 300 take 20 or double 280 add on 20. Children then complete your prepared questions. Tell them to record their methods as well as the answers. They check their answers with a partner and compare methods.
DIFFERENTIATION	More able: challenge them to find as many different methods as possible using near doubles to find the solution. Less able: ensure children are confident with two-digit numbers before moving on to three-digit numbers.
PLENARY	Invite children to answer addition questions when some help about doubles has been given first, eg *Double 40 is 80, what is 39 + 40? Double 80 is 160 what is 78 + 83? Double 170 is 340 what is 174 + 168?*

LESSON 7

RESOURCES
Dice and/or digit cards; pencils and paper.

PREPARATION
Provide dice and 0–9 digit cards for each pair.

LEARNING OUTCOMES:

ORAL AND MENTAL STARTER
● Consolidate knowing by heart addition and subtraction facts for all numbers to 20.

MAIN TEACHING ACTIVITY
● Consolidate knowing by heart addition and subtraction facts for all numbers to 20.

VOCABULARY
Take away; how many are left?; how much less?; how much more?; how many more to make?; difference between; decrease; inverse; minus (–) sign; more; add; total; altogether; sum; increase; plus (+) and equals (=) signs; prime number.

ORAL AND MENTAL STARTER
TOP TWENTY: Repeat the activity from Lesson 3, Unit 1 and focus on using different vocabulary to ask the questions. Then check on addition of doubles ranging from 1 + 1 to 20 + 20, using quick-fire questions.

MAIN TEACHING ACTIVITY
UP TO 20: Tell the children that they are going to make up addition and subtraction questions with answers that are up to 20. Write on the board examples of the type of questions they could use: for addition, *Find the total of two numbers..., Add up three single-digit numbers..., Find the sum of 3, 7 and 4, What do 6, 5 and 9 add up to?*; for subtraction, *What is 5 less than 17?, 19 take away 5?* Include number sentences with missing numbers, eg 7 + ? + 3 = 16 and ones where there are choices for a correct answer, eg ? + 5 + ? + 2 = 20. Introduce the use of half, eg *If I have 7½ what do I need to make 20? What is 12½ plus ½?* Include some doubling and halving questions. The children then work in pairs to produce their own examples of these types of questions. Remind them that the answers should never be more than 20. They can use dice or digit cards to generate numbers. Set them targets, eg ten questions involving addition, five subtraction calculations, five involving both addition and subtraction, five involving doubling and halving.

DIFFERENTIATION
More able: challenge them to produce five other questions in which a negative number has been used, eg –5 + 12, –3 + 2 + 6, and so on
Less able: check that they are confident with the more straightforward questions before they move on to more complicated tasks.

PLENARY
Ask for volunteers to make 'stories' about numbers less than 20 for the other children to solve, eg *My number is the total of 5, 6 and 4. It is 19 – 6. It is double 7½. What is it?* (15) Introduce more detailed vocabulary: *It is greater than 10 but less than 15. It is a prime number. Its digits add up to 2. What is the number?* (11).

LESSON 8

RESOURCES
Copies of photocopiable page 32 ('Back to school'); sets of plastic coins; pencils.

PREPARATION
Prepare money problems that use numbers above 20 and involve at least two processes to solve, eg 'Ann is given a 50p coin and a 20p coin. She then spends 35p on a notebook. How much does she have left?' Photocopy 'Back to school' (page 32) one per child. Provide sets of coins for some groups.

LEARNING OUTCOMES
ORAL AND MENTAL STARTER
● Consolidate knowing by heart addition and subtraction facts for all numbers to 20.

MAIN ACTIVITY
● Use addition and subtraction to solve word problems involving numbers in 'real life' and money using one or more steps.

VOCABULARY

Calculate; money; coin; note; penny; pound; cost; buy; bought; sold[sell[pay[change[how much?; how many?.

ORAL AND MENTAL STARTER

TOP TWENTY: Repeat the activity from Lesson 3, Unit 1 but this time asking questions in the context of money that require the children to carry out at least two processes, eg *Add together 12p and 5p and take away 6p*; *How much change would you have from 20p after buying items costing 5p and 10p?* Check their understanding of changing pence into pounds and vice versa, eg *How many pence in £3.52?*

MAIN TEACHING ACTIVITY

MONEY PROBLEMS: Work through your prepared word problems showing the children how to pick out the number processes from the words in order to solve the problem, eg *David saves a 50p coin, a 10p coin and a 5p coin. How much more does he need to save to buy a toy costing 99p?* First find the total of his coins (65p) and work out the difference between that and the cost of the toy (99p). Children then work on their own to complete 'Back to school' (page 32).

DIFFERENTIATION

More able: use more double-process situations with larger numbers and extend to number processes where three steps are involved.
Less able: restrict to single-process problems first with smaller more manageable numbers and let them use the coins to help in their calculations.

PLENARY

Invite children to write up one of their questions on the board for others to solve. Compare and discuss strategies used. Ask: *Is there a right or wrong method providing the solution is correct?* Or provide coins and ask children to make up a money story around it.

RESOURCES
Dice and/or 0–9 digit cards; pencils and paper.

PREPARATION
Provide dice and/or 0–9 digit cards for each child.

LEARNING OUTCOMES
ORAL AND MENTAL STARTER
● Use the relationship between addition and subtraction.

MAIN TEACHING ACTIVITY
● Recognise the outcome of sums or differences of pairs of odd/even numbers.
● Check with the inverse operation.

VOCABULARY

Sum; difference; odd; even; inverse; check; calculation.

ORAL AND MENTAL STARTER

IN THE FAMILY: Check that the children can say a subtraction fact corresponding to an addition fact and the reverse. Begin with simple numbers, eg *If 7 + 9 is 16 what is 16 – 9 and 16 – 7?* Move on to larger two-digit numbers, eg *If 27 + 19 = 46 what is 46 – 19 and 46 – 27?* Also start with subtraction, eg *67 – 24 = 43 so what is 67 – 43? 43 + 24? 24 + 43?*

MAIN TEACHING ACTIVITY

ODDS AND EVENS: Explain to the children that they are going to add and subtract odd and even numbers to establish general rules and to check the answers by using the inverse operation. Work through some examples on the board. Start with small two-digit numbers, eg 24 + 18 = 42 (even + even = even); 19 + 31 = 50 (odd + odd = even); 21 + 24 = 45 (odd + even = odd); 38 + 27 = 65 (even + odd = odd). Then check subtraction of odd and even numbers, eg 28 – 12 = 16 (even – even = even); 37 – 15 = 22 (odd – odd = even); 49 – 26 = 23 (odd – even = odd); 60 – 33 = 27 (even – odd = odd). Then show children how to check their answers are correct by using the inverse operation, eg in 24 + 18 = 42, 42 – 18 = 24 and 42 – 24 = 18. Children then use dice to generate their own two-digit numbers. They add and subtract odd/even numbers to prove the rules suggested above. They then use the inverse operation to check answers.

DIFFERENTIATION

More able: extend to three-digit numbers in HTU + TU examples to see if the rules still apply, again using the inverse operation for checking.
Less able: restrict to smaller two-digit numbers until confident. Remind them that all odd numbers end with 1, 3, 5, 7 or 9 and all even numbers with 0, 2, 4, 6 or 8.

PLENARY

Check through the children's findings. Reinforce teaching points on the inverse operation: addition questions can be checked by subtracting each of the numbers from the answer and subtraction questions can be checked by adding the answer to each of the original numbers.

LESSON 10

RESOURCES	Write up these word problems on the board: 'A farmer has 17 sheep in one field, 14 sheep in another and 24 sheep in a third field. How many sheep does he have altogether?'; 'There are 30 days in September, 31 in March and 28 in February (non leap year). What is the total number of days in these months?'; 'John has 32 books on one shelf of his bookcase, 12 on another and 27 on another. How many books does the bookcase hold?' Write up 10 sums. Start with addition of three or four single-digit numbers or of small two-digit numbers then increase to addition of three larger two-digit numbers.
LEARNING OUTCOMES	**ORAL AND MENTAL STARTER** ● Understand the principle (not the name) of the commutative law as it applies to addition. **MAIN TEACHING ACTIVITY** ● Use addition to solve word problems involving numbers in 'real life'. ● Check the sum of several numbers by adding in reverse order.
ORAL AND MENTAL STARTER	MAKE TEN: Repeat the activity from Lesson 1. Then give the children three single-digit numbers to be added in different orders. Stress that they all make the same total in whichever order they are added. Try for sets of small two-digit numbers.
MAIN TEACHING ACTIVITY	CHANGE THE ORDER: Tell the children they are going to solve some word problems involving real-life situations by adding numbers together. They then work through the examples you have written on the board. Then change the order of the numbers in each question by writing up the sums 24 + 14 + 17, 28 + 30 + 31 and 12 + 32 + 27 for them to work out. After they have solved each one ask: *Does changing the order of the numbers change the result?* Then point to the ten sums you have written up on the board for the children to work out. Challenge them, in pairs, to make up a real-life story about the numbers in each question. Tell them to change the order of the numbers to check their answers.
DIFFERENTIATION	More able: go on to use dice to generate two-digit numbers and use these to make up number stories. Less able: work with this group initially to help with the adding of three single-digit or small two-digit numbers.
PLENARY	Write on the board the numbers from one of the questions in at least three different orders, eg 27 + 15 + 19, 19 + 15 + 27, 15 + 19 + 27. Ask: *What can you tell me about the answer?* They should say it is the same total (61). Give other examples.

Clever one

One way to add 9 to any number is to add 10 and take away 1.

Add 9 to these numbers:

15   27   45   68   125   376   452   809

One way to take away 9 from any number is to take away 10 and add 1.

Subtract 9 from these numbers:

18   25   56   74   169   587   753   905

One way to add 11 to any number is to add 10 and then add 1 more.

Add 11 to these numbers:

28   33   64   89   121   159   625   829

One way to take away 11 from any number is to take away 10 and then take away 1 more.

Subtract 11 from these numbers:

42   58   73   99   253   408   734   988

Work out your own method to add/subtract 19 with these numbers:

31   49   55   68   212   573   864   922

What would you have to do to add/subtract 29 using the same method?

Find a way to add/subtract 21 with these numbers:

29   54   73   92   259   306   552   847

What would you have to do to add/subtract 31 using the same method?
Show your workings on the back of this sheet.

Back to school

Answer these money problems and write your workings out underneath each question.

Back to school bargains! Less than £1!

1. How much would it cost to buy a pencil and a rubber?

2. If you bought a notebook and a stapler how much would it cost?

3. You buy a ruler, a pencil and a notebook. What does your bill come to?

4. If you went into the shop with 50p and bought a sharpener, how much change would you get?

5. How could you pay for a rubber using the least number of coins?

6. You have 80p. What is left over after buying a pencil and a notebook?

7. You only have £1. How much would you need to borrow from your friend if you wanted a sharpener and the crayons?

8. Add up the cost of a ruler, a stapler and a rubber. Write down the least number of coins you could use to buy these items.

Now make up your own word problems using the same list of items.

UNITS 4-6

ORGANISATION (13 LESSONS)

	LEARNING OUTCOMES	ORAL AND MENTAL STARTER	MAIN TEACHING ACTIVITY	PLENARY
LESSON 1	● Derive quickly all number pairs that total 100; all pairs of multiples of 50 with a total of 1000.	MAKE 100: Give the other number in the pair to make 100 or 1000.	MAKE 1000: Give the other number in the pair to make 100 or 1000; find missing numbers.	Check results.
LESSON 2	● Use, read and write standard metric units of length including their abbreviations. **● Know and use the relationships between familiar units of length.**	CLAP COUNTER: Count on and back in steps of 10 then 100.	MEASURE FOR MEASURE: Measure lines to the nearest half centimetre.	Revise metric units for measuring length.
LESSON 3	● Know the equivalent of one half, one-quarter, three-quarters and one-tenth of 1km and 1m. Convert up to 1000 centimetres to metres, and vice versa.	CLAP COUNTER: Count on and back in steps of 1000.	METRIC FRACTIONS: Find fractions of different metric lengths and convert to different units of measure.	Revise key fractions.
LESSON 4 +5	● Suggest suitable units and measuring equipment to estimate or measure length. Record estimates and readings from scales to suitable degrees of accuracy.	FIND THE NUMBER: Find the number from the given clue.	MEASURE IT UP: Choose appropriate equipment for different measuring tasks.	Check equipment and units used; discuss results.
LESSON 6 +7	● Calculate the perimeter and area of rectangles and other simple shapes, using counting methods and standard units (cm and cm^2).	NUMBER SPLITS 1: Add two numbers by splitting into hundreds, tens and units.	FENCES: Find the area and perimeter of simple shapes.	Check results and clarify understanding of area and perimeter.
LESSON 8	● Use addition and subtraction to solve word problems using one or more steps.	COUNT UP: Find differences by counting up.	LONG AND SHORT OF IT: Solve length problems written in words.	Review and discuss strategies used.
LESSON 9 +10	● Describe and visualise 2-D shapes. **Classify polygons.**	NEAR DOUBLES: Use near doubles to add two numbers.	2-D SHAPES: Sort 2-D shapes in two different ways.	Check properties of 2-D shapes.
LESSON 11 +12	● Describe and visualise 3-D shapes. ● Make shapes and discuss properties.	MAKE 100: Give the other number in the pair to make 100.	3-D SHAPES: Make a cube using two different methods.	Display models; revise 3-D shape vocabulary.
LESSON 13	● Make and investigate a general statement about familiar shapes by finding examples that satisfy it.	THOUSAND UP: Give the other number in the pair to make 1000.	SORTING SHAPES: Sort triangles and other polygons.	Reinforce statements made and investigated.

ORAL AND MENTAL SKILLS Derive quickly all number pairs that total 100; all pairs of multiples of 50 with a total of 1000. Count on or back in repeated steps of 10, 100, 1000. Consolidate knowing by heart addition and subtraction facts for all numbers to 20. Partition into hundreds, tens and ones, adding the hundreds first. Find a small difference by counting up. Identify near doubles, using known doubles.

Lessons 2, 4, 9 and 11 are shown in full, with Lessons 5, 10 and 12 provided in outline as developments from them. Lessons 1, 3, 6, 7, 8 and 13 are an extension of what has already been taught so are shown in outline.

RESOURCES	Number fans prepared for Lesson 1, Unit 1; pencils and paper. **ORAL AND MENTAL STARTER** ● Derive quickly all number pairs (of multiples of 5) that total 100. ● Derive quickly multiples of (100) with a total of 1000.
LEARNING OUTCOMES	**MAIN TEACHING ACTIVITY** ● Derive quickly all number pairs that total 100; all pairs of multiples of 50 with a total of 1000.
ORAL AND MENTAL STARTER	MAKE 100: Give the children a multiple of 5 for them to show on their number fan the other one in the pair that totals 100, eg 25 they show 75. Then ask them to say how many steps of 5 must be taken to count on or count back from 100, eg 65 to 100 (7 steps to make 35), 100 back to 85 (3 steps to make 15). Repeat for multiples of 100 that total 1000 and then for the number of steps of 100 to count on or back from 1000.
MAIN TEACHING ACTIVITY	MAKE 1000: Write a multiple of 50 on the board for the children to show on their number fans the other one in the pair to total 1000, eg you write up 750, they show 250. Record on the board questions that have missing numbers, eg ? + 24 = 100; ? + 850 = 1000. Work these out together then provide further examples of each type of question for them to complete.
DIFFERENTIATION	More able: go on to provide their own pairs of numbers to make 100 and 1000. Less able: ensure children are confident using multiples of 5 to make 100 and multiples of 100 to make 1000 before moving on.
PLENARY	Ask children for number pairs they have completed and record these on the board. Reinforce the teaching points.

RESOURCES

Copies of photocopiable page 41, 'Measure for measure'; 30cm rulers, same type for each child; squared/lined paper; pencils.

PREPARATION:

Photocopy 'Measure for measure' (page 41), one per child.

LEARNING OUTCOMES:

ORAL AND MENTAL STARTER:
● Count on or back in repeated steps of 10 or 100.

MAIN TEACHING ACTIVITY:
● Use, read and write standard metric units of length including their abbreviations.
● **Know and use the relationships between familiar units of length.**

ORAL AND MENTAL STARTER

CLAP COUNTER: Repeat the activity from the first part of the Main teaching activity in Lesson 2, Units 2–3, including counting in tens.

MAIN TEACHING ACTIVITY

MEASURE FOR MEASURE: Make sure the children know which metric units are used to measure length. Write the words and their abbreviations on the board, eg millimetres (mm). Explain that inches, feet and miles also measure length but these are called Imperial units. Reinforce the relationship between the measures, eg how many mm in a cm? (10), how many cm in m? (100) and how many m in a km? (1000). Record these on the board. Point out the pattern: each unit is ten times bigger than the previous one. Give

---

VOCABULARY

Measure; size; metric unit; measuring scale; estimate; length; centimetre; millimetre, metre, kilometre and their abbreviations cm, mm, m and km.

each child a 30cm ruler and discuss how each centimetre on the ruler is divided into 10mm with 5mm as the halfway point. Show the point on the ruler where lines should be measured from and how to read off to the nearest centimetre. Children then complete 'Measure for measure' (page 41).

DIFFERENTIATION

More able: measure to the nearest millimetre.
Less able: work with these children to start with to ensure they are reading measurements accurately from the ruler.

PLENARY

Ensure through discussion that children know the main units of length measurement and their abbreviations and the relationships between them, eg *How many centimetres are there to the metre?* (100) *How many millimetres make half a centimetre?* (5) Check lines have been measured correctly.

RESOURCES	Copies of photocopiable page 42, one per child; pencils.
LEARNING OUTCOMES	**ORAL AND MENTAL STARTER** ● **Count on or back in repeated steps of 1000.** **MAIN TEACHING ACTIVITY** ● Know the equivalent of one half, one-quarter, three-quarters and one-tenth of 1km and 1m. ● Convert up to 1000 centimetres to metres, and vice versa.
ORAL AND MENTAL STARTER	**CLAP COUNTER:** Repeat the activity from the first part of the **Main teaching activity** in Units 2–3, Lesson 2 but this time count up and back in thousands.
MAIN TEACHING ACTIVITY	METRIC FRACTIONS: Check first, using the board, that children know the main fractional parts of 10, 100, 1000 and 10,000: one-quarter of 10 is 2½, one-half of ten is 5, three-quarters of 10 is 7½ and one-tenth of ten is 1; for 100 the fractions would be 25, 50, 75 and 10 and so on. Tell them that because 100cm make a metre, half a metre would be 50cm, one-quarter would be 25cm, three-quarters would be 75cm and one-tenth 10cm. Repeat for a kilometre (1000m). Explain that an easy way to find one-quarter is to halve a half; similarly, three-quarters is one-quarter and one-half added together. Check conversion from cm to m and vice versa – for example, 500cm = 5m, 3m = 300cm. Children then complete 'Metric fractions' (page 42).
DIFFERENTIATION	More able: in conversion questions link whole numbers and fractions together, eg *How many cm in 3½m?* (350cm) and *Write 4½km in m* (4250m). Less able: ensure halves are correctly calculated and then assist with other fractions.
PLENARY	Put fraction and conversion questions up on the board and ask for volunteers to fill them in, eg ½m = ?cm, ¾km = ?m, 10cm = ?m, 750m = ?km.

RESOURCES

30cm rulers; metre sticks; tape measures; trundle wheel; A4 paper; card; pencils.

PREPARATION

Draw this table on to the board for the children to copy:

Item measured	Estimate	Measurement (nearest ½cm)

Write out on pieces of card the items to be measured. Items might include:
- length/width of exercise books, pieces of paper/card
- length/width/height of work tables
- length/width/height of sink area
- length/width/height of doorways and windows
- length/width/height of carpeted area
- length/width/height of display boards/bookcases
- perimeter of the classroom (length ×2 + width ×2)
- perimeter of outside play area (as above) ... adult supervision needed here
- height of children on wall height chart.

Give two or three of these to each group of three or four, along with the measuring equipment, and A4 paper for the recording chart.

LEARNING OUTCOMES

ORAL AND MENTAL STARTER
- Consolidate knowing by heart addition and subtraction facts for all numbers to 20.

MAIN TEACHING ACTIVITY
- Suggest suitable units and measuring equipment to estimate and measure length. Record estimates and readings from scales to suitable degrees of accuracy.

VOCABULARY
Length; width; height; depth; breadth; long; short; low; high; longer than; shorter than; taller than; longest; shortest; tallest; highest; distance apart/ between/to/ from; metre; centimetre; millimetre; ruler; metre stick; tape measure; trundle wheel.

ORAL AND MENTAL STARTER

FIND THE NUMBER: Ask quick-fire questions that require children to find the number from the given clue, for numbers up to 20. For example: *I am the total of 12 and 7; I am the difference between 19 and 5; I am 5, 12 and 4 added together; I am 16 decreased by 9; I am double 9; I am half of 16; I am the difference between 13½ and 20; I am the missing number if this sequence 5 + ? + 7 = 20.*

MAIN TEACHING ACTIVITY

MEASURE IT UP: Explain to the children that during the next two lessons they are going to carry out measuring tasks in the classroom to find out how long, how high, how wide a number of objects are. In pairs or small groups, they will make an estimate (intelligent guess) of the measurement first and then measure it as accurately as they can using their equipment. They should record their results on the chart, giving their measurements to the nearest half centimetre. Discuss what equipment would be used for the different tasks. *What would be best to measure the length of a book? The width of the room? The height of a child?* Examine the types of scales used on the equipment and discuss what units will be used to record the results (mm, cm or m). Then let the groups start the recording.

DIFFERENTIATION

More able: record results more accurately, eg to the nearest mm or cm or record results in another way, eg 8m 25cm as 825cm long or 243mm as 24cm 3mm long.
Less able: pair them up with children who can assist them with the measuring tasks or use an adult helper if they are available.

PLENARY

Discuss the measuring tasks. Ask such questions as: *Did you choose the right equipment? Did you choose the correct units? Were scales easy to read? Which ones were difficult? How close were your estimates? Did this help or hinder the measuring process?*

LESSON 5

For the **Oral and mental starter** repeat the activity but this time ask a child to record how many numbers are guessed correctly within a set time. For the **Main teaching activity** the children continue working through the different measuring tasks. Then in the **Plenary** let them share their results. Record these on the board for discussion.

LESSON 6 + 7

RESOURCES	Simple shapes drawn onto squared paper, then enlarged for display; copies of photocopiable page 43 ('Fences'), one per child; cm squared paper (1cm and 2cm); pegboards; elastic bands; dotty paper; pencils.
LEARNING OUTCOMES	**ORAL AND MENTAL STARTER** ● Partition into hundreds, tens and ones, adding the hundreds first. **MAIN TEACHING ACTIVITY** ● Calculate the perimeter and area of rectangles and other simple shapes, using counting methods and standard units (cm and cm²).
ORAL AND MENTAL STARTER	NUMBER SPLITS: Repeat the activity from Lesson 4, Units 2–3.
MAIN TEACHING ACTIVITY	FENCES: Discuss differences between area (the amount of surface in a shape) and perimeter (the distance around the outside of a shape). Display the simple shapes you have drawn on to squared paper and demonstrate how to calculate area by counting squares. Introduce square centimetres as being the correct unit of measurement. Show the children how this is written as cm². Stress that while area is a measurement of the surface, perimeter is a measurement of distance. Look at quicker ways to find the perimeter of a shape other than counting all the units around the outside. For example, in a square you multiply the length by 4 and in a rectangle you multiply the length by 2 and the width by 2 and then add the two results together. Children then work through 'Fences' (page 43). Set other tasks for those who complete this activity, eg find as many octominoes as possible (shapes with an area of eight squares); draw different shapes all with the same perimeter; find shapes which have the same number for both the area and the perimeter. They continue working on these tasks in **Lesson 7**.
DIFFERENTIATION	More able: when children work on the octominoes task, ask them to use half squares as well as whole ones. Less able: children draw in the squares on the dotty paper before counting them up to find the area. Give them help with calculating the perimeters.
PLENARY	Check children are able to define what the words area and perimeter mean. Ask them to hold up a book or a piece of paper. Watch as they rub their hand over the surface to show area and point round the edge with their finger to show perimeter. Together check results for the different tasks attempted.

LESSON 8

RESOURCES	Copies of photocopiable page 44 ('Sports day'), one per child; rulers; measuring tapes and sticks for reference purposes; pencils.
LEARNING OUTCOMES	**ORAL AND MENTAL STARTER** ● Find a small difference by counting up. **MAIN TEACHING ACTIVITY** ● Use addition and subtraction to solve word problems using one or more steps.
ORAL AND MENTAL STARTER	COUNT UP: Repeat the activity from Lesson 3, Units 2–3.
MAIN TEACHING ACTIVITY	LONG AND SHORT OF IT: Explain that the focus of the lesson will be solving length problems that have been written in words. Say that they will involve both adding and subtracting. Work through some examples on the board, eg *Two pieces of wood measure 42cm and 53cm. What is their total length?* (adding); *A piece of string is 29cm long but 17cm is cut off. How much is left?* (subtracting); *What is the perimeter of a 5m² lawn?* (adding). Include some two step processes, eg *Add together the lengths of two pencils 89mm and 47mm long and give the answer in cm* (13cm 6mm or 13.6cm). In pairs, the children complete 'Sports day' (page 44).
DIFFERENTIATION	More able: devise their own word problems for others to solve. Less able: keep measures simple and digits to two figures. Help them to extract the calculations from the word problems. Let them use equipment where needed.
PLENARY	Go through the questions. Discuss the processes used. Look at strategies. Compare methods. Check units used for the answers. Then let those who have produced their own word problems give them to the class to solve.

LESSON 9 +10

RESOURCES
Collection of card/plastic 2-D shapes; prepared record sheets, one per child; squared/dotty/isometric paper; pegboards; elastic bands; rulers; pencils.

PREPARATION
Draw the recording chart shown here, then photocopy, one per child – if you are using large shapes, enlarge the chart to A3 size.

Provide each group with a tray containing the selection of shapes, and give them pegboards and elastic bands.

	Regular	Irregular
8 sides		
7 sides		
6 sides		
5 sides		
4 sides		
3 sides		

LEARNING OUTCOMES
ORAL AND MENTAL STARTER
● Identify near doubles, using known doubles.

MAIN TEACHING ACTIVITY:
● Describe and visualise 2-D shapes.
● **Classify polygons.**

VOCABULARY
Shape; 2-D; two-dimensional; line; side; base; angle; vertex; vertices; straight; regular; irregular; circle; triangle; rectangle; square; circular; rectangular; triangular; quadrilateral; pentagon; hexagon; heptagon; octagon; polygon.

ORAL AND MENTAL STARTER
NEAR DOUBLES: Repeat the activity from Lesson 6, Units 2–3, extending to three-digit numbers.

MAIN TEACHING ACTIVITY
2-D SHAPES: Explain the term '2-D, two dimensional', also known as flat shapes. Show the children the main 2-D shapes, the square, rectangle, triangle and circle, for them to name. Discuss the properties of each shape as they are shown, eg the number of sides, number of corners, length of sides, and so on. Discuss key vocabulary, eg 'sides', 'angles', 'corners' ('vertices'). Discuss the meaning of regular/irregular in relation to 2-D shapes. Introduce the word polygon – flat shapes with three or more straight sides. Explain that in regular polygons all the sides and angles are equal. In irregular polygons they are not. Introduce the heptagon (seven sides) and revise the pentagon, hexagon and octagon. Then hand out the chart and explain that they are to sort the 2-D shapes into the boxes, drawing round each shape to record it. They then make examples of 2-D shapes using pegboards and elastic bands or on dotty/squared/isometric paper and record them on the chart.

DIFFERENTIATION
More able: encourage children to become more precise in their recording of shapes using words such as rhombus, parallelogram and trapezium in the quadrilateral family.
Less able: restrict the sorting task to triangles and quadrilaterals first, then progress to other polygons.

PLENARY
Revise the 2-D shapes shown at the beginning of the **Main teaching activity**, their names and properties. Then ask individual children to give a full description of a 2-D shape for others to guess its name.

LESSON 10
In the **Oral and mental starter** start with three-digit numbers. In the **Main teaching activity** the children carry on making shapes to add to their recording sheet. Revise the vocabulary in the **Plenary**.

LESSON 11 +12

RESOURCES
Number fans prepared for Lesson 1, Unit 1; collection of 3-D shapes for display and discussion; squared paper (5cm squares are best); construction- or artstraws; glue; sticky tape; large version of net of cube; scissors; pencils, rulers; ready-made paper cube and skeletal cube; pencils; felt-tipped pens.

PREPARATION
Make a large version of the net of a cube, including flaps for attaching it together, and also make up an actual paper cube from an identical net. Make a skeletal cube from artstraws.

LEARNING OUTCOMES

ORAL AND MENTAL STARTER
● Derive quickly all number pairs that total 100.

MAIN TEACHING ACTIVITY
● Describe and visualise 3-D shapes.
● Make shapes and discuss properties.

VOCABULARY
Shape; curved; straight; hollow; solid; corner; point; face; edge; construct; net; surface; base; vertex; vertices; 3-D; three-dimensional; cube; cuboid; pyramid; sphere; cone; cylinder; prism; tetrahedron; polyhedron.

ORAL AND MENTAL STARTER
MAKE 100: Repeat the activity from Lesson 1, Units 4–6.

MAIN TEACHING ACTIVITY
3-D SHAPES: Start with the cube. Talk about its properties and introduce key words: 'faces' (6), 'shape' of each face (square), 'edges', a straight line where two faces meet, (12), and 'vertices' or 'corners', a point where three or more edges meet, (8). Tell the children they are going to construct two cubes – one from paper using a net and the other in skeletal form using straws. Show them the large version of the net of the cube and how it is made up. Show them the skeletal version of the cube. Then discuss other 3-D shapes that the children know. Ask them to describe them and their properties. Then show them the shape and check if they are correct. Include cuboid, cone, cylinder, tetrahedron (triangular based pyramid), Egyptian pyramid (square based) and triangular prism. Explain that the word 'polyhedron' means many sided solid shape. Return to the cube. Put up the large version of the net. Give out large squared paper. Ask children to draw it, cut it out and decorate it ready for fixing together. To make the skeletal version, they will need 12 edges (pieces of artstraws) all the same size plus sticky tape for fixing the corners. (Edges of length 10cm make a good sized model.)

DIFFERENTIATION
More able: using squared paper, investigate other nets that can be made up into a cube. Less able: provide straws already cut to length. Show them the example to help with construction. Assist them with assembly.

PLENARY
Exhibit models that the children have made. Discuss properties of the cube. Reinforce the meaning of words such as 'face', 'edge' and 'vertex'.

LESSON 12
In the **Oral and mental starter** start with three-digit numbers. In the **Main teaching activity** the children complete their cubes and go on to make other nets for cubes. Discuss these nets in the **Plenary** and hold up the other 3-D shapes that were discussed in the previous lesson for the children to name.

RESOURCES	Number fans prepared for Lesson 1, Unit 1; selection of equilateral and isosceles triangles; selection of regular and irregular polygons; rulers; paper; pencils; two charts drawn on the board:

Equilateral triangles	Isosceles triangles

Regular polygons	Irregular polygons

LEARNING OUTCOMES	**ORAL AND MENTAL STARTER** ● Derive quickly all pairs of multiples of 50 with a total of 1000. **MAIN TEACHING ACTIVITY** ● Make and investigate a general statement about familiar shapes by finding examples that satisfy it.
ORAL AND MENTAL STARTER	THOUSAND UP: Repeat the activity from Lesson 1 but this time for number bonds for 1000 and counting on/back in steps of 50.
MAIN TEACHING ACTIVITY	SORTING SHAPES: Introduce the children to equilateral triangles – triangles with all three sides the same length. Introduce isosceles triangles – triangles that have two equal sides and one different. Revise the words regular and irregular. Explain that, in small groups, they are going to sort the triangles provided into equilateral and isosceles sets by using rulers to measure their sides. They copy the chart from the board then draw round the triangles on paper to record them under the correct headings. They then do the same to sort the polygons provided into regular and irregular shapes.
DIFFERENTIATION	More able: challenge children to make their own equilateral and isosceles triangles and their own regular/irregular polygons on squared, dotty and isometric paper. Less able: work with this group and assist with the measuring of sides when sorting shapes.
PLENARY	Discuss how the triangles and polygons were sorted. Display and discuss shapes that the children have made. Reinforce statements investigated.

Measure for measure

Use your 30cm ruler to measure these lines to the nearest half centimetre. Write your answers in two different ways, eg 7cm is the same as 70mm and $5\frac{1}{2}$ cm is the same as 55mm.

1.

2.

3.

4.

5.

6.

7.

8.

9.

10.

On the back of the sheet draw some lines of your own. Then ask your partner to measure them.

Metric fractions

UNITS 4–6

| Remember: | 10mm = 1cm | 100cm = 1m | 1000m = 1km |

Fill in the gaps with the missing distances:

	$\frac{1}{4}$	$\frac{1}{2}$	$\frac{3}{4}$	$\frac{1}{10}$
metres	25cm			
kilometres		500m		

Fill in the missing distances:

200cm = ☐ m   4m = ☐ cm   4000m = ☐ km

500cm = ☐ m   7m = ☐ cm   7000m = ☐ km

900cm = ☐ m   6m = ☐ cm   6km = ☐ m

300cm = ☐ m $2\frac{1}{2}$ m = ☐ cm   9km = ☐ m

100cm = ☐ m $3\frac{1}{4}$ m = ☐ cm $3\frac{1}{2}$ km = ☐ m

If 125cm = 1m 25cm and 2m 40cm = 240cm, fill in these missing distances:

136cm = ☐ m ☐ cm $5\frac{1}{2}$ m = ☐ cm

245cm = ☐ m ☐ cm $6\frac{3}{4}$ m = ☐ cm

438cm = ☐ m ☐ cm $2\frac{1}{4}$ m = ☐ cm

670cm = ☐ m ☐ cm $7\frac{1}{10}$ m = ☐ cm

792cm = ☐ m ☐ cm   1m 20cm = ☐ cm

805cm = ☐ m ☐ cm   3m 65cm = ☐ cm

Fences

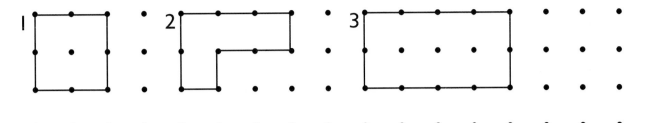

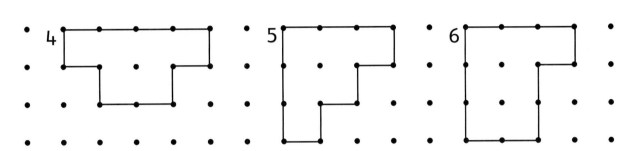

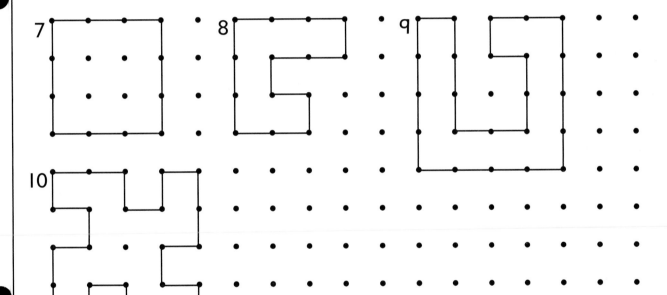

The 'fence' gives this shape an area of 3 squares and a perimeter of 8 units.

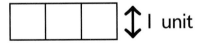
↕ 1 unit

This shape also has an area of 3 squares and a perimeter of 8 units.

Find the areas and perimeters of all the shapes opposite. Do any of them have the same area and perimeter?

Use dotty paper to make your own 'fence' shapes.

UNITS 4–6

 # Sports day

The children at Easton School have just had a Sports Day. They did some long jump and high jump events. Find the answers to these measurement questions. As you work them out, write down the numbers and the operations you use underneath the question.

1. Josh jumps three metres and Rob jumps $2\frac{1}{2}$ m. Add their jumps together.

2. Ravinder jumps $2\frac{1}{2}$ m and Paul jumps $1\frac{1}{2}$ m. How much further did Ravinder jump?

3. Ajay jumps 2m 75cm. How much further would he need to jump to reach 3m?

4. Sita jumped 3m 25cm. How much further than 3m is this?

5. What is the difference between Paul's jump of 4m and Jenny's jump of 3m 50cm?

6. The high jump bar was set at 80cm to start. How much less than 1m is this?

7. Parveen jumped 1m 10cm. How many centimetres is this?

8. Amrit and Ajay are in the top class. Amrit jumped 1m 20cm and Ajay jumped 1m 45cm. What is the total height?

9. Add up these heights and find the difference between their total and 4m: 124cm, 1m 13cm and 1m 52cm.

10. Find the difference between these two high jumps, 90cm and 1m 56cm.

Discuss your answers with a partner. Did you work them out the same way?

UNIT 7: Assess & Review

Choose from the following activities over the two lessons. During the group activities, some children can complete Assessment worksheets 1a and 1b, which assess their skills in: reading, writing and ordering whole numbers to at least 10 000; partitioning numbers into hundreds, tens and ones when adding; adding three two-digit multiples of 10; understanding the commutative law. The specific assessment criteria for the assessment sheets can be found at the bottom of each sheet.

RESOURCES

Pencils; paper; number fans or digit cards; rulers; length measuring equipment including tapes and sticks; cards labelled with the fractions half, one-quarter, three-quarters and one-tenth and with the measurements 50m, 25cm, 75cm, 10cm, 250cm, 500cm, 750cm and 100cm; prepared pairs of paper strips showing equivalent measures, eg 300cm and 3m; metric conversion cards; collections of 2-D and 3-D shapes.

ORAL AND MENTAL STARTER

ASSESSMENT
● Can the children: show they know by heart addition and subtraction facts for all numbers to 2; derive quickly all number pairs that total 100?

NUMBERS TO 20: Give the children a number, say 18, and ask them to write down all pairs of numbers that total 18, eg 14 + 4. Ask them to write down as many subtraction facts as they can starting with this number, eg 18 – 6 = 12. Then ask them to write down groups of three numbers that total 18, eg 3 + 6 + 9. Check through the answers together.
NUMBER PAIRS TO MAKE 100: Give children a multiple of 10 and ask them to use their number fans to show you the other number in the pair to make 100, eg you say 60, they show 40. Then move to multiples of 5, eg you say 15, they show 85. Finally, move to random pairs, eg you say 27, they show 73.

GROUP ACTIVITIES

ASSESSMENT
● Can the children: use, read and write standard metric units (of length), including their abbreviations (cm, m and km)?
● Do the children: know the equivalent of one half, one quarter, three quarters and one tenth of 1km, 1m? Can they: convert up to 1000 centimetre to metres, and vice versa?
● Can the children: describe and visualise 2-D and 3-D shapes?

MEASURING METRIC LENGTH: The children draw five straight lines using a 30cm ruler. They give the lines to their partner who has to measure them to the nearest half centimetre (or millimetre if possible) and then write the measurement alongside the line. Discuss using the ruler, reading scales and choosing the right equipment for different length measuring tasks.
LENGTH FRACTIONS: Lay the fraction and distance cards face up on the table. After some discussion, invite children to match up one of the fractions with the correct distance. Do fractions of a metre first then fractions of a kilometre. Display the prepared paper strips with pairs of equivalent distances, one showing the distance in metres, the other in centimetres. Ask children to pair them up. Start with easier pairs such as 300cm = 3m, then use some fractions eg 4½m = 450cm and finally, try pairs such as 516cm = 5m 16cm.
SHAPE GAME: Put the 2-D and 3-D shapes on the table. Ask the children to choose one of the 2-D shapes and write a short but detailed description of it, eg 'It is a quadrilateral. All of its sides are the same length. It has four right angles (square).' They then take turns to read out their description for the others to guess the shape. Repeat for 3-D shapes.

UNIT 7

Assessment 1a

Write these numbers in words, eg 134 is one hundred and thirty-four.

273 _____   506 _____

1286 _____   3792 _____

7049 _____

Write these numbers in figures, eg two hundred and seventy-nine is 279.

three hundred and twenty-four _____   five hundred and seventeen _____

one thousand nine hundred and fourteen _____

five thousand six hundred and forty _____   eight thousand and seven _____

Give the value of the digits shown in brackets, eg 5(7)2 = 70

5(9) _____   (2)003_____   (9)6 _____   40(6)1_____

              6(1)4 _____   (5)394 _____

(8)93 _____   80(5)0 _____   174(5) _____   987(2) _____

Place these numbers in order of size, starting with the smallest first.

| 21   12   102   120   112 | 215   512   355   533   251   152 |

| 95   59   105   115   119   109 | 75   17   57   107   77 |

| 752   275   205   725   502   75 |

| 1121   1111   1211   1002   2111   2001 |

| 3542   3425   5243   5324   535   5432 |

| 9999   9119   9111   9911   9101   9001 |

● Read and write whole numbers to at least 10 000 in figures and words, and know what each digit represents.
● Order a set of whole numbers less than 10 000.

Assessment 1b

Add these numbers by splitting them into hundreds, tens and ones,
eg 157 + 49 = 100 + 90 + 16 = 206.

45 + 74 _____

135 + 67 _____

243 + 98 _____

314 + 28 _____

472 + 567 _____

703 + 371 _____

Find the answers to these addition questions. Then change the order of
the numbers, write them down and add them again. Check your answers.
eg 27 + 59 = 86   59 + 27 = 86   86 – 59 = 27

43 + 86 _____

30 + 40 + 10 _____

52 + 11 + 51 _____

214 + 55 + 24 _____

459 + 302 _____

Check the answers to these addition questions by using subtraction:

15	43	156	359	258
+29	+72	+ 73	+ 77	+372
44	115	229	436	630

● Partition into hundreds, tens and ones (when adding). ● Consolidating understanding of relationship between + and –.
● Understand the principle (not the name) of the commutative law. ● Check with the inverse operation.

UNIT 8

ORGANISATION (5 LESSONS)

LEARNING OUTCOMES	ORAL AND MENTAL STARTER	MAIN TEACHING ACTIVITY	PLENARY
LESSON 1 ● Derive quickly doubles of all whole numbers to 50 and the corresponding halves.	ADD 10 AND ADJUST: Add 9 or 11 by adding 10 then adjusting by 1.	BIG FIVE-0: Double and halve numbers to 50.	Understand that doubling and halving are inverse operations.
LESSON 2 ● **Know by heart multiplication facts for the 3 × table.** ● **Derive quickly division facts corresponding to the 3 × table.**	TABLES BINGO: Use knowledge of 2, 5 and 10 times tables to play bingo.	TIMES THREE: Work using the 3 times table (x and ÷).	Discuss patterns formed by the 3 times table.
LESSON 3 ● **Know by heart multiplication facts for the 4 × table.** ● **Derive quickly division facts corresponding to the 4 × table.**	DIVISION QUIZ: Answer division questions related to 2, 5 and 10 times tables.	TIMES FOUR: Work using 4 times table (x and ÷).	Discuss patterns formed by the 4 times table.
LESSON 4 ● Recognise odd/even numbers up to 1000 and some of their properties.	TABLES BINGO: Use knowledge of 3 and 4 times tables to play bingo.	ODD AND EVEN: Sort two- and three-digit numbers into odd and even sets and order numbers.	Children show examples of their own odd/even numbers.
LESSON 5 ● Make and investigate a general statement about familiar numbers.	DIVISION QUIZ: Answer division questions related to 3 and 4 times tables.	MAGIC SQUARES: Make magic squares.	Discuss magic squares created.

ORAL AND MENTAL SKILLS Add or subtract the nearest multiple of 10, then adjust. Derive quickly doubles of all whole numbers to 50 and the corresponding halves. **Know by heart multiplication facts for 2, 3, 4, 5 and 10 times tables. Derive quickly division facts corresponding to 2, 3, 4, 5 and 10 times tables.**

Lessons 1, 2, 4 and 5 are shown in full. Lesson 3 is provided as a development of the previous lesson.

RESOURCES

Copies of prepared random doubling/halving numbers exercise; dice; calculators; pencils.

PREPARATION

On a sheet of A4, draw two boxes and fill them with random numbers and their doubles and halves. Photocopy, one per child.

LEARNING OUTCOMES

ORAL AND MENTAL STARTER
● Add or subtract the nearest multiple of 10, then adjust.

MAIN TEACHING ACTIVITY
● Derive quickly doubles of all whole numbers to 50 and the corresponding halves.

ORAL AND MENTAL STARTER

ADD 10 AND ADJUST: Repeat the activity from Lesson 5, Units 2–3, using three-digit numbers.

VOCABULARY

Double; twice; half; halve; whole; divide by 2; divide into 2; ½ (as one half).

MAIN TEACHING ACTIVITY

BIG FIVE-0: Stress that halving is the inverse of doubling. Write on the board *Double 7 is 14 and half of 14 is 7; if half of 22 is 11 then double 11 is 22.* Ask quick-fire questions for doubles of numbers up to 50. Repeat for halving, starting with even numbers then include odd numbers, eg *Half 35 is ?.* Together create number chains doubling up from a starting number, eg 6, 12, 24, 48. Repeat for halving, eg 44, 22, 11, 5½ (stop when a fraction is reached). Give out your prepared sheet and tell the childdren to find the doubles and halves within the boixces and list the relevant pairs alongside.

DIFFERENTIATION

More able: use a calculator to continue halving a number when they reach a fraction, eg half of 5½ is 2.75.
Less able: focus on doubling even numbers first especially those up to 20 and halving questions that do not produce a half.

PLENARY

Check through their answers. Reinforce that doubling and halving are inverse operations. Ask questions such as: *If double 32 is 64, what is half of 64? If half of 96 is 48, what is 48 doubled?*

LESSON 2 + 3

RESOURCES

Prepared bingo cards; copies of photocopiable resource sheet B ('1-100 square'); crayons; prepared function machines; 0–50 digit cards, one set per child (for Lesson 3).

PREPARATION

Prepare different bingo cards with numbers from the 2, 5 and 10 times tables, one per child, and write corresponding questions. Prepare function machines for children to fill in the missing numbers, one set for the 3 times table and one set for the 4 times table, eg:

(×3)				(÷3)	
in	Out			in	out
6	?			30	?
4	?			18	?
?	21			?	5

Prepare questions for DIVISION QUIZ for Lesson 3. Photocopy '1-100 square' (resource sheet B), one per child.

LEARNING OUTCOMES

ORAL AND MENTAL STARTER
● **Know by heart multiplication facts for 2, 3, 4, 5 and 10 times tables**
● **Derive quickly division facts corresponding to 2, 3, 4, 5 and 10 times tables.**

MAIN TEACHING ACTIVITY
● **Know by heart multiplication facts for the 3 and 4 times tables.**
● **Derive quickly division facts corresponding to the 3 and 4 times tables.**

ORAL AND MENTAL STARTER

TABLES BINGO: Read out questions from the 2, 5 and 10 times tables, eg 6 times 2, 5 multiplied by 10, seven fives, what is the product of 6 and 10? The children cover up the correct answers on their bingo card. The winner is the first child to cover the whole card.

VOCABULARY

Times-table; multiply; times by; lots of; product; divide; divided by; share; groups of; quotient; function; digit; pattern.

MAIN TEACHING ACTIVITY

TIMES THREE: Chant through the 3 times table from 3 to 30 and then back again. Ask questions to do random checks, eg *What number comes before/after (21) in the 3 times table?* You may need to write up the 3 times table on a number line on the board to help initially. If so cover up numbers and ask children to fill in the gaps. Ask questions that involve division facts using a range of vocabulary, eg *Divide 30 by 3; How many threes are there in 9?; What is the quotient of 3 and 18?* Tell the children to colour in each third square on their 100 square, 3, 6, 9, 12 and so on, to complete a pattern of the 3 times table up to 100. Ask them to make links with other tables, eg *Which members of the 3 times table belong to the 2, 5 and 10 times tables as well?* Use the prepared function machines to reinforce knowledge of this table.

DIFFERENTIATION

More able: investigate the 3 times table by adding the digits that are produced, eg 3(3), 6(6), 9(9), 12(3), 15(6), 18(9), 21(3) .... *What pattern is made?* (3, 6, 9 is repeated). Tell them to check this through the rest of the table. Where adding two digits gives a double-digit number they should be added again, eg 39: 3 + 9 = 12 and 1 + 2 = 3.
Less able: let them start with the 3 times table up to 30 and then give help beyond this point.

PLENARY

Chant up and down the 3 times table. Check before and after numbers. Discuss the pattern the 3 times table has made on the 100 square. Discuss links with 2, 5 and 10 times tables. Ask the more able group to report on the pattern formed by adding the digits of the 3 times table numbers.

LESSON 3

For the **Oral and mental starter** play DIVISION QUIZ. Remind the children that all even numbers are members of the 2 times table, all members of the 5 times table end with 5 or 0 and that members of the 10 times table always end with zero. Then ask division questions related to the 2, 5 and 10 times tables that have answers of no more than 50, which they must answer by holding up the relevant digit card, eg *How many twos in 18?; 25 divided by 5; What is the quotient of 50 and 10; Share 45 by 5; How many groups of 2 can I get out of 20?* Repeat the **Main teaching activity** from Lesson 2, but this time for the 4 times table. For **Differentiation** help the less able colour the numbers beyond 40. Let the more able look for a pattern in the units digits of the 4 times table, eg *The end digit pattern goes 4, 8, 2, 6, 0/4, 8, 2, 6, 0. Does this pattern continue up to 100?* In the **Plenary** write up parts of the table on the board and ask the children to fill in the gaps. Discuss the pattern formed on the 100 square and links with other tables. Ask the more able group to report on the pattern found in the end digits.

LESSON 4

RESOURCES

Prepared bingo cards; dice, one per pair/small group; number fans (prepared for Lesson 1, Unit 1), one per child; pencils and paper.

PREPARATION

Prepare different bingo cards with numbers from the 3 and 4 times tables, one per child, and write corresponding questions.

LEARNING OUTCOMES

ORAL AND MENTAL STARTER
● **Know by heart multiplication facts for the 3 and 4 times tables.**

MAIN TEACHING ACTIVITY
● Recognise odd and even numbers up to 1000 and some of their properties.

VOCABULARY

Odd; even;
alternate;
every other;
sequence;
pattern;
predict.

ORAL AND MENTAL STARTER

TABLES BINGO: Repeat the activity from Lesson 2 but using questions from the 3 and 4 times tables. Include questions that reinforce the fact that division is the inverse of multiplication, eg *If 9 × 3 = 27, what is 27 ÷ 3?*

MAIN TEACHING ACTIVITY

ODD AND EVEN: Tell the children that you are going to say a two-digit number that they must make on their number fan and hold up in their right hand if it is even and in their left hand if it is odd. Repeat for various two-digit numbers. Then ask them to show the even number that comes after 52 (shown in their right hand), the odd number that comes before 53 and so on (shown in their left hand). Ask for an odd number between 50 and 70, an even number between 45 and 65 and so on. Discuss results.

Repeat for three-digit numbers. Talk about the system used to number buildings along most roads – odd along one side and even along the other. Ask children to tell you their door numbers. Others have to hold up this number on their fan, again showing if it is odd or even.

In pairs, or groups of three or four, children throw the dice three times and from these three numbers make as many odd three-digit numbers as possible, and then as many even numbers. They record each number list in descending order. They repeat for another three throws of the dice.

DIFFERENTIATION

More able: children suggest statements about odd and even numbers and test them out, eg 'after one, every second number is odd'; 'odd + odd always equals even'.
Less able: check they understand that all even numbers end with the digits 0, 2, 4, 6, 8 and all odd numbers end with the digits 1, 3, 5, 7, 9.

PLENARY

Invite children out to write three-digit numbers on the board. Others have to say whether it is odd or even and give the numbers in that sequence that come immediately before and after it, eg 376 (even), before 374, after 378. Ask groups to report back on the statements they investigated.

RESOURCES

0–50 digit cards, one set per child; squared paper; large magic square.

PREPARATION

Prepare questions for DIVISION QUIZ. Draw a 3 × 3 square on the board. Put in the digits 1 to 9 in the places as shown here.

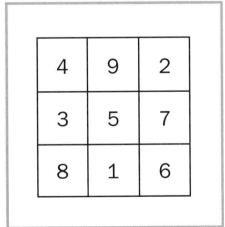

VOCABULARY

Pattern,
puzzle,
calculate,
calculation,
answer, right,
wrong,
correct, what
could we try
next? How did
it work out?
sum, total,
difference
between.

LEARNING OUTCOMES

ORAL AND MENTAL STARTER
● **Derive quickly division facts for 3 and 4 times tables.**

MAIN TEACHING ACTIVITY
● Make and investigate a general statement about familiar numbers.

ORAL AND MENTAL STARTER

DIVISION QUIZ: Repeat the activity from Lesson 3, but for the 3 and 4 times tables, again including questions that reinforce that multiplication is the inverse of division. Remind the children that all members of the 4 times table are even numbers.

MAIN TEACHING ACTIVITY

MAGIC SQUARES: Tell the children that the number square on the board is called a magic square. Explain that magic squares are squares in which the numbers in each vertical line, horizontal line and the two diagonals always add up to the same total. They were first derived by the Chinese thousands of years ago. Add up each line – vertical, horizontal and diagonal – to show they each total 15. Provide the children with squared paper. Ask them to arrange the same nine digits in the square to make it remain a magic square. Each digit can only be used once. *How many different solutions can you find?* Ask them to make a general statement about magic squares: 'in a magic square the numbers in each line always add up to the same total'.

DIFFERENTIATION

More able: make their own 3 x 3 magic squares using numbers of their choice.
Less able: provide them with a partially complete magic square (different to the one on the board) for them to find the missing numbers by adding two numbers from a line and subtracting from 15 to get the third number.

PLENARY

Check through solutions the children have made using the digits 1–9. For example:

8	3	4
1	5	9
6	7	2

4	3	8
9	5	1
2	7	6

8	1	6
3	5	7
4	9	2

Discuss the general statement about what a magic square is.

UNITS 9–10

ORGANISATION (10 LESSONS)

	LEARNING OUTCOMES	ORAL AND MENTAL STARTER	MAIN TEACHING ACTIVITY	PLENARY
LESSON 1	● Extend understanding of the operation of × and its relationship to + and ÷.	TIMES TABLES FACTS: Answer multiplication questions for 2, 5 and 10 times tables and play tables bingo.	MULTIPLICATION FACTS: Investigate multiplication as adding and as the inverse of division.	Revise key vocabulary; check examples.
LESSON 2	● Extend understanding of the operation of ÷ and its relationship to − and x. ● **Find remainders after division.**	TIMES TABLES FACTS: Answer multiplication questions for 3 and 4 times tables and play tables bingo.	DIVISION FACTS: Investigate division as repeated subtraction and as the inverse of multiplication.	Reinforce main teaching points.
LESSON 3	● Use doubling or halving, starting from known facts eg double/halve two-digit numbers by doubling/halving the tens first.	BIG FIVE-0: Double and halve numbers to 50.	DOUBLE AND HALVE: Double and halve larger two-digit numbers.	Check correct method has been used.
LESSON 4 +5	● Use doubling or halving, starting from known facts, using other examples.	TRUE OR FALSE?: Answer division questions for 2, 5 and 10 times tables. DIVISION QUIZ: Adapt from Lesson 3, Unit 8.	DOUBLE METHODS: Develop other methods of doubling numbers.	Check through methods that have been used.
LESSON 6	● Use known number facts and place value to multiply and divide integers by 10.	IS IT A FACT & DIVSION QUIZ?: Answer division questions for 3 and 4 times tables.	MOVING PLACES: Use quick ways to multiply and divide by 10.	Reinforce methods.
LESSON 7	● Approximate first. Use informal pencil and paper methods to support, record and explain multiplications.	TIMES TEN: Answer quick-fire questions that involve multiplying by 10.	GRID METHOD: Use the grid method for multiplying.	Check and compare answers found.
LESSON 8	● Use informal pencil and paper methods to support, record and explain divisions. ● **Find remainders after division.** Round up or down after division, depending on the context.	DIVIDE BY TEN: Answer quick-fire questions that involve dividing by 10.	REMAINDERS: Solve divisions with remainders and rounding up/down.	Discuss and compare methods used.
LESSON 9	● Use all four operations to solve word problems involving numbers in 'real life', including money.	MAKE £1: Give the number to make £1.	WORD PROBLEMS: Solve real-life problems.	Check answers.
LESSON 10	● Check with an equivalent calculation.	NUMBER SPLITS 1: Add two or three numbers by splitting into hundreds, tens and units.	HERE'S ANOTHER WAY: Check answers using equivalent operation.	Compare and discuss operations used.

ORAL AND MENTAL SKILLS   Know by heart multiplication facts for 2, 3, 4, 5 and 10 times tables; derive quickly division facts corresponding to 2, 3, 4, 5 and 10 times tables. Derive quickly doubles of all whole numbers to 50 and the corresponding halves. Use known number facts and place value to multiply and divide integers by 10. Derive quickly all number pairs that total 100. Partition into hundreds, tens and ones, adding hundreds first.

Lessons 1, 2, 4, 6, 7 and 8 are shown in full. Lesson 5 is provided as a development of the previous lesson. Lessons 3, 9 and 10 are an extension of what has already been taught so are shown in outline.

LESSON 1

RESOURCES

Number fans prepared for Lesson 1, Unit 1, one per child; bingo cards prepared for Lesson 2, Unit 8 and prepared questions; multiplication statements; 0–100 tables squares (from Lesson 2, Unit 8); pencils and paper.

PREPARATION

Write questions for TABLES BINGO. Write ten multiplication statements on the board, such as 3 × 9 = 27.

LEARNING OUTCOMES

ORAL AND MENTAL STARTER
● **Know by heart multiplication facts for 2, 5 and 10 times tables.**

MAIN TEACHING ACTIVITY
● Extend understanding of the operation of × and its relationship to + and ÷.

VOCABULARY

Times; multiply; multiplied by; product; multiple; inverse; the times (×) sign.

ORAL AND MENTAL STARTER

TIMES TABLES FACTS: Children use their number fans to show answers to multiplication questions about the 2, 5 and 10 times tables, eg: *6 × 2, 4 × 5, 7 × 10; What are 7 twos?; 9 multiplied by 2?; 6 multiplied by 5?; What is the product of 10 and 2?* Then play TABLES BINGO from Lesson 2, Unit 8.

MAIN TEACHING ACTIVITY

MULTIPLICATION FACTS: Establish first that children understand that multiplication is a quick way of adding. Show examples on the board eg 2 × 6 is 6 + 6 and 5 × 2 is 2 + 2 + 2 + 2 + 2. Also work examples where multiplication is shown to be the inverse of division and can be used to check answers, eg 6 × 3 = 3 × 6 = 18 so 18 ÷ 6 = 3 and 18 ÷ 3 = 6. Show examples where any number x1 leaves the number unchanged by getting the children to check the results on their calculator, eg 17 × 1 = 17, 256 × 1 = 256 and 3974 × 1 = 3974. Repeat to illustrate that any number times zero is always zero. In pairs or individually, ask the children to write down ten examples from their table chart to show that multiplication is a quick way to add eg 6 × 3 = 3 + 3 + 3 + 3 + 3 + 3 = 18. Then ask them to write other × and ÷ facts using the same numbers for the ten multiplication statements shown on the board, eg you write 3 × 9 = 27 they write 9 × 3 = 27, 27 ÷ 3 = 9 and 27 ÷ 9 = 3.

DIFFERENTIATION

More able: give the children three numbers only and tell them to work out their own × and ÷ facts from them, eg 9, 2, 18 would produce 2 × 9 = 18, 9 × 2 = 18, 18 ÷ 2 = 9 and 18 ÷ 9 = 2.
Less able: give support on how to use the tables squares to look up multiplication and division facts.

PLENARY

Revise key vocabulary with the children especially 'multiply', 'times', 'product', 'inverse'. Ask children out to give examples of how multiplication and addition is linked. Check other examples that show how division is the inverse of multiplication.

RESOURCES
Numbers fans prepared for Lesson 1, Unit 1, one per child; bingo cards prepared for Lesson 2, Unit 8 and prepared questions; calculators; 0–100 tables squares (from Lesson 2, Unit 8); pencils and paper.

PREPARATION
Write questions on the 3 and 4 times tables for TABLES BINGO.

LEARNING OUTCOMES

ORAL AND MENTAL STARTER
● **Know by heart multiplication facts for 3 and 4 times tables.**

MAIN TEACHING ACTIVITY
● Extend understanding of the operation of ÷ and its relationship to – and ×.
● **Find remainders after division.**

VOCABULARY
Share; group; divide; divided by; divided into; divisible by; factor; quotient; remainder; inverse.

ORAL AND MENTAL WORK

TIMES TABLES FACTS: Repeat the activity from Lesson 1, but this time for the 3 and 4 times tables.

MAIN TEACHING ACTIVITY

DIVISION FACTS: Tell the children that dividing can be carried out using repeated subtraction. Show this example on the board: 12 ÷ 3; take one group of three away leaves 9 (12 – 3 = 9), take two groups of three away leaves six (12 – 3 – 3 = 6), take three groups of three away leaves three (12 – 3 – 3 – 3 = 3), take the last group of three away leaves zero (12 – 3 – 3 – 3 – 3 = 0), so there are *four* groups of three in 12. Show other examples. Also work examples where division is shown to be the inverse of multiplication, eg if 15 ÷ 3 = 5 and 15 ÷ 5 = 3 then 3 × 5 = 15 and 5 × 3 = 15. Show examples where any number divided by 1 leaves the number unchanged by getting the children to check the results on their calculator, eg 20 ÷ 1 = 20. Remind the children that when division questions do not work out exactly, a remainder is left. Show examples such as 19 ÷ 3 = 6 remainder 1 and 34 ÷ 4 = 8 remainder 2. Using the tables square, make as many equal groups as possible and then show what is left over as the remainder. Get the children to follow on their tables square as you demonstrate. Then, in pairs, ask the children to use their tables squares to record:
● ten examples of dividing using repeated subtraction
● five examples of multiplication statements being turned into division statements, eg 7 × 3 = 21 becomes 21 ÷ 3 = 7 and 21 ÷ 7 = 3
● five simple division questions that leave remainders, eg 10 ÷ 3 = 3 remainder 1 and 32 ÷ 5 = 6 remainder 2.
Tell them to use the tables worked on so far: 2, 3, 4, 5 and 10 times tables.

DIFFERENTIATION

More able: give them sets of three numbers from which they should make up their own division statements, eg 24, 8, 3 gives 24 ÷ 8 = 3 and 24 ÷ 3 = 8.
Less able: give them help in using the tables square. Encourage them to use small numbers for repeated subtraction and small numbers for remainder questions.

PLENARY

Revise key vocabulary especially 'share', 'group', 'divide', 'divided by', 'divided into'. Ask children to show and discuss examples. Reinforce the main teaching points of the lesson.

LESSON 3

RESOURCES	Dice or 0–9 digit cards, per child; pencils and paper.
LEARNING OUTCOMES	**ORAL AND MENTAL STARTER** ● Derive quickly doubles of all whole numbers to 50 and the corresponding halves. **MAIN TEACHING ACTIVITY** ● Use doubling or halving, starting from known facts, eg double/halve two-digit numbers by doubling/halving the tens first.
ORAL AND MENTAL STARTER	BIG FIVE-O: Repeat the whole class work part of the Main teaching activity in Lesson 1, Unit 8.
MAIN TEACHING ACTIVITY	DOUBLE AND HALVE: Show the children how to use the partition method to double and halve larger two-digit numbers: for double 75, double the tens first, double 70 is 140, and then double the units, double 5 is 10 and add the two results together to get the answer, 140 + 10 = 150; to halve 86, half of 80 is 40, half of 6 is 3 so the answer is 40 + 3 = 43. Children then use digit cards or dice to produce two-digit numbers, which they can then double and halve. Ask them to try ten of each.
DIFFERENTIATION	More able: repeat for doubling three-digit numbers looking at the hundreds first, then the tens, then the units. Less able: work with two-digit numbers less than 50 until they have the confidence to progress.
PLENARY	Revise quick-fire doubling/halving for numbers up to 50. Check that in the children's calculations they have doubled/halved the tens first followed by the units.

LESSON 4 + 5

RESOURCES

0–9 digit cards, one set per child; pencils and paper.

PREPARATION

None.

LEARNING OUTCOMES

ORAL AND MENTAL STARTER
● **Derive quickly division facts corresponding to 2, 3, 4, 5 and 10 times tables.**

MAIN TEACHING ACTIVITY
● Use doubling or halving, starting from known facts, using other examples.

VOCABULARY

Times; multiply; multiplied by; multiple; times table; double; halve; method.

ORAL AND MENTAL STARTER

TRUE OR FALSE?: Revise division facts from the 2, 5 and 10 times tables. Remind children that multiples of 2 are known as even numbers, multiples of 5 always end in 5 or 0 and that multiples of 10 always end in 0. Children should answer true or false to questions such as: *Are these numbers divisible exactly by 2: 8, 11, 17, 20, 24? Are these numbers divisible exactly by 5: 13, 18, 20, 26, 30? Are these numbers divisible exactly by 10: 17, 30, 52, 60, 74?*

MAIN TEACHING ACTIVITY

DOUBLE METHODS: Tell the children that one way to multiply a number by 4 is to double and double again. Write up and go through some examples on the board, eg 6 × 4 = 6 × 2 × 2 = 24. Similarly, one way to multiply a number by 5 is to multiply by 10 and halve the answer, eg 32 × 5 = 32 × 10 ÷ 2 = 160. One way to multiply by 20 is to multiply by 10 and then double the answer, eg 6 × 20 = 6 × 10 × 2 = 120. The children then work individually using their digit cards to make five single-digit numbers and five two-digit numbers. They then multiply each of these numbers by 4 using the method shown in the lesson. They repeat the process to multiply by 5 and then to multiply by 20, producing 30 answers by the end of the two lessons.

DIFFERENTIATION

More able: investigate possible links between the 3 and 6 times tables and the 4 and 8 times tables.
Less able: work only with single-digit numbers until confident enough to move on.

PLENARY

Reinforce the main teaching points: times 4 is double and double again; times 5 is times 10 and halve; times 20 is times 10 and double. Check through their examples.

LESSON 5

For the **Oral and mental starter** play DIVISION QUIZ from Lesson 3, Unit 8 for the 2, 5 and 10 times tables. In the **Main teaching activity** remind the children of the three methods, then let them continue with the 30 multiplications. In the **Plenary** discuss other ways to use doubling/halving to make multiplication easier.

LESSON 6

RESOURCES

0–9 digit cards; prepared multiply and divide by 10 questions; pencils.

PREPARATION

Provide the digit cards, one set per child. On a sheet of paper write about 12 questions that involve multiplying by 10 (of the type $14 \times 10 = ?$; $750 = ? \times 10$; $1247 \times 10 = ?$) followed by a list of numbers with the instruction 'Make these numbers 10 times bigger'. Then add 12 questions that involve dividing by 10 (of the type $? \div 10 = 90$; $290 \div ? = 29$; $840 = 8400 \div ?$), followed by a list of numbers with the instruction *Divide these numbers by 10*, then photocopy, one per child.

LEARNING OUTCOMES

ORAL AND MENTAL STARTER
● **Derive quickly division facts corresponding to 3 and 4 times tables**.

MAIN TEACHING ACTIVITY
● Use known number facts and place value to multiply and divide integers by 10.

VOCABULARY

Digit; place; zero; multiply; divide; tenth; ten times bigger; ten times smaller.

ORAL AND MENTAL STARTER

IS IT A FACT?: Revise division facts for the 3 and 4 times tables. Remind the children that in the 3 times table the digits always add up to 3, 6 or 9. Children answer true or false to question such as: *Are these numbers exactly divisible by 3: 8, 12, 17, 24, 29?* Then play DIVISION QUIZ with these tables (see Lesson 3, Unit 8).

MAIN TEACHING ACTIVITY

MOVING PLACES: Tell the children that a quick way to multiply whole numbers by 10 is to move the digits one place to the left, leaving the units column with a zero. Start with single-digit numbers, eg $7 \times 10 = 70$. Show examples using two-digit numbers, eg $14 \times 10 = 140$. Write on the board some examples of statements with missing numbers for the children to solve, eg $42 \times ? = 420$ and $? \times 10 = 760$. Explain that a quick way to divide a number that ends in 0 by 10 is to move the digits one place to the right which means there is no 0 in the answer, eg $80 \div 10 = 8$. Repeat for two-digit numbers, eg $360 \div 10 = 36$. Provide missing number statements for them to solve, eg $40 \div ? = 4$ and $? \div 10 = 64$. Children then complete the questions you have prepared.

DIFFERENTIATION

More able: ask children to generate questions in which words are used in place of signs, eg *37 multiplied by 10*; *Make 52 ten times bigger*; *590 divided by 10*; *What is one tenth of*

610?, for a partner to solve.
Less able: limit multiplying by 10 to single-digit numbers and two-digit numbers ending in 0 to start with.

PLENARY

Reinforce the main teaching points. Work through some of the questions devised by the children. Invite children out to solve questions on the board, eg *Make 43 ten times bigger, what is one tenth of 750?*

LESSON 7

RESOURCES

Dice; digit cards; tables squares from Lesson 2, Unit 8; pencils and paper.

PREPARATION

Provide each pair with 2, 3, 4, 5 digit cards and one dice.

LEARNING OUTCOMES

ORAL AND MENTAL STARTER
● Use known number facts and place value to multiply integers by 10.

MAIN TEACHING ACTIVITY
● Approximate first. Use informal pencil and paper methods to support, record and explain multiplications.

VOCABULARY
Times; multiply; multiplied by; grid; tens; units; product; approximate; approximately; × sign.

ORAL AND MENTAL STARTER

TIMES TEN: Ask quick-fire questions that involve multiplying single- and two-digit numbers by 10, eg 6 × 10, 19 × 10…. Then give the children statements to complete such as 9 × ? = 90, ? × 10 = 210, *Make 34 ten times bigger, Multiply 29 by 10, What is the product of 46 and 10?*

MAIN TEACHING ACTIVITY

GRID METHOD: On the board remind the children of an informal written method for multiplying TU by U, the grid method introduced in Year 3. Use times tables that have already been worked on: 2, 3, 4, 5 and 10 times tables. Start with 53 × 5. Ask the children to approximate first, eg 50 × 5 would be 250. Then show them how to multiply using the grid method, partitioning the two-digit number to multiply the tens and units separately and then adding together the results to give the answer. 50 × 5 is 250, 3 × 5 is 15 and 250 + 15 gives the answer 265.

x	50	3	
53 × 5: 5	250	15	= 265

Work through other examples together, eg 69 × 4. Then, in pairs, one child throws a dice twice to generate a two-digit number (TU), the other child chooses a digit card for the single digit (U). They approximate the answer first then use the grid method, recording their work. Let them use their tables squares to check their calculations.

DIFFERENTIATION

More able: go on to multiply HTU by U using the grid method.
Less able: work with this group to assist with approximate answers and to ensure the method is being following correctly.

PLENARY

Put up some sample questions on the board and invite children up to work them through.

Discuss how to approximate the answer first. *How does the approximate answer help us to see if the final answer is correct?* Try these examples 29 × 3, 42 × 3, 58 × 4 and 73 × 5.

RESOURCES

Prepared division questions; tables squares from Lesson 2, Unit 8; pencils and paper.

PREPARATION

Write 20 division questions on the board of the type TU ÷ U. All should have remainders and should involve 2, 3, 4, 5 and 10 times tables.

LEARNING OUTCOMES

ORAL AND MENTAL STARTER
● Use known number facts and place value to divide integers by 10.

MAIN TEACHING ACTIVITY
● Use informal pencil and paper methods to support, record and explain divisions.
● **Find remainders after division**. Round up or down after division, depending on the context.

VOCABULARY

Share; group; divide; divided by; divided into; divisible by; remainder; ÷ sign; quotient; left over.

ORAL AND MENTAL STARTER

DIVIDE BY TEN: Ask quick-fire questions that involve dividing two- and three-digit numbers by 10, eg 80 ÷ 10, 170 ÷ 10…. Then give the children statements to complete such as *50 ÷ ? = 5, ? ÷ 10 = 130, What is the quotient of 370 and 10, What is one tenth of 960?*

MAIN TEACHING ACTIVITY

REMAINDERS: Remind children that remainders are what is left over after dividing and that they are always written as a whole number. Work through some examples on the board using the times tables featured so far (2, 3, 4, 5 and 10 times). For example, 19 ÷ 2 = 9 remainder 1, 23 ÷ 3 = 7 remainder 2, 41 ÷ 4 = 10 remainder 1, 29 ÷ 5 = 5 remainder 4 and 63 ÷ 10 = 6 remainder 3. Show the children how these can be written in a different way. In order they would be 19 = 9 × 2 + 1, 23 = 7 × 3 + 2, 41 = 10 × 4 + 1, 29 = 5 × 5 + 4 and 63 = 6 × 10 + 3. Explain that in some practical situations it is necessary to round down or round up to get a sensible answer. Read these questions out and ask the children whether rounding down or rounding up is needed. Then work through them on the board:
● *I have £47. Tickets cost £5 each. How many can I buy?* 47 ÷ 5 = 9 remainder 2. I can only buy 9 tickets (rounding down).
● *I have 44 pencils. Boxes of pencils hold 10. How many boxes can I fill?* 44 ÷ 10 = 4 remainder 4. I can only fill 4 boxes (rounding down).
● *I have 28 CDs. Holders hold 5 CDs. How many holders do I need?* 28 ÷ 5 = 5 remainder 3. I need six holders to store them (rounding up).
● *In the classroom, tables seat four children. There are 26 children. How many tables do I need?* 26 ÷ 4 = 6 remainder 2. I need 7 tables to seat them all (rounding up).
    The children then work through the 20 questions on the board, working out the remainders then writing the answers in the two ways, eg 39 ÷ 4 = 9 remainder 3 and 39 = 9 × 4 + 3. Let them use their tables squares to check their calculations.

DIFFERENTIATION

More able: go on to make up 'real life' situations for rounding up or down – these will be useful in the next lesson.
Less able: start with questions using small two-digit numbers and division by 2, 5 or 10.

PLENARY

Check through the questions. Ask different children to show the different methods. Discuss how, in these cases, division is the inverse of multiplication and addition when expressing remainders.

LESSON 9

RESOURCES	Sets of plastic coins; copies of photocopiable page 61 ('At the greengrocer's'), one per child; copies of resource sheet C ('Times tables square').
LEARNING OUTCOMES	**ORAL AND MENTAL STARTER** ● Derive quickly all number pairs that total 100. **MAIN TEACHING ACTIVITY** ● Use all four operations to solve word problems involving numbers in 'real life', including money.
ORAL AND MENTAL STARTER	MAKE £1: Tell the children to make the amount you give them up to 100p or £1. Start with multiples of 10 eg 60p, they answer 40p. Go on to multiples of 5, eg you say 45p, they answer 55p. Then choose amounts at random, eg 73p, they answer 27p. Then give them two amounts to add and then work out the change from £1, eg you say 40p and 35p, they answer 25p.
MAIN TEACHING ACTIVITY	WORD PROBLEMS: Give children some single process word problems for all four operations and ask them to pick out the processes, numbers and operations involved, eg *There are 27 cows in one field and 19 in another. How many cows altogether?* 'Add: 27 + 19 = 46'; *I had a 50p coin and spent 38p on some sweets. How much did I receive?* 'Subtract: 50p – 38p = 12p'; *A beetle has six legs. How many legs do 8 beetles have?* 'Multiply: 8 × 6 = 48'; *Pencils are packed in boxes of 10. How many boxes will 70 pencils fill?* 'Divide: 70 ÷ 10 = 7'. Then move on to two-step questions, such as *Mum bought two tins of paint costing £2.25 each. How much change did she get from £5?* 'Add and then subtract: £2.25 + £2.25 = £4.50 and £5 – £4.50p = 50p. *20 children in the class bring chocolate bars. A quarter of them have Zip Bars and the rest have Zap Bars. How many have each type?* 'Divide and then subtract: 20 ÷ 4 = 5 and 20 – 5 = 15'. Also use examples where it is necessary to round up/down following a division question with a remainder (see the previous lesson). Children then complete 'At the greengrocer's' (page 61).
DIFFERENTIATION	More able: make up their own real-life two-step problems for others to solve. Less able: use the 100 square and the multiplication square to aid calculations.
PLENARY	Go through the questions on the worksheet. One child reads out the questions, another child writes on the board the numbers and correct signs needed to solve the problem and a third child calculates the answer.

LESSON 10

RESOURCES	Copies of photocopiable 62 ('Check it out'), one per child; copies of resource sheet C ('Times tables square').
LEARNING OUTCOMES	**ORAL AND MENTAL STARTER** ● Partition into hundreds, tens and ones adding hundreds first. **MAIN TEACHING ACTIVITY** ● Check with an equivalent calculation.
ORAL AND MENTAL STARTER	NUMBER SPLITS 1: Repeat the activity from Lesson 4, Units 2–3. Start by adding two two-digit numbers, move on to adding three two-digit numbers, then try examples of HTU + TU.
MAIN TEACHING ACTIVITY	HERE'S ANOTHER WAY: On the board show children examples of how to check calculations using an equivalent process or operation, eg 50 + 37 could be checked as 50 + 30 +7 to get 87; 90 – 53 could be checked as 90 – 50 – 3 to get 37; 72 × 5 could be checked as 70 × 5 + 2 × 5 to make 360; 63 ÷ 3 could be checked as 60 ÷ 3 + 3 ÷ 3 to make 21. In pairs, children work through 'Check it out' (page 62).
DIFFERENTIATION	More able: challenge children to find more than one method of checking the calculation. Suggest partition method for adding/subtracting, and doubling/halving for multiplication/division. Less able: let them use the times tables square to assist calculations.
PLENARY	Work through the questions with the children. Write different methods on the board. Discuss which of the methods they found easier and why. Discuss the importance of being able to self-check work.

Name

 **At the greengrocer's**

Here are the prices of some fruit and vegetables at the greengrocer's shop.

| apples 7p each | tomatoes 6p each | cabbage 48p each | cauliflower 50p each | bananas 7p each |

| cucumber 37p each | oranges 22p each | pears 12p each | grapes 89p per bunch |

Work out these word problems, writing the numbers and operations you use underneath the question, as well as the answer.

1. Find the cost of an apple, an orange and a pear.

2. How much would a cabbage and a cucumber cost to buy?

3. What change would there be from a £1 coin after buying a bunch of grapes?

4. You only have 50p. How much more would you need to buy an orange and a cauliflower?

5. How much more than a pear does a cucumber cost?

6. What would you have to pay for four apples and three tomatoes?

7. Find the total cost of two oranges and five bananas.

8. If you bought five pears what change would you get from £1?

9. Paul and Alison decide to buy four oranges between them. How much do they need to pay each?

10. At the end of the day, cabbages, pears and tomatoes are reduced to half price. What would you pay for two cabbages, three pears and five tomatoes?

Check it out

Work with a partner. For questions a–e one of you answer the question in the usual way while the other one looks for another method, either using the same operation or a different one. Then check to see if your answers are the same. Swap round for questions f–j.

> 60 + 28 could be worked out as 60 + 20 + 8 = 88
> or 50 − 24 could be worked out as 50 − 20 − 4 = 26
> or 28 × 3 could be worked out as 28 + 28 + 28 = 84.

a) 70 + 34 _____

b) 150 + 73 _____

c) 160 + 158 _____

d) 48 × 4 _____

e) 42 ÷ 2 _____

Now swap round. Remember that both of you must use different methods.

f) 80 + 52 _____

g) 180 + 49 _____

h) 57 × 3 _____

i) 125 × 5 _____

j) 123 ÷ 3 _____

Discuss your results. Did you both get the same answers? Which method did you find easiest? Now find a third way to answer each question.

UNIT 11

ORGANISATION (5 LESSONS)

	LEARNING OUTCOMES	ORAL AND MENTAL STARTER	MAIN TEACHING ACTIVITY	PLENARY
LESSON 1	● Use fraction notation.	IT'S CLOSE: Find differences by counting up.	SPLIT INTO FRACTIONS 1: Make simple fraction diagrams.	Review and discuss diagrams made.
LESSON 2	● **Recognise simple fractions that are several parts of a whole.**	TOP TWENTY: Answer quick-fire addition and subtraction questions based on a number less than 20.	SPLIT INTO FRACTIONS 2: Make fraction diagrams showing several parts of a whole.	Look at simple fraction equivalents.
LESSON 3	● **Recognise simple fractions that are several parts of a whole and mixed numbers.**	MAKE 100: Give the other number in the pair to make 100.	MIXED NUMBERS: Draw fraction diagrams for mixed numbers.	Make mixed numbers.
LESSON 4 + 5	● Begin to relate fractions to division and find simple fractions of numbers and quantities.	THOUSAND UP: Give the other number in the pair to make 1000.	FRACTIONS AND DIVISION: Find fractions of amounts.	Find fractional amounts of groups of numbers.

ORAL AND MENTAL SKILLS Find a small difference by counting up. Consolidate knowing by heart addition and subtraction facts for all numbers to 20. Derive quickly all number pairs that total 100. Derive quickly all pairs of multiples of 50 with a total of 1000.

Lessons 1 and 4 are shown in full. Lessons 2 and 3 are extensions of what has already been taught so are shown in outline. Lesson 5 is a development of the previous lesson.

RESOURCES
Squared paper; interlocking cubes; large squared paper for board; crayons.

PREPARATION
Attach a sheet of large squared paper to the board.

LEARNING OUTCOMES

ORAL AND MENTAL STARTER
● Find a small difference by counting up.

MAIN TEACHING ACTIVITY
● Use fraction notation.

ORAL AND MENTAL STARTER
IT'S CLOSE: Repeat the activity from the first part of the **Main teaching activity** in Lesson 3, Units 2–3, starting with two-digit numbers.

MAIN TEACHING ACTIVITY
SPLIT INTO FRACTIONS 1: On the squared paper, colour in half of a large square and label it ½ (Figure 1) . Explain that half means that you have coloured one part out of two.

VOCABULARY
Parts; equal parts; fraction; whole; half; quarter; eighth; fifth; tenth; twentieth.

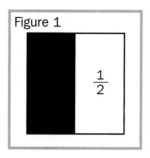

Figure 1

Now colour one quarter of a square and label it ¼ (Figure 2). Explain that one quarter means one part out of four.

Ask: *How many halves make a whole one? How many quarters make a whole one?* Repeat the process for one-third, one-fifth, one-sixth, one-eighth and one-tenth. Children then make their own fraction strips using squared paper (Figure 3). On a row of two squares they find ways to show the fraction a half. On a row of four squares they find the different ways to record one-quarter, eg:

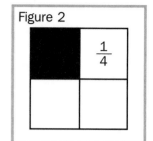

Figure 2

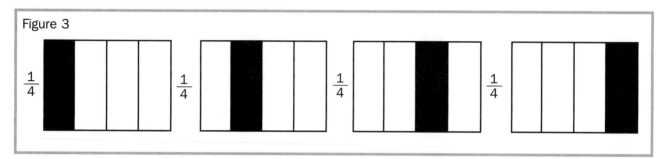

Figure 3

Repeat the process with one-third, one-fifth and one-tenth.

DIFFERENTIATION

More able: draw rectangles with a different number of squares, eg four by two, and shade correct fractions of these shapes.

Less able: use solid objects of different colours such as interlocking cubes to show one-half, one-quarter and so on by using different colours.

PLENARY

Children come to the board to show examples of fraction drawings they have made. Check variations. How many different solutions for one-quarter are there? Were all the possible answers recorded?

LESSON 2

RESOURCES	Squared paper; interlocking coloured cubes; crayons.
LEARNING OUTCOMES	**ORAL AND MENTAL STARTER** ● Consolidate knowing by heart addition and subtraction facts for all numbers to 20. **MAIN TEACHING ACTIVITY** ● **Recognise simple fractions that are several parts of a whole.**
ORAL AND MENTAL STARTER	TOP TWENTY: Repeat the activity from Lesson 3, Unit 1 but this time ask quick-fire questions based on one number between 0 and 20. For example, 12. Ask for all the number pairs that will total 12, then ask for number trios. Give the children subtraction facts to complete, eg 12 – 7 = ? and number sentences to complete, eg 7 + 4 + ? = 12. Start with 12 and subtract two numbers for the children to answer.
MAIN TEACHING ACTIVITY	SPLIT INTO FRACTIONS 2: Show the children how to illustrate and record simple fractions that are several parts of a whole, eg show three-quarters by shading three squares out of four, show three-fifths by shading three squares out of five. They then draw their own diagrams of different fractions.
DIFFERENTIATION	More able: match up fraction shapes to show equivalences, eg a half is the same as two-quarters, one-quarter is the same as two-eighths. Less able: use interlocking cubes of different colours to show examples of simple fractions.
PLENARY	Share the equivalence activity with the rest of the class. Ask children to come up in pairs to show two fractions that are the same. Also show how fractions can be paired up to make a whole, eg one-quarter and three-quarters.

LESSON 3

RESOURCES	Large squared paper, attached to board; squared paper; crayons.
LEARNING OUTCOMES	**ORAL AND MENTAL STARTER** ● Derive quickly all number pairs that total 100. **MAIN TEACHING ACTIVITY** ● **Recognise simple fractions that are several parts of a whole and mixed numbers.**
ORAL AND MENTAL STARTER	MAKE 100: Repeat the activity from Lesson 1, Units 4–6.
MAIN TEACHING ACTIVITY	MIXED NUMBERS: Explain that a mixed number is a mixture of a whole number and a fraction. Show some examples using the large squared paper on the board, eg show 2¼ as two whole coloured squares and one-quarter of a whole square. On squared paper, the children then record mixed numbers of their own. You may want to write examples on the board, eg two and a half, five and two-thirds.
DIFFERENTIATION	More able: ask the children to calculate what they need to add on to the mixed number to reach the next whole one, eg three and three-quarters + one-quarter = four. Less able: restrict mixed numbers to whole numbers and only one fraction part to start with, eg two and a half, four and one-quarter.
PLENARY	Call out a mixed number and ask the children to come out and record it on the board. Start with whole numbers and one fraction part only, eg two and one-quarter. Then ask them to work out how many fraction parts they are worth, eg one and one-quarter is 5 quarters, three and two-thirds is 11 thirds.

LESSON 4 + 5

RESOURCES

Copies of photocopiable page 67 ('Finding fractions'); squared paper; number lines; times tables charts; crayons; pencils.

PREPARATION

Photocopy 'Finding fractions' (page 67), one per child. Provide times tables charts and 0–10 number lines prepared from photocopiable resource sheet A.

LEARNING OUTCOMES

ORAL AND MENTAL STARTER
● Derive quickly all pairs of multiples of 50 with a total of 1000.

MAIN TEACHING ACTIVITY
● Begin to relate fractions to division and find simple fractions of numbers and quantities.

ORAL AND MENTAL STARTER

THOUSAND UP: Repeat the activity from Lesson 13, Units 4–6.

MAIN TEACHING ACTIVITY

FRACTIONS AND DIVISION: Tell the children that fractions can be linked to division. Demonstrate on the board an example that finding one-half of a number is the same as dividing by 2, eg $\frac{1}{2}$ of 12 is equivalent to 12 ÷ 2. Use other examples; $\frac{1}{3}$ of 9 is 9 ÷ 3 and $\frac{1}{10}$ of 50 is 50 ÷ 10. Show them that when a whole cake is divided into four equal parts each piece is one-quarter of the cake. So 1 ÷ 4 = $\frac{1}{4}$. Demonstrate other examples on the board, eg 1 ÷ 3 = $\frac{1}{3}$ and 1 ÷ 10 = $\frac{1}{10}$. Give examples involving finding fractions of certain amounts, eg *What fraction of £1 is 50p?*; *25p is what fraction of £1?* Children then work through 'Finding fractions' (page 67).

DIFFERENTIATION

More able: encourage children to make links between fractions and metric measures, eg *Find one-quarter, a half and three-quarters of one metre, one kilogram and one litre.*

Less able: start with halving of round numbers, eg ½ of 10; ½ of 20. Let them use table charts and number lines when dividing.

PLENARY

On the board write a fraction alongside a series of numbers for the children to answer, eg write up a ½ and then the numbers 20, 24, 30, 48, 60, and so on. Repeat for one-fifth with multiples of 5 and one-tenth with multiples of 10.

LESSON 5

Repeat the **Oral and mental starter** from Lesson 4. For the **Main teaching activity** work through some examples together then let the children complete the photocopiable sheet, started in the previous lesson. They can then go on to show fractional amounts in shapes other than squares, eg rectangles or equilateral triangles. Alternatively, give them two shapes and ask them to relate one fraction to another. For example:

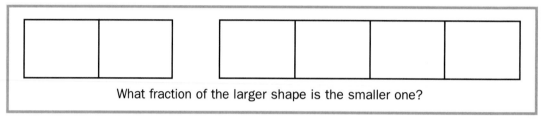

What fraction of the larger shape is the smaller one?

Ask the children to place fractions on number lines, eg *Show the fraction halfway between three and four* (arrow 1); *What fraction is shown by arrow 2?*

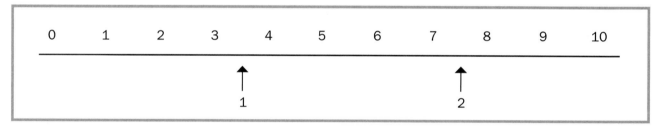

In the **Plenary** give the children different fractions to work on with different series of numbers.

Name

Finding fractions

Remember: Finding a half is the same as dividing by two; finding one-quarter is the same as dividing by four.

1. Find a half of these numbers:

8	12	26	34	40	50	56	72	84	100

2. Find one-quarter of these numbers:

12	16	24	36	40	48	56	64	72	80

3. Find one-fifth of these numbers:

10	20	25	35	40	55	65	70	85	100

4. Find one-tenth of these numbers:

10	30	40	50	80	90	100	120	220	250

5. What is one half, one-quarter, one-fifth and one-tenth of £1?

6. What is one half, one-quarter, one-fifth and one-tenth of a metre?

7a. What fraction of £1 is 10p?   b. What fraction of £1 is 50p?

  c. What fraction of £1 is 20p?   d. What fraction of £1 is 25p?

8a. What fraction of a metre is 50cm?   b. What fraction of a metre is 25cm?

  c. What fraction of a metre is 10cm?   d. What fraction of a metre is 20cm?

9. If a cake is divided equally between two children, what fraction do they get each?

10. If a pizza is divided equally between four children, what fraction do they get each?

UNIT 12

ORGANISATION (5 LESSONS)

	LEARNING OUTCOMES	ORAL AND MENTAL STARTER	MAIN TEACHING ACTIVITY	PLENARY
LESSON 1	● Consolidate understanding of relationship between + and –. ● Check with the inverse operation.	CLEVER ONE: Add numbers close to multiples of 10.	TAKE IT AWAY: Use addition to check answers to subtraction.	Revise subtraction vocabulary and inverse operation.
LESSON 2	● Partition into hundreds, tens and units (when adding and subtracting).	SUBTRACT 10 AND ADJUST: Subtract 9 or 11 by subtracting 10 then adjusting by 1.	SPLIT UP 1: Add using the partition method.	Go over questions generated by the children.
LESSON 3	● Use informal pencil and paper methods to support, record or explain additions/ subtractions.	PAIR UP: Pair up numbers to make 10 to aid addition.	SPLIT UP 2: Revise methods for adding and subtracting.	Go through examples. Revise key vocabulary.
LESSON 4 + 5	● Use, read and write the vocabulary related to time. Read the time from an analogue clock to the nearest minute and from a 12-hour digital clock.	FIVES AND TENS: Revise 5 and 10 times tables.	WHAT'S THE TIME? Read and write times on clock faces.	Show times in different ways.

ORAL AND MENTAL SKILLS Add or subtract the nearest multiple of 10, then adjust. Add three or four small numbers, finding pairs totalling 10. **Know by heart multiplication facts for 5 and 10 times tables.**

Lessons 1 and 4 are shown in full. Lessons 2 and 3 are an extension of what has already been taught so are shown in outline. Lesson 5 is a development of the previous lesson.

LESSON 1

RESOURCES

1–100 number lines; dice or 0–9 digit cards; pencils and paper.

PREPARATION

Prepare 1–100 number lines from photocopiable resource sheet A.

LEARNING OUTCOMES

ORAL AND MENTAL STARTER
● Add or subtract the nearest multiple of 10, then adjust.

MAIN TEACHING ACTIVITY
● Consolidate understanding of relationship between + and –.
● Check with the inverse operation.

ORAL AND MENTAL STARTER

CLEVER ONE: Repeat the activity from the classwork part of the **Main teaching activity** in Lesson 5, Units 2–3.

MAIN TEACHING ACTIVITY

TAKE IT AWAY: Use number questions to test the children's knowledge of vocabulary associated with subtraction, eg *46 take away 9, Decrease 46 by 17, What is the difference between 27 and 45?, What has to be taken away from 35 to leave 17? How many less than 56 is 27?* Revise the fact that subtraction is the inverse of addition and that subtraction questions can be checked by using addition. Work through examples on the board, eg *When*

VOCABULARY

Take away; subtract; how many are left?; how much less?; difference between; how much more?; how many more to make?; decrease; inverse; minus (–) sign.

29 is taken away from 53, the answer is 24. This can be checked by adding together 29 and 24. If they total 53, the question has been correctly worked out. Reinforce the fact that subtracting zero from any number leaves the number unchanged. Children then use dice or digit cards to generate their own numbers for subtraction questions which they then check by adding. Start with ten examples of TU – U, then move to ten examples of TU – TU.

DIFFERENTIATION

More able: move on to HTU – TU.
Less able: ensure children are successful with TU – U before progressing to larger numbers. More work may need to be done on the subtraction process using apparatus.

PLENARY

Work through some of the children's examples on the board. Ask for words and phrases used for the subtraction process and write them up on the board. Discuss the meaning of the term 'inverse operation' to check understanding.

RESOURCES	Number lines; 0–9 digit cards or dice; pencils and paper.
LEARNING OUTCOMES	**ORAL AND MENTAL STARTER** ● Subtract the nearest multiple of 10, then adjust. **MAIN TEACHING ACTIVITY** ● Partition into hundreds, tens and units (when adding and subtracting).
ORAL AND MENTAL STARTER	SUBTRACT 10 AND ADJUST: Repeat the activity from Lesson 5, Units 2–3, but for subtraction. Then use the method to add 19 by taking away 20 and adding on 1 and similarly for subtracting 29 by adding 30 and taking away 1.
MAIN TEACHING ACTIVITY	SPLIT UP 1: Remind the children of the partitioning method, adding the tens first and then the units, eg 36 + 27 becomes 30 + 20 = 50 and 6 + 7 = 13 giving 50 + 13 = 63. Give an example involving hundreds then demonstrate how to use the method for subtraction by partitioning the number that is being subtracted, eg 96 – 58 = 96 – 50 – 8 = 46 – 8 = 38. In pairs, children use digit cards or dice to generate numbers for addition and subtraction questions to practice these methods. Aim for ten of each.
DIFFERENTIATION	More able: progress to HTU + TU, then HTU + HTU using partition. Less able: restrict to adding initially and support calculations with use of number lines.
PLENARY	Work through the example 152 + 367 on the board, asking individual children to talk through each stage, eg adding the hundreds would be 100 + 300 = 400, the tens would be 50 + 60 = 110, adding the units would be 2 + 7 = 9. This produces 400 + 110 + 9, which totals 519.

RESOURCES	Prepared addition and subtraction questions of the type practised in Lessons 1–7, Units 2–3; number lines; digit cards or dice; pencils.
LEARNING OUTCOMES	**ORAL AND MENTAL STARTER** ● Add three or four small numbers, finding pairs totalling 10. **MAIN TEACHING ACTIVITY** ● Use informal pencil and paper methods to support, record or explain additions/subtractions.
ORAL AND MENTAL STARTER	PAIR UP: Give the children quick-fire number trios for mental additions. Remind them to pair up numbers that make 10 first. Start with single-digit numbers, then include a small two-digit number and then increase to four numbers. Give them two numbers that make 10 and a total and ask them to find the missing number, eg 3 + ? + 7 = 19.
MAIN TEACHING ACTIVITY	SPLIT UP 2: Revise the mental calculation strategies and informal written methods of adding and subtracting which have been introduced so far particularly those in the Lessons 1–7, Units 2–3. Children then work through your prepared questions.
DIFFERENTIATION	Refer to Lessons 1–7, Units 2–3.
PLENARY	Children provide examples of questions to work through with the class. Reinforce key vocabulary. Revise the points of any problem areas.

RESOURCES

Prepared bingo cards; large clock face; printed sheets of blank clocks, analogue and digital; copies of photocopiables pages 71 and 72 ('Telling the time' 1 and 2); pencils.

PREPARATION

Prepare different bingo cards with numbers from the 5 and 10 times tables, one per child, and write corresponding questions. Prepare a sheet of blank clock faces, then photocopy, one per child. Photocopy 'Telling the time' 1 and 2 (pages 71 and 72), one of each per child.

LEARNING OUTCOMES

ORAL AND MENTAL STARTER

● **Know by heart multiplication facts for 5 and 10 times tables**.

MAIN TEACHING ACTIVITY

● Use, read and write the vocabulary related to time. Read the time from an analogue clock to the nearest minute and from a 12-hour digital clock.

VOCABULARY

Day; morning; afternoon; evening; night; midnight; noon; mid-day; hour minute; second; a.m. (before noon); p.m. (afternoon); analogue; digital.

ORAL AND MENTAL STARTER

FIVES AND TENS: Count up in fives from 0 to 60 eg 5, 10, 15, 20, 25.... Reverse and count back from 60 to 0. Repeat for tens. Count in groups of five and leave gaps, eg 15, 20, ?, 30 and 40, ?, 30, 25 and ask the children to fill the gaps. Repeat with tens. Tell them to answer 15 × 2, 15 × 3 and 15 × 4 to reinforce that one-quarter of an hour is 15 minutes, half an hour is 30 minutes, three-quarters of an hour is 45 minutes and a full hour is 60 minutes.

MAIN TEACHING ACTIVITY

WHAT'S THE TIME?: Revise time vocabulary and the units of measure, 60 seconds = one minute and 60 minutes = one hour. On a large clock face remind the class that the long hand is the minute hand and the short hand is the hour hand. Move the minute hand around the clock face clockwise counting every five minutes, eg five, ten, fifteen, (quarter of an hour), twenty, twenty-five, thirty (half an hour) until you reach 'o'clock' again. Show times past o'clock and times to o'clock. Discuss am and pm times and the points that separate them: noon and midnight. On the board show how the same time can be written in a number of different ways, eg quarter past 4 as 4:15, or 6:35 as 35 minutes past 6 or 25 minutes to 7. Explain that an analogue clock face shows the time using hands on and that a digital clock face shows the time in numbers only. Show a variety of times on the clock face and ask children what the time is. Ask for the digital equivalent. The children then work individually to complete 'Telling the time 1' (page 71).

DIFFERENTIATION

More able: work to the nearest minute and write times in at least two different ways.
Less able: use a large clock face to work to the nearest five minutes.

PLENARY

Ask a child to come out and show some times on the clock face. Others have to say what the times are. Can they use several ways of saying the same time?

LESSON 5

In the **Oral and mental starter** repeat the TABLES BINGO activity from Lesson 2, Unit 8 for the 5 and 10 times tables. In the **Main teaching activity** ask individual children to show given times on the analogue clock face. The children then work individually to complete 'Telling the time 2' (page 72). Then give them the blank clock faces for them to record their own times, eg time they get up, time school starts, when they go to bed. For **Differentiation**, see Lesson 4. In the **Plenary** ask a child to say a time, for another child to show it on the clock face and a third volunteer to write on the board as a digital time.

Telling the time 1

1. Draw the minute and hour hands on these clock faces to show the times given underneath. Remember the minute hand should be longer than the hour hand. The first one is done for you.

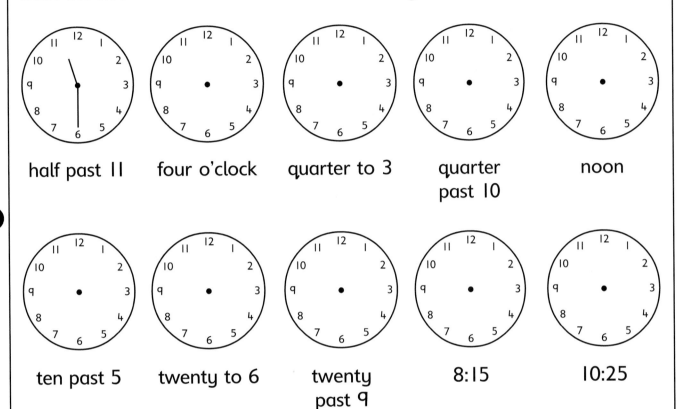

half past 11   four o'clock   quarter to 3   quarter past 10   noon

ten past 5   twenty to 6   twenty past 9   8:15   10:25

2. These are the faces of digital clocks. Write numbers into the boxes to show the times given underneath.

3 o'clock $\frac{1}{2}$ past 7   5 o'clock $\frac{1}{4}$ to 7 $\frac{1}{4}$ past 2

20 past 4   20 to 11   five to 12   five past 9   25 past 4

3. Use some blank clock faces to make up some times. Then swap with a partner and write down the times shown on their clock faces.

Telling the time 2

1. Look carefully at the position of the hands on these clock faces and then write down the times underneath.

half past two _____   _____   _____   _____

_____   _____   _____   _____   _____

2. Look carefully at the faces of these digital clocks and then write down the times in words underneath.

| 4:00 | 7:30 | 3:15 | 11:45 | 9:20 |

four o'clock _____   _____   _____   _____

| 6:05 | 2:50 | 3:10 | 4:25 | 1:35 |

_____   _____   _____   _____   _____

3. Use some blank clock faces to show your own times. Show the answer on the clock face and write the times underneath.

UNIT 13

ORGANISATION (5 LESSONS)

	LEARNING OUTCOMES	ORAL AND MENTAL STARTER	MAIN TEACHING ACTIVITY	PLENARY
LESSON 1	● Solve a problem by collecting quickly, organising, representing and interpreting data.	TOP TWENTY: Quick-fire questions on addition and subtraction using numbers up to 20.	ALL ABOUT US: Collect information to set up a database.	Review findings produced by the database.
LESSON 2 +3	● Solve a problem by collecting quickly, organising, representing and interpreting data in tally charts.	BIG FIVE-0: Double and halve numbers to 50.	TALLY-HO: Record, then interpret information from tally charts.	Check through results of tally chart tasks.
LESSON 4 +5	● Solve a problem by collecting quickly, organising, representing and interpreting data in pictograms.	NEAR DOUBLES: Use near doubles to add 2 two-digit numbers.	IN THE PICTURE: Make and use pictograms.	Display the pictograms made and discuss and explain findings.

ORAL AND MENTAL SKILLS Consolidate knowing by heart addition and subtraction facts for all numbers to 20; derive quickly doubles of all whole numbers to 50 and the corresponding halves. Identify near doubles, using known doubles.

Lessons 1, 2 and 4 are shown in full. Lessons 3 and 5 are provided as developments of the previous lessons.

RESOURCES

Personal record chart; pencils; computer database.

PREPARATION

Create the following personal record charts then photocopy, one per child:

My personal record sheet	
First name	
Surname	
Boy/Girl	
Birth date	
Age in months	
Hair colour	
Eye colour	
Height (cm)	
Shoe size	
Pets	

LEARNING OUTCOMES

ORAL AND MENTAL STARTER
● Consolidate knowing by heart addition and subtraction facts for all numbers to 20.

MAIN TEACHING ACTIVITY
● Solve a problem by collecting quickly, organising, representing and interpreting data.

VOCABULARY

Survey;
questionnaire;
data; sort;
represent;
database;
organise;
interpret;
more/less;
most/least;
common;
popular.

ORAL AND MENTAL STARTER

TOP TWENTY: Repeat the version of the activity from Lesson 2, Unit 11.

MAIN ACTIVITY

ALL ABOUT US: Discuss what is involved in data handling. Explain that once a theme has been decided, data needs to be: collected, organised or sorted, recorded or represented then interpreted or analysed. Discuss what each stage entails. Explain to the children that they are going to make a database of information about themselves. Hand out the personal record charts and ask them to record the information. Tell them to ask a partner for help with measurements they can't do on their own. Then, in pairs, ask them to devise questions they might want to find answers to once the database is complete. These might include: *Are there any birthday twins? How many children are older than 100 months? What is the most popular pet in the class?* While they are doing this, photocopy all the record sheets, one set per group of three. Then organise the class to take turns to collate their information on the computer database. The other children work in groups of three to find out the answers to agreed questions, by interrogating the data record sheets. Once the database is complete, the children can take turns to use it to answer their questions.

DIFFERENTIATION

More able: encourage them to use the database for questions which relate two pieces of information to each other, eg *Are girls in the class taller on average than boys?*
Less able: assist with filling in the information, especially some of the numerical data.

PLENARY

Ask children for examples of the questions they devised. *Which questions were most popular? What information would it be most useful to know?* Revise the stages of the data handling process. Can the children list them in the correct order?

LESSON 2 + 3

RESOURCES

Squared paper; pencils and paper.

PREPARATION

None.

LEARNING OUTCOMES

ORAL AND MENTAL STARTER
● Derive quickly doubles of all numbers to 50 and the corresponding halves.

MAIN TEACHING ACTIVITY
● Solve a problem by collecting quickly, organising, representing and interpreting data using a tally chart.

VOCABULARY

As previous
lesson plus
tally chart,
bundles of
five.

ORAL AND MENTAL STARTER

BIG FIVE-0: Repeat the whole class work part of the **Main teaching activity** in Lesson 1, Unit 8.

MAIN TEACHING ACTIVITY

TALLY-HO: Show the children on the board how to record items in a count by using tallying. Explain that it involves bundles of five. Four items are recorded by short vertical strokes while the fifth tally mark consists of a diagonal line across them: ‖‖‖ .

Then gather information from the class, for example on the pets children keep. Let different children take turns to do the tallying on the board. For example:

type of pet	number of pets	total
dog	ЖЖ	
cat	ЖЖ ЖЖ III	
rabbit	III	
hamster	ЖЖ I	
gold fish	III	

The children then work in pairs or small groups to devise questions that will enable them to interrogate the tally chart, eg *Which is the most/least popular pet? How many pets are there all together? How many pets live inside the house?* They should then use the chart to answer their questions.

DIFFERENTIATION

More able: devise their own topic for the survey and collect the information themselves. Less able: provide help when counting in fives or converting information into tally marks and with writing the questions.

PLENARY

Put up some low numbers on the board and ask children to come out and record them using the tallying method, eg 7 would be IIII II and 21 would be ЖЖ ЖЖ ЖЖ ЖЖ I. Children then provide questions they have devised for the pets survey and give the answers.

LESSON 3

Repeat the **Oral and mental starter** from Lesson 2. In the **Main teaching activity** provide the children with the following information or devise another topic: 'The favourite fruits of children in two classes in a school – apples 18, oranges 10, peaches 6, grapes 9, kiwi fruit 4, pear 2, strawberry 5 and melon 6'. Children should convert the information into a tally chart using bundles of five on squared paper and again devise a set of questions based on their results. For **Differentiation** see Lesson 2. In the **Plenary** ask children to show how they recorded results. Ask them for the questions they devised and together check the answers. Some may be able to provide their own data to discuss.

LESSON 4 +5

RESOURCES

Squared paper; cardboard/plastic stencils of vehicles; copies of photocopiable page 77 ('Music time'); pencils.

PREPARATION;

Provide a set of stencils for each group. Photocopy 'Music time' (page 77), one per child.

LEARNING OUTCOMES

ORAL AND MENTAL STARTER
● Identify near doubles using known doubles.

MAIN TEACHING ACTIVITY
● Solve a problem by collecting quickly, organising, representing and interpreting data using pictograms.

ORAL AND MENTAL STARTER

NEAR DOUBLES: Repeat the activity from Lesson 6, Units 2–3 and this time include three-digit numbers.

VOCABULARY

As for previous lessons plus pictograms, symbol, units.

MAIN TEACHING ACTIVITY

IN THE PICTURE: Revise the main stages in the process of handling data, from Lesson 1. Check that they know what a pictogram is: a type of chart or graph that shows information using diagrams or drawings. Explain that the diagram or symbol used can represent one unit but can also show more than one unit. Show some examples on the board where one symbol can represent one or two, five or ten.

These two symbols could mean two apples, four apples, ten apples or twenty apples depending on what each symbol represents.

Display this information: Cars 32; lorries 6; vans 15; buses 1; motor cycles 12; bicycles 4.

In pairs, the children decide what each symbol should represent and then make a pictogram by drawing a pair of axes on squared paper, then drawing round the stencils of the vehicles. If stencils are not available, they should draw their own pictures. Explain that the pictures can be placed horizontally or vertically. The pictogram will need a title and the chart must show many items each symbol stands for:

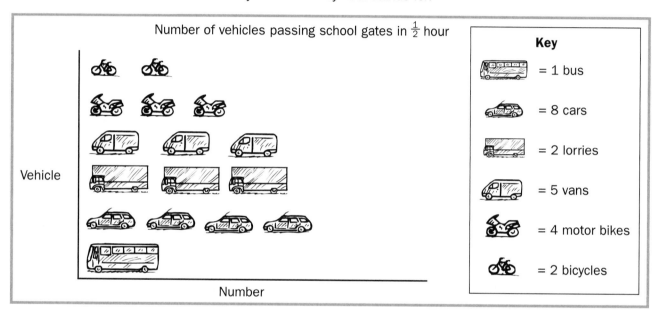

They then prepare questions that can be answered by looking at the pictogram and swap these with another pair to answer, eg *Which vehicle was seen most/least? What was the total number of motor vehicles?*

DIFFERENTIATION

More able: encourage them to provide a question first and then collect information for a pictogram in order to find a solution, eg *Do more cars than buses pass the school gates in a particular half hour period? Why might this happen?*

Less able: ensure they fully understand how to use a pictogram with a one-to-one representation before moving on to other units.

PLENARY

Ask children out to display and discuss the pictograms they have made. *What information did the traffic survey provide? What questions did it help answer? Why do you think there were more cars than anything else? Can you explain why there was only one bus in the half hour period? Did the time of day chosen matter? Why?*

LESSON 5

In the **Oral and mental starter** repeat NEAR DOUBLES from Lesson 4, but with different numbers. In the **Main teaching activity** children complete 'Music time' (page 77). For **Differentiation** ask the more able children to devise some more questions of their own for a partner to answer. Work with the less able to give support where it is needed. In the **Plenary** go through the children's answers and discuss their findings.

Music time

Some children at Weston School were asked to name their favourite percussion instruments. This information was turned into a pictogram. Each picture represents five instruments. Look carefully at the pictogram and then answer the questions.

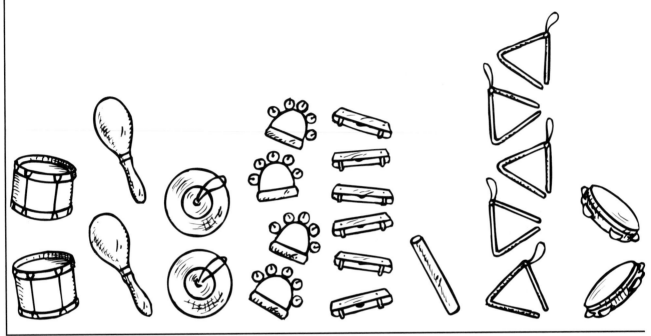

| drums | maracas | cymbals | sleigh bells | chime bars | claves | triangles | tambourines |

1. How many cymbals are there? _____

2. How many triangles are there? _____

3. How many claves and drums are there altogether? _____

4. Which instrument is there least of? _____

5. Which instrument is there most of? _____

6. Which four instruments were chosen by the same number of children?

_____

7. How many children took part in the survey?_____

8. Which of these is your favourite instrument? _____

UNIT 14: Assess & Review

Choose from the following activities over the next two lessons. During the group activities, some of the children can complete assessment worksheets 2a and 2b. These assess skills in adding/subtracting 1, 10, 100 and 1000 to/from any integer and counting on/back in tens, hundreds, thousands from any whole number up to 10000; rounding any positive integer less than 1000 to the nearest 10 or 100; multiplying or dividing any integer up to 1000 by 10 (whole number answers) and understanding the effect; beginning to multiply by 100; recognising simple fractions that are several parts of a whole and mixed numbers.

RESOURCES

Tables bingo cards from Lesson 2, Unit 8; division questions related to the 2, 5 and 10 times tables for number up to 50; set of cards each with number between 0 and 50 written on and the corresponding double or half on another card; cards for doubling/halving; prepared word problems in story form, and options; coloured counters/beads/cubes; information for pictogram; squared paper; rulers, coloured pencils.

ORAL AND MENTAL STARTER

ASSESSMENT

● Can the children: show they **know by heart multiplication and division facts for the 2, 3, 4, 5 and 10 times tables**; derive quickly doubles of all whole numbers to 50 and the corresponding halves?

MULTIPLICATION AND DIVISION FACTS: Use the games TABLES BINGO (Lesson 2, Unit 8) and DIVISION QUIZ (Lesson 3, Unit 8) more formally to check children know the 2, 3, 4, 5 and 10 times tables. For TABLES BINGO collect cards in to check the answers with the children. Check correct answers cards are held up when playing DIVISION QUIZ.

BIG FIVE-0: Split the doubles and halves cards into two piles and ask children to pair them up. Play doubles first, eg 16 pairs with 32. Then switch to halves, eg 22 pairs with 11.

GROUP ACTIVITIES

ASSESSMENT

● Can the children: use all four operations to solve word problems involving numbers in 'real life', money and measures; begin to relate fractions to division and find simple fractions of numbers or quantities; solve a problem by collecting, organising, representing and interpreting data in tables including pictograms?

WORD PROBLEMS: Give the children the prepared word problems in story form and provide them with a range of options for working them out, eg *David saves 70p one week and 25p the next week. How much has he saved so far?* Options: *Which operation should you use: 70p + 25p, 70p ÷ 25p or 70p + 25p?* They then work out the correct answer. Ask children to make up their own stories with a range of answer options and swap them within the group.

USING FRACTIONS: Remind the children that a half of 20 is another way of saying $20 \div 2$, that one-quarter of 8 is $8 \div 4$ and one-tenth of 70 is $70 \div 10$. Ask questions such as: *What is a half of 10? What is a quarter of 16? What is a third of 15? What is a fifth of 30? What is a tenth of 30?* Children should assemble the correct number of coloured counters, beads or cubes to show the right answer.

PICTOGRAMS: Provide the children with some suitable information that they can then in pairs make into a pictogram. For example, number of children in the class who have travelled in the following vehicles: Plane: 25; Car: 31; Bicycle: 29; Bus: 26; Lorry: 4; Van: 7. Discuss important issues with the group: *What information needs to be shown? How will the pictogram be drawn using axes? What symbols will be used? How many items will each symbol represent? What questions will be needed to interpret the information? What answers will they produce? What problems does this help to solve?*

Assessment 2a

Fill in the gaps in these number sequences

75	76	77	☐	☐	80	81
99	☐	☐	☐	103	104	105
115	125	135	☐	☐	165	175
675	775	☐	975	☐	☐	
4563	5563	6563	☐	☐	9563	

Add 1 to these numbers

89 ☐   197 ☐   2000 ☐   3054 ☐

Add 10 to these numbers

86 ☐   145 ☐   2000 ☐   6540 ☐

Add 100 to these numbers

92 ☐   257 ☐   954 ☐   1876 ☐

Add 1000 to these numbers

17 ☐   917 ☐   1645 ☐   8074 ☐

Subtract 1 from these numbers:
100   204   1794   9999
☐   ☐   ☐   ☐

Subtract 10 from these numbers:
86   145   2000   6540
☐   ☐   ☐   ☐

Subtract 100 from these numbers:
125   652   5672   8124
☐   ☐   ☐   ☐

Subtract 1000 from these numbers:
1005   2836   7490   8006
☐   ☐   ☐   ☐

● Add/subtract 1, 10, 100 and 1000 to/from an integer and count on or back in tens, hundreds, thousands from any whole number up to 10 000.
● **Round any positive integer less than 1000 to the nearest 10 or 100.**

Name

Assessment 2b

Multiply by 10:

a. 7   b. 15   c. 152   d. 263   e. 509

Divide by 10:

a. 60   b. 180   c. 240   d. 510   e. 6300

Multiply by 100:

a. 9   b. 12   c. 53   d. 79   e. 145

Complete these statements:

a. $\boxed{} \times 10 = 210$ c. $\boxed{} \times 100 = 2500$ e. $640 \div \boxed{} = 64$

b. $47 \times \boxed{} = 470$ d. $\boxed{} \div 10 = 8$ f. $53 \times \boxed{} = 5300$

Used squared paper and coloured pencils to show these fractions and mixed numbers:

a. $\frac{1}{2}$ e. $1\frac{1}{2}$

b. $\frac{3}{4}$ f. $3\frac{1}{4}$

c. $\frac{2}{3}$ g. $2\frac{1}{5}$

d. $\frac{7}{10}$ e. $3\frac{4}{10}$

● Multiply or divide any integer up to 1000 by 10. Begin to multiply by 100.
● **Recognise simple fractions that are several parts of a whole and mixed numbers.**

TERM 2

Term 2 introduces written methods for column addition and subtraction and refines written methods for multiplication and division. Work on remainders is developed and children are taught when to round up and when to round down. Children are introduced to the symbols < (less than) and > (greater than) and are taught to use them, with = (equals), to compare numbers. They learn to recognise and extend number sequences. In measurement, the focus is on mass. In fractions, children are introduced to the relationship with decimals and to equivalent fractions and pairs of fractions that total 1. Children classify shapes using different criteria and use co-ordinates to describe different points. Bar charts and sorting diagrams are introduced in data-handling work and understanding of pictograms is developed.

ENLARGE THIS SHEET TO A3 AND USE IT AS YOUR MEDIUM-TERM PLANNING GRID.

Oral and mental: Multiply any integer up to 1000 by 10, and understand the effect; begin to multiply by 100. Count on or back in tens, hundreds or thousands up to 10000. **Use known number facts and place value to add or subtract mentally, including any pair of two-digit whole numbers.** Consolidate knowing by heart addition and subtraction facts for all numbers to 20. Derive quickly doubles of all whole numbers to 50; doubles of multiples of 10 to 500 and of 100 to 5000, and the corresponding halves. Extend number sequences formed by counting from any number in steps of constant size. Derive quickly all number pairs that total 100.

UNIT	TOPIC	OBJECTIVES: CHILDREN WILL BE TAUGHT TO...
1	Place value, ordering and rounding Reading numbers from scales	● Read and write the vocabulary of comparing and ordering numbers. **Use symbols correctly, including less than (<), greater than (>), equals (=).** Give one or more numbers lying between two given numbers and order a set of whole numbers less than 10000. ● Read and write the vocabulary of estimation and approximation. **Round any positive integer less than 1000 to the nearest 10 or 100.** ● Recognise negative numbers. ● Record estimates and readings from scales to a suitable degree of accuracy.
2–3	Understanding + and – Mental calculation strategies (+ and –) Pencil and paper procedures (+ and –) Money and 'real life' problems Making decisions and checking results	● Consolidate understanding of relationship between + and –. Understand the principles (not the names) of the commutative and associative laws as they apply or not to addition and subtraction. ● Identify near doubles, using known doubles. ● Partition into tens and units, adding the tens first. ● Add 3 or 4 small numbers, finding pairs totalling 10, or 9 or 11. Add three two-digit multiples of 10. ● Use informal pencil and paper methods to support, record or explain additions/subtractions. ● **Choose and use appropriate number operations and appropriate ways of calculating (mental, mental with jottings, pencil and paper) to solve problems.** ● Use all four operations to solve word problems involving numbers in 'real life', including money. ● Check with the inverse operation.
4–6	Measures, including problems Shape and space Reasoning about shapes	● Use, read and write standard metric units. ● **Know the relationships between familiar units of length, mass and capacity.** ● Suggest suitable units and measuring equipment to estimate or measure length, mass or capacity. Know the equivalent of one-half, one-quarter and one-tenth of 1km, 1m, 1kg and 1l in m, cm, g, ml. Convert up to 1000 centimetres to metres and vice versa. ● Record estimates and readings from scales to a suitable degree of accuracy. ● Use all four operations to solve word problems involving measures. ● Measure and calculate the perimeter and area of rectangles and other simple shapes, using counting methods and standard units (cm, cm²). ● Sketch the reflection of a simple pattern in a mirror line parallel to one side. ● Describe and find the position of a point on a grid of squares where the lines are numbered. ● Recognise and use the eight compass directions. ● **Classify polygons using criteria such as symmetry properties.** ● Make and investigate a general statement about familiar shapes by finding examples that satisfy it.
7	Assess and review	See the key objectives listed on the relevant pages.

Oral and mental: Know by heart multiplication facts for 2, 3, 4, 5 and 10 times tables. Extend number sequences formed by counting from any number in steps of constant size. Begin to know multiplication facts for 6, 7, 8 and 9 times tables. **Derive quickly division facts corresponding to 2, 3, 4, 5 and 10 times tables. Recognise simple fractions, and the equivalence of simple fractions.**

UNIT	TOPIC	OBJECTIVES: CHILDREN WILL BE TAUGHT TO...
8	Properties of numbers Reasoning about numbers	● Recognise and extend number sequences formed by counting from any number in steps of constant size, extending beyond zero when counting back. ● Recognise odd and even numbers up to 1000, and some of their properties. ● Explain methods and reasoning about numbers orally and in writing. ● Solve mathematical problems or puzzles, recognise and explain patterns and relationships, generalise and predict. Suggest extensions by asking 'What if...?' ● Make and investigate a general statement about familiar numbers by finding examples that satisfy it.
9–10	Understanding × and ÷ Mental calculation strategies (× and ÷) Pencil and paper procedures (× and ÷) Money and 'real life' problems Making decisions and checking results	● Begin to know multiplication facts for 6, 7, 8 and 9 times tables. ● Extend understanding of × and ÷, and their relationship to each other and to + and –. Understand the principles of the commutative, associative and distributive laws as they apply to multiplication. ● **Find remainders after division.** ● Use doubling or halving, starting from known facts. ● Partition. ● Use the relationship between multiplication and division. ● Approximate first. Use informal pencil and paper methods to support, record or explain multiplications and divisions. Develop and refine written methods for TU × U, TU ÷ U. ● Use all four operations to solve word problems involving numbers in 'real life' and money. ● Check with the inverse operation.
11	Fractions and decimals	● Use fraction notation. **Recognise simple fractions that are several parts of a whole; recognise the equivalence of simple fractions.** Identify two simple fractions with a total of 1. ● Order simple fractions. ● Begin to relate fractions to division and find simple fractions of numbers, quantities or shapes.
12	Handling data	● Solve a problem by collecting quickly, organising and representing data in charts and pictograms.
13	Assess and review	See the key objectives listed on the relevant pages.

UNIT 1

ORGANISATION (3 LESSONS)

	LEARNING OUTCOMES	ORAL AND MENTAL STARTER	MAIN TEACHING ACTIVITY	PLENARY
LESSON 1	● Read and write the vocabulary of comparing and ordering numbers. **Use symbols correctly, including less than (<), greater than (>), equals (=).** Give one or more numbers lying between two given numbers and order a set of whole numbers less than 10000.	CHANGE POSITION: Multiply by 10 and 100.	MORE OR LESS: Complete number sentences using <, > and = symbols.	Order numbers.
LESSON 2	● Record estimates and readings from scales to a suitable degree of accuracy. ● Recognise negative numbers.	NUMBER CHAINS: Count on and back in 10s, 100s and 1000s.	PLUS AND MINUS: Order negative numbers.	Do number counts that extend into negative numbers.
LESSON 3	● Read and write the vocabulary of estimation and approximation. **Round any integer less than 1000 to the nearest 10 or 100.**	DIGIT ADDITION: Add mentally single-digit numbers.	ROUND TO THE NEAREST TEN: Round numbers to the nearest 10.	Share examples and extend to rounding to the nearest hundred.

ORAL AND MENTAL SKILLS   Multiply any integer up to 1000 by 10, and understand the effect; begin to multiply by 100. Count on or back in tens, hundreds or thousands from any whole number up to 10000. **Use known number facts and place value to add or subtract mentally.**

Lessons 1 and 2 are shown in full. Lesson 3 is provided in outline as an extension of what has already been taught.

RESOURCES

Number fans prepared for Lesson 1, Unit 1, Term 1; washing line; pegs; 0–30 number cards; large <, >, = signs; copies of photocopiable page 86 ('Comparing numbers'); number cards from the range 0–10000; pencils.

PREPARATION

Hang the washing line where the children can reach it and have integer and sign cards and pegs readily available. Prepare the set of 0–30 number cards and random number cards from the range 0–10000.

LEARNING OUTCOMES

ORAL AND MENTAL STARTER
● Multiply any integer less than 1000 by 10 (whole-number answers) and understand the effect. Begin to multiply by 100.

MAIN TEACHING ACTIVITY
● Read and write the vocabulary of comparing and ordering numbers. **Use symbols correctly, including less than (<), greater than (>), equals (=).** Give one or more numbers lying between two given numbers and order a set of whole numbers less than 10000.

ORAL AND MENTAL STARTER

CHANGE POSITION: Remind children that when they multiply by 10 the whole number moves one position to the left leaving the units column with a zero. Do not say you add a nought. Call out a number, the children multiply this by 10 and show their answer on their number fans. Repeat for other numbers, eg 56 × 10, 125 × 10. Explain to the children that when you multiply by 100 the whole number moves two positions to the left, leaving both the units and the tens column with zeros. Give some examples then call out single-digit numbers for the children to multiply by 100, then two-digit numbers.

MAIN TEACHING ACTIVITY

MORE OR LESS: Display two number cards, say 5 and 12. Say: *12 is bigger than, or greater than, 5. This can be written as 12 > 5.* Point out that the wider part of the symbol > faces the larger number. Write 5 < 12 and say this means 5 is less than, (or smaller than) 12. Again point out that the wider part of the symbol faces the larger number. Peg the two cards and the relevant sign on to the washing line. Then select two other numbers and invite a child to peg the numbers and the appropriate symbol on the line. Ask: *Is there another way they can be positioned?* Repeat for other numbers. Write a simple addition on the board, eg 5 + 7, then write = and ask a child to complete the number sentence. Next write 5 + 7 > and ask a child to complete the number sentence. Let several children give different answers, then point out that there is only one answer to 5 + 7 = but a whole range of answers for 5 + 7 >. Repeat for 5 + 7 <. Then write on the board 10 < ? < 25 and peg up the numbers and symbols on the washing line. Ask different children to complete the number sentence by pegging a number in the gap. In pairs, they then complete 'Comparing numbers' (page 86).

DIFFERENTIATION

More able: go on to generate their own number sentences using several numbers.
Less able: give them the digits 0 to 10 and < and > signs and ask them to make up 'greater than' and 'less than' number sentences.

PLENARY

Go through their answers. Then hold up number cards from the range 0–10,000 and ask children to peg them on the washing line. As each number is added it should be placed in 'order'. Ask: *Is it bigger than...? Is it smaller than...? Which comes next?*

RESOURCES

–100 to +100 class number line; thermometer; drawn thermometer; sets of cards of positive and negative whole numbers; pencil and paper.

PREPARATION

On a large sheet of paper draw a thermometer with a scale from –10 to +30°C. Prepare one set of positive and negative whole numbers per group of four, within a range suitable for that ability level.

LEARNING OUTCOMES

ORAL AND MENTAL STARTER
● Count on or back in tens, hundreds or thousands from any whole number up to 10000.

MAIN TEACHING ACTIVITY
● Record estimates and readings from scales to a suitable degree of accuracy.
● Recognise negative numbers.

ORAL AND MENTAL STARTER

NUMBER CHAINS: Start from 10, and together count on in tens up to at least 200, then from 200 count back in tens. Next start at 5 and count on in tens up to 205, and then back again. Repeat with other starting points, eg 17, 66, 154, 3405. Next, repeat the activity counting on and back in 100s; and then in 1000s.

MAIN TEACHING ACTIVITY

PLUS AND MINUS: Write 'negative numbers' on the board and explain that these are numbers that are less than zero. Show them on the number line. Together count from 0 to 10 then backwards through 0 to –1, –2 ... up to –10. Then use the number line to count in 2s, 5s, 10s and so on, each time counting forwards from zero for at least ten steps and then backwards through zero. Show children a thermometer and display the one you have drawn. Discuss the scale. Tell them that when negative numbers show on the thermometer it means the temperature is below freezing. Say temperatures from –10 to +30ºC for individual children to show you on the scale. Then give them sets of positive and negative numbers, say, 20, –15, 8, –2, and 15, for them to put in order. List those that are < zero and those that are > zero. In groups of four, the children then play PLUS AND MINUS. Remove the class number line out of view before they start play.

They start by dealing two of the plus and minus number cards to each child, placing the remaining cards face down in a pile. The first player places his/her cards in order on the table. The next child must add his/her cards in sequence. They then take it in turns to select a card from the pile to add to the sequence. When all the cards are placed they record the sequence before playing again.

DIFFERENTIATION

More able: give them a selection of positive and negative numbers from a set range for them to put in order and complete the set.
Less able: limit the range of the cards they use in the game, eg –10 to +10.

PLENARY

Check their number sequences from the game on the class number line. Use different starting numbers for counts in 2s, 5s, 10s within the range –100 to + 100.

LESSON 3

RESOURCES	Number fans; class number line with tens and hundreds marked in a different colour; individual number lines for less able group, prepared from photocopiable resource sheet A; 0–9 dice, one per pair; paper and pencils.
LEARNING OUTCOMES	**ORAL AND MENTAL STARTER** ● **Use known number facts and place value to add or subtract mentally.** **MAIN TEACHING ACTIVITY** ● Read and write the vocabulary of estimation and approximation. **Round any integer less than 1000 to the nearest 10 or 100.**
ORAL AND MENTAL STARTER	DIGIT ADDITION: Call out a series of single-digit numbers for children to add mentally, holding up their number fans with the answer. Start with two numbers, eg 7 + 6, and build up to five or six, eg 5 + 6 + 8 + 9 + 7 + 4.
MAIN TEACHING ACTIVITY	ROUND TO THE NEAREST TEN: Ask the children for examples when we do not always need to know exact quantities and can round numbers up or down. Give supermarket shopping as an example: by rounding prices to the nearest 10p or even £1 and totalling we can keep track of how much we are spending as we fill our trolley. Ask: *What do you think 17 rounded to the nearest ten would be?* Refer to the number line and ask a child to point out 17. Ask: *Which is the nearest multiple of ten to 17?* Repeat for other numbers, then give 35. Children may suggest either 30 or 40. Remind them that when a number ends in 5 they should always 'round *up*'. In pairs, the children roll their dice twice to generate a two-digit number, recording the original number in one column, and the number rounded to the nearest 10 in the other column.
DIFFERENTIATION	More able: roll the dice three times to generate three-digit numbers. Round to the nearest 100 as well as the nearest 10. Less able: encourage them to find the number on the number line then look for the nearest 10.
PLENARY	Reinforce the principles of rounding. Let children explain some of the examples they have generated. Introduce rounding to the nearest 100 using examples from the more able group.

Comparing numbers

1. Complete these number sentences using the =, < or > symbols.

a. 45 + 39 ☐ 80

b. 86 – 28 ☐ 62

c. 98 – 67 ☐ 50

d. 58 + 35 ☐ 93

2. Complete these number sentences:

a. 36 + 23 > ☐

b. 76 – 34 < ☐

c. 5 + 25 = ☐

d. 84 – ☐ > 53

e. 56 + ☐ < 100

f. 48 – ☐ > 20

g. ☐ + ☐ = 76

h. ☐ – ☐ = 44

i. ☐ + ☐ < ☐ + ☐

j. ☐ + ☐ > ☐ + 5

k. ☐ + 7 < 19 < ☐ – 6

l. ☐ – 5 > 12 < ☐ – 8

m. 46 – 27 > 17 + ☐

n. 58 + 10 > ☐ + ☐

o. ☐ + 13 < ☐ + 13

p. 26 – ☐ > 26 – ☐

q. Which questions could you have answered in a different way?

3. Write some number sentences of your own, using the =, < and > symbols.

UNITS 2-3

ORGANISATION (10 LESSONS)

LEARNING OUTCOMES	ORAL AND MENTAL STARTER	MAIN TEACHING ACTIVITY	PLENARY
LESSON 1 ● Consolidate understanding of relationship between + and –. Understand the principles (not the names) of the commutative and associative laws as they apply or not to addition and subtraction. ● Use informal pencil and paper methods to support, record or explain additions/subtractions.	DIGIT ADDITION: Add mentally single-digit numbers.	CHECK MY ADDING: Create number sentences.	Share and check calculations.
LESSON 2 ● Identify near doubles, using known doubles. ● Partition into tens and units, adding the tens first.	NUMBER CHAINS: Count on and back in 10s, 100s and 1000s.	DOUBLE UP: Calculate doubles, near doubles and halves.	Chant number chains for doubling, then for halving.
LESSON 3 ● Add three or four small numbers, finding pairs totalling 10, or 9 or 11. Add three two-digit multiples of 10.	MAKE 20: Make number bonds for 10, then for 20.	NEARLY TEN: Look for pairs totalling 9, 10 or 11 to aid addition.	Add three multiples of ten.
LESSON 4 ● Use informal pencil and paper methods to support, record or explain additions/subtractions.	MISSING NUMBER: Complete addition and subtraction sentences.	THAT'S HOW: Use pencil and paper for addition and subtraction.	Discuss methods and share recordings.
LESSON 5 ● **Choose and use appropriate number operations and appropriate ways of calculating (mental, mental with jottings, pencil and paper) to solve problems.** ● Check with the inverse operation. ● Check with an equivalent calculation.	WHICH NUMBER?: Guess the number from a given number sentence.	WHICH OPERATION?: Choose operations to solve problems and check results.	Compare methods used for calculating and for checking.
LESSON 6 +7 ● **Develop and refine written methods for column addition and subtraction for two whole numbers less than 1000, and addition of more than two such numbers.**	DOUBLE/HALVE NUMBER CHAINS: Chant number sequences for doubling.	COLUMN ADDITION: Calculate HTU + HTU sums using column addition.	Introduce addition of more than two integers less than 1000. Check answers.
LESSON 8 +9 ● **Develop and refine written methods for column addition and subtraction for two whole numbers less than 1000, and addition of more than two such numbers.** ● Check with the inverse operation.	MAKE 20: Make number bonds for 20.	COLUMN SUBTRACTION: Calculate HTU – TU using decomposition method.	Reinforce methods. Stress correct positions of digits. Use inverse operation to check answers.
LESSON 10 ● Use all four operations to solve word problems involving numbers in 'real life' and money, using one or more steps.	EQUATION GAME: Give equivalent sums.	REAL-LIFE PROBLEMS: Use all four operations to solve problems.	Identify appropriate operation to solve problems.

ORAL AND MENTAL SKILLS Consolidate knowing by heart addition and subtraction facts for all numbers to 20. Count on or back in 10s, 100s or 1000s. Derive quickly doubles of all whole numbers to 50 and the corresponding halves. **Use known number facts and place value to add and subtract mentally.**

Lessons 1, 2, 4, 5, 6 and 8 are shown in full. Lessons 3 and 10 are shown in outline. Lessons 7 and 9 are developments of the previous lessons.

RESOURCES

Number fans; pencils and paper.

PREPARATION

Provide the number fans prepared for Lesson 1, Unit 1, Term 1.

LEARNING OUTCOMES

ORAL AND MENTAL STARTER
● Consolidate knowing by heart addition and subtraction facts for all numbers to 20.

MAIN TEACHING ACTIVITY
● Consolidate understanding of relationship between + and −. Understand the principles (not the names) of the commutative and associative laws as they apply or not to addition and subtraction.
● Use informal pencil and paper methods to support, record or explain additions/ subtractions.

VOCABULARY

Add; addition; subtract; subtraction; sum; total; sign; minus; leaves; inverse; equals; operation; digit.

ORAL AND MENTAL STARTER:

DIGIT ADDITION: Repeat the activity from Lesson 3, Unit 1, Term 2.

MAIN TEACHING ACTIVITY

CHECK MY ADDING: Write on the board *48 + 39* and *39 + 48* and ask the children to work out the answers. They may remember from previous work that the two answers will be the same as the order in which the numbers are added doesn't matter. Give other examples, then ask them to work out 87 − 48 and 87 − 39. Discuss the results. Point out that we can check the results of additions and subtractions by using the inverse operations, eg 48 + 39 = 87. Ask: *What would be the result of 48 minus 87?* They may say you cannot do it or may give the result as a negative number (−39). Point out that this is not the same as 87 − 48 and that with subtraction the order of the numbers *does* make a difference (commutative law does not apply to subtraction.) Give them three numbers to add, say 39, 48 and 66. Does the order matter? (Associative law of addition). Point out that a useful way to check an answer is to add the numbers in a different order. Write 38 + 29 + 47 on the board. In pairs, the children use the numbers to create number sentences. Ask them to record their work, showing their informal calculations and methods. Possible answers: 38 + 29 = 67; 38 + 47 = 85; 29 + 47 = 76; 67 + 47 = 114; 67 − 38 = 29; 114 − 38 = 76; 114 − 29 = 85. They can then repeat for three more two-digit integers of their choice.

DIFFERENTIATION

More able: use three-digit integers, eg 254, 123, 422.
Less able: use single-digit integers instead.

PLENARY

Ask the children to share examples. Reinforce the principles of commutativity and of using the inverse operation to check addition and subtraction.

RESOURCES

0–9 dice; 0–5 dice; pencils and paper.

PREPARATION

Provide 0–9 dice, one per pair and 0–5 dice for less able pairs.

LEARNING OUTCOMES
ORAL AND MENTAL STARTER
● Count on or back in tens, hundreds or thousands from any whole number up to 10,000.

MAIN TEACHING ACTIVITY
● Identify near doubles, using known doubles.
● Partition into tens and units, adding the tens first.

VOCABULARY

Double; twice; half; halve; whole; divide by 2; divide into 2.

ORAL AND MENTAL STARTER

NUMBER CHAINS: Repeat the activity from Lesson 1, Unit 1, Term 2, counting on in 10s, 100s and 1000s.

MAIN TEACHING ACTIVITY

DOUBLE UP: Give children numbers up to 50 for doubling such as 6, 10, 25, 40 (known doubles). Then ask: *What about double 36?* Explain that double 36 is the same as double 30 plus double 6. Record on the board: double 36 = double 30 + double 6 = 60 + 12 = 72. Repeat for other two-digit numbers. Point to the first example, double 36, and ask: *What happens if we halve 72?* Ensure that they remember that halving is the same as dividing by 2, in this instance to give 36. Explain that this can be calculated as half of 70 giving 35, plus half of 2 which is 1 making 36 in total. Repeat for the other numbers. Then remind the children of how to use known doubles to work out 'near doubles'. Write 25 + 26 on the board and explain that it is the same as (double 25) + 1. Give other examples. Next, look at doubles of multiples of 10, eg 70 + 70. Ask: *What is double 7?* Explain that double 70 is ten times 14 (giving 140). Give other examples. Repeat for near doubles, eg 120 + 130 calculated as double 120 plus 10. Give other examples. Then in pairs, the children each throw their 0–9 dice to generate a number from 10–99. They record this number and then its double. They repeat for five other numbers. They then join up with another pair, tell them the double and the other pair has to work out the half of that number.

DIFFERENTIATION

More able: work out what happens when they double their doubles, and halve their halves.
Less able: use 0–5 dice instead.

PLENARY

Together chant number chains, starting from 2 and doubling: 2, 4, 8, and so on, and then halving: 8, 4, 2. Repeat for other start numbers. Ask quick-fire doubling and halving questions around the class, including near doubles. Ask children to explain how they have worked out their answers.

LESSON 3

RESOUCES	Number fans, one per child; 0–9 dice, one per pair; pencils and paper.
LEARNING OUTCOMES	**ORAL AND MENTAL STARTER** ● Consolidate knowing by heart addition and subtraction facts for all numbers to 20. **MAIN TEACHING ACTIVITY** ● Add three or four small numbers, finding pairs totalling 10, or 9 or 11. Add three two-digit multiples of 10.
ORAL AND MENTAL STARTER	MAKE 20: Ask quick-fire questions for number bonds to make 10, then to make 20. Children should use their number fans to show the answers.
MAIN TEACHING ACTIVITY	NEARLY TEN: Call out three single-digit numbers for the children to add quickly and show their answer using their number fans. Discuss which are the easiest numbers to pair together. Remind them that they should be looking for pairs of numbers that make 9, 10 or 11 so that they can add 10 and then add or subtract 1 to adjust. In pairs, they roll their 0–9 dice three times then total the numbers, recording their calculations and answers.
DIFFERENTIATION	More able: add more than three numbers. Less able: use 0–5 dice.
PLENARY	Discuss what happens when multiples of ten are added.

LESSON 4

RESOURCES
Number fans; pencils and paper.

PREPARATION
Prepare a variety of addition and subtraction calculations for the group activities, using one-, two- and three-digit numbers.

LEARNING OUTCOMES

ORAL AND MENTAL STARTER
● **Use known number facts and place value to add and subtract mentally, including any pair of two-digit whole numbers.**

MAIN TEACHING ACTIVITY
● Use informal pencil and paper methods to support record or explain additions/ subtractions.

VOCABULARY
Add; subtract; calculate; method; right; correct; wrong; how did you work it out?

ORAL AND MENTAL STARTER

MISSING NUMBER: Say a number sentence with a missing number, for children to show the missing number on their number fans on the count of 3, eg *20 minus 'something' equals 13*; *5 plus 'something' plus 4 equals 14*.

MAIN TEACHING ACTIVITY

THAT'S HOW: Write 375 + 49 on the board and ask children to explain how they worked out their answer. Record their calculation on the board. For example, add the hundreds to get 300, then 70 to 40 to get 110, then 5 to 9 to get 14, and then add the totals to get 424. Another method may be 375 + 50 = 425, 49 = 50 – 1 so 375 + 49 = 425 – 1 = 424. Record both methods and ask: *Which is easiest?* Repeat for other sums. Stress that there is no right or wrong way as long as the calculations are correct, but some ways are quicker than others. Give children calculations to work out. Allow them to work in groups to explain, discuss and record their methods.

> Point out that different methods are more appropriate for some calculations. For example, for 299 + 399 the easiest way is:
>
> 299 = 300 – 1399 = 400 – 1
>
> *so* 299 + 399 = 300 – 1 + 400 – 1
> = 700 – 2
> = 698

DIFFERENTIATION

Differentiate by varying the complexity of the calculations for different groups. For example, more able 368 + 589; less able: 39 + 26.

PLENARY

Discuss methods, share strategies and allow children to explain and demonstrate their recording.

LESSON 5

RESOURCES

1–10 number cards; prepared number problems; pencils and paper.

PREPARATION

Prepare 1–10 number cards, one set for you and one set per child. Write on the board a problem of the type: 'I am going shopping and I have £15 to spend. My bus fare is £1.50 each way. I buy three books at £1.95 each. I share the money I have left with my two friends. How much do they get each?'. Prepare other examples of this type.

LEARNING OUTCOMES

ORAL AND MENTAL STARTER
● **Use known number facts and place value to add and subtract mentally, including any pair of two-digit whole numbers.**

MAIN TEACHING ACTIVITY
● **Choose and use appropriate number operations and appropriate ways of calculating (mental, mental with jottings, pencil and paper) to solve problems.**
● Check with the inverse operation.
● Check with an equivalent calculation.

VOCABULARY

Total; inverse; equals; calculate; calculations; method; answer.

ORAL AND MENTAL STARTER

WHICH NUMBER?: Select a number card and hide it from view. Give children a number sentence involving at least two operations whose answer is the number on your card. They guess the number. Children hold up a number card to show their answer. Turn over your card to reveal the number.

MAIN TEACHING ACTIVITY

WHICH OPERATION?: Tell the children that you are going to give them a number problem in words and you want them to tell you the operation they would use to solve it. Give one stage examples to start with, eg *Crisps cost 30p a packet. How much for six packets?*; *Plants can be packed in trays of 12. How many trays are needed for 100 plants?*; *Jack has eaten ¼ of his chocolate bar. How much is left?* Then discuss the problem on the board before asking the children in pairs to work it out, recording their calculations. Tell them to use different ways to check their answers. Remind them about inverse operations and that subtraction is the inverse of addition and division is the inverse of multiplication. If time, they work on your other prepared examples.

DIFFERENTIATION

More able: record the checking of their calculations.
Less able: give them a simpler problem with fewer operations.

PLENARY

Go through the solution to the problem and methods the children have used.

RESOURCES

Base 10 equipment; squared paper; pencils.

PREPARATION

Prepare HTU + HTU type addition sums for different ability levels, either taken from books or created yourself.

LEARNING OUTCOMES

ORAL AND MENTAL STARTER
● Derive quickly doubles of all whole numbers to 50 and the corresponding halves.

MAIN TEACHING ACTIVITY
● **Develop and refine written methods for column addition and subtraction for two whole numbers less than 1000, and addition of more than two such numbers.**

VOCABULARY

Add; addition; sum; total; exchange; column; units; tens; hundreds.

ORAL AND MENTAL STARTER

DOUBLE NUMBER CHAINS: Repeat the activity from Lesson 2, Unit 1, Term 2 but this time for doubling.

MAIN TEACHING ACTIVITY

COLUMN ADDITION: Remind the children that there are a variety of written methods for column addition, but in this lesson they are going to use the standard way. Write up the sum 245 + 353 and tell them to look at the place value of each of the digits. 245 is 2 hundreds, 4 tens and 5 units, 353 is 3 hundreds, 5 tens and 3 units. Show them how to write the sum vertically. Stress that the units must be directly under each other in the unit column and similarly for the tens and the hundreds columns:

Explain as you write that you are going to add the units first: *5 units plus 3 units equals 8 units.* Stress that the 8 must be recorded under the units column:

$$\begin{array}{r} 245 \\ + \ 353 \\ \hline 8 \end{array}$$

Now add the tens, 4 from the first number and 5 from the second, 90. Avoid just saying 4 add 5 is 9, talk about tens:

$$\begin{array}{r} 245 \\ + \ 353 \\ \hline 8 \\ 90 \end{array}$$

Then go to the hundreds: 2 hundreds plus 3 hundreds gives 500. Then add the three numbers to give the answer:

$$\begin{array}{r} 245 \\ + \ 353 \\ \hline 8 \\ 90 \\ 500 \\ \hline 598 \end{array}$$

This can also be demonstrated using base 10 apparatus or Big base. Write up another sum for a child to work out on the board, using this column method, say 624 + 273. Repeat for 327 + 545. In this example children will be prepared for carrying. Explain that we can reduce the number of lines that we use by writing for the first sum:

$$\begin{array}{r} 245 \\ + \ 353 \\ \hline 598 \end{array}$$

Talk this through as above starting with the least significant digit (the units). Then give them the sum 327 + 545. Explain and record the working as follows:

$$\begin{array}{r} 327 \\ + \ 545 \\ \hline 872 \\ {\scriptstyle 1} \end{array}$$

Again starting with the units, 7 units plus 5 units, gives 12 units, but 12 is one ten and two units. We can't put tens in the unit column so we can only write the 2 in the answer box and we must add on the ten in the tens column. This can be written underneath the line in the tens column. We now add the tens column, 2 tens and 4 tens equals 6 tens, but we have an extra ten to add on, giving us 7 tens. We can now write 7 in the tens column of the answer. Finally, we add up the hundreds, 3 hundreds plus 5 hundreds gives us 8 hundreds. We can write 8 in the hundreds column of the answer box. Our final answer is 872.

Again this can be reinforced using base 10 apparatus. Give a third example, say 578 + 246, for one child to write the sum vertically, and another to go through the addition process. Children then complete your prepared examples, on squared paper so that they keep the digits in their correct columns.

DIFFERENTIATION

More able: give them some examples involving zero in the answers and larger numbers, eg 783 + 117.
Less able: give them examples that do not involve carrying, or carrying from just units to tens. Let them use base 10 materials to add practically, exchanging ten units for a ten, ten tens for a hundred.

PLENARY

Introduce adding three integers less than 1000. Explain that the process is the same. Give an example where more than one ten or hundred is carried, eg 346 + 159 + 268.

LESSON 7

For the **Oral and mental starter** repeat the activity from Lesson 6 but this time for halving. For the **Main teaching activity** go through similar examples to Lesson 6, adding three numbers less than 1000 then four numbers, eg 104 + 36 + 50. Write a selection of numbers on the board, eg 299, 145, 403, 38, 87, 30, 576, for children to use to write their own sums and calculate the answers. For **Differentiation** work with the less able group to demonstrate practically using base 10 materials. Tell the more able children to add more numbers together, find the total of all the given numbers, find combinations of the numbers and check the overall totals. Use the **Plenary** to check answers. Ask a more able child to demonstrate the addition of the whole list of numbers.

LESSON 8 + 9

RESOURCES

Number fans; base 10 apparatus; 0–9 dice, one per pair; squared paper and pencils.

PREPARATION

Prepare some examples that do not involve decomposition for the less able group. These may be taken from published materials.

LEARNING OUTCOMES

ORAL AND MENTAL STARTER

● Consolidate knowing by heart addition and subtraction facts for all numbers to 20.

MAIN TEACHING ACTIVITY

● **Develop and refine written methods for column addition and subtraction for two whole numbers less than 1000, and addition of more than two such numbers.**

ORAL AND MENTAL STARTER

MAKE 20: Repeat the activity from Lesson 3, but just for number bonds for 20, and with two teams playing against each other against the clock.

MAIN TEACHING ACTIVITY

COLUMN SUBTRACTION: Write on the board 376 – 87. Demonstrate using decomposition:

376					
− 87 =		300 +	70 +	6	376 is three hundreds, seventy and six
	−		80 +	7	minus 87 which is eighty and seven
=		300 +	60 +	16	We can exchange one ten from the seventy, leaving sixty
	−		80 +	7	and add it to the six to make sixteen
=		200 +	160 +	16	We can exchange one hundred from the three hundred
	−		80 +	7	leaving two hundred and add it to the sixty to make 160
= 289		200 +	80 +	9	When we subtract each column the result is 289

VOCABULARY

Sum; total;
altogether;
subtract;
exchange;
column.

Give another example (546 – 59) and ask one child to write it vertically and another child to work through it on the board with help from the rest of the class. Remind them about putting the digits in the correct place and that we start at the right and work towards the left. Demonstrate using base 10 apparatus. Then, in pairs, children throw a dice three times to generate a three-digit number and then twice to generate a two-digit number to be subtracted from the first number. Tell them to set the sum out vertically and work through it in the way demonstrated.

DIFFERENTIATION

More able: encourage them to check their results using the inverse operation.
Less able: give them examples that do not involve decomposition. Let them use base 10 apparatus to work through the calculation practically.

PLENARY

Go through the method again. Then let children demonstrate their own calculations for the class. Reinforce the correct positioning of the digits.

LESSON 9

Repeat the **Oral and mental starter** and see if they can beat their previous score. In the **Main teaching activity** go through similar examples to Lesson 8. Then give the children examples from published materials to work through. Tell them to practise using their own informal methods and then use the standard method to check their answers. For **Differentiation**, vary the level of questions you provide for each group. In the **Plenary** go through examples together.

LESSON 10

RESOURCES	Prepared number problem of the type on the photocopiable sheet, but with only three questions; copies of photocopiable page 95 ('Downtown/Uptown School'), one per child; pencils and paper.
LEARNING OUTCOMES	**ORAL AND MENTAL STARTER** ● **Use known number facts and place value to add and subtract mentally, including any pair of two-digit whole numbers.** **MAIN TEACHING ACTIVITY** ● Use all four operations to solve word problems involving numbers in 'real life', including money, using one or more steps.
ORAL AND MENTAL STARTER	EQUATION GAME: Go through the prepared number problem. Give the children an addition or subtraction question and ask them for an equivalent question with the same answer, eg you say *26 plus 19*, they respond *9 plus 36*.
MAIN TEACHING ACTIVITY	REAL-LIFE PROBLEMS: The children work on their own to complete 'Downtown/Uptown School' (page 95). The answers are as follows: 1) 48, 51, 52; 2) 151; 3) 73 girls, 78 boys; 4) 505; 5) 302; 6) 453; 7) 30, 121; 8) 226, 1130; 9) 327; 10) six with 38, two with 37.
DIFFERENTIATION	More able: go on to write similar questions related to own school. Less able: work with this group, ensuring they know which operations to use.
PLENARY	Go through each question asking different children to identify the operation involved and show how they calculated the answer.

Downtown/Uptown School

Sam and Katie go to Downtown Infants School and their sister Olivia goes to Uptown Junior School. In the Infant School there are six classes. the two Reception classes have 24 children each, the two Year 1 classes have 25 and 26 children and the two Year 2 classes have 26 children in each class.

1. How many children are there in each year group?

2. How many children are there in the Infant School?

3. There are five more boys than girls in the Infant School,
How many girls are there? How many boys are there?

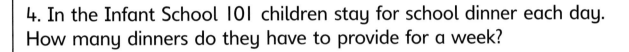

4. In the Infant School 101 children stay for school dinner each day. How many dinners do they have to provide for a week?

5. There are twice as many children in the Junior School than in the Infant School. How many children are in the Junior School?

6. How many children go to the Infant and Junior School altogether?

7. There were five children absent from each class one day in November. How many children were absent in the Infant School on that day? How many children attended the Infant School on that day?

8. 125 more children stay for dinner each day in the Junior School than in the Infant School. How many children stay each day in the Junior School? How many dinners does the kitchen have to make each week?

9. The Junior School is also going to provide the dinners for the infants. How many dinners does the kitchen have to provide each day?

10. In the Junior School there are eight classes, six have the same number of children in each, the remaining two have one less children in each. How many children are there in each class?

UNITS 4–6

ORGANISATION (13 LESSONS)

	LEARNING OUTCOMES	ORAL AND MENTAL STARTER	MAIN TEACHING ACTIVITY	PLENARY
LESSON 1 + 2	● Use, read and write standard metric units. ● **Know the relationships between familiar units of length, mass and capacity.** ● Suggest suitable units and measuring equipment to estimate or measure length, mass or capacity.	NUMBER CHAINS: Count on and back in 2s, 4s, 5s; 20s, 25s, 50s.	WHICH MEASURE?: Estimate then find actual measurements.	Recap on units of measurement. Discuss accuracy of estimates.
LESSON 3	● Know the equivalent of one-half, one-quarter and one-tenth of 1km, 1m, 1kg and 1l in m, cm, g, ml. Convert up to 1000 centimetres to metres, and vice versa.	AT SPEED: Give quick answers to addition and subtraction sums.	FRACTIONS OF A MEASURE: Record items that are exactly or near to $\frac{1}{2}$, $\frac{1}{4}$ and $\frac{1}{10}$ of the unit of measure.	Recap on ways to record measurements.
LESSON 4	● Record estimates and readings from scales to a suitable degree of accuracy.	DIGIT ADDITION: Add mentally single-digit numbers.	READING SCALES: Read measurements from different scales.	Discuss rounding when reading scales.
LESSON 5	● Use all four operations to solve problems involving measures.	WHICH NUMBER?: Guess the number from a given number sentence.	PARTY TIME: Work out quantities of ingredients for party cooking.	Check and explain answers.
LESSON 6	● Measure and calculate the perimeter and area of rectangles and other simple shapes, using counting methods and standard units (cm, cm^2).	MAKE 20: Make number bonds for 20.	COUNTING SQUARES: Count and measure perimeter and area of shapes.	Work out areas of shapes that involve counting part squares.
LESSON 7	● Sketch the reflection of a simple pattern in a mirror line parallel to one side (all sides parallel or perpendicular to the mirror line).	WHICH NUMBER?: Guess the number from a given number sentence.	REFLECTIONS: Draw reflections of shapes.	Share work. Discuss any difficulties.
LESSON 8	● Describe and find the position of a point on a grid of squares where the lines are numbered.	DOUBLING AND HALVING: Double and halve three-digit numbers.	CO-ORDINATE PICTURES: Draw pictures by locating co-ordinates.	Share work and use co-ordinates.
LESSON 9	● Recognise and use the eight compass directions.	NUMBER CHAINS: Count on and back in 2s, 4s, 5s, 20s, 25s, 50s.	COMPASS DIRECTIONS: Label a plan from given compass directions.	Children give compass directions for another child to follow.
LESSON 10	● **Classify polygons using criteria such as symmetry properties.**	EQUATION GAME: Give equivalent sums.	SHAPE SORT: Draw in lines of symmetry and sort shapes.	Discuss how the shapes were sorted. Investigate lines of symmetry.
LESSON 11	● Make and investigate a general statement about familiar shapes by finding examples that satisfy it.	MAKE 100: Make number bonds for 100.	GUESS MY SHAPE: Give clues for others to guess their shape.	Challenge the class with shape clues.

LEARNING OUTCOMES	ORAL AND MENTAL STARTER	MAIN TEACHING ACTIVITY	PLENARY
● Make and investigate a general statement about familiar shapes by finding examples that satisfy it.	GUESS MY SHAPE: Give clues for others to guess their shape.	SHAPE TREE: Classify shapes using tree diagrams.	Compare answers. Discuss shape trees.

LESSON 12 + 13

ORAL AND MENTAL SKILLS Extend number sequences formed by counting from any number in steps of constant size. **Use known number facts and place value to add or subtract mentally, including any pair of two-digit whole numbers.** Consolidate knowing by heart addition and subtraction facts for all numbers to 20; derive quickly all number pairs that total 100, doubles of multiples of 10 to 500 and of 100 to 5000.

Lessons 1, 3, 6, 8, 10 and 11 are shown in full. Lessons 2, 12 and 13 are developments of the previous lessons. Lessons 4, 5, 7 and 9 are shown in outline.

LESSON 1 + 2

RESOURCES

Variety of measuring apparatus, rulers, tape measures, scales, measuring jugs etc; pencils and paper.

PREPARATION

None.

LEARNING OUTCOMES

ORAL AND MENTAL STARTER
● Extend number sequences formed by counting from any number in steps of constant size.

MAIN TEACHING ACTIVITY
● Use, read and write standard metric units.
● **Know the relationships between familiar units of length, mass, and capacity.**
● Suggest suitable units and measuring equipment to estimate or measure length, mass or capacity.

ORAL AND MENTAL STARTER

NUMBER CHAINS: Repeat Lesson 2, Unit 1, Term 2, but this time count on and back in 2s, 4s and 5s to 100.

MAIN TEACHING ACTIVITY

WHICH MEASURE?: Brainstorm and record on the board any units of measurement that the children know. Explain that units such as feet, inches and miles are imperial measures. Tell them that you are going to be looking at metric measures. Go through basic relationships between familiar measures – mm, cm, m, km, g, kg, ml, l – giving examples of approximations of these, eg *the room is about 5m wide, a bag of sugar is 1kg, lemonade may be in 1 or 2 litre bottles*. Write on the board *10mm = 1cm* and *100cm = 1m*. Ask: *How many mm equal one metre?* Then write *1000mm = 1m*. Point out that 'milli' means one thousandth. Ask: *How many millilitres do you think would be in one litre?* Stress *milli*litres. Write *1000ml = 1l*. Ask: *How many grams in a kilogram?* Point out that 'kilo' means one thousand, then write *1000g = 1kg*. Ask children to estimate some measurements, eg *How tall is the door? How long is a pencil case? How much water will a vase hold? How much does a bag of clay weigh?* Discuss their estimates and then ask individual children to find the actual measurements. Remind them that a length of 125cm can also be written as 1.25m, similarly with mass and capacity. Then, in pairs, the children list items available in the classroom that they could measure, recording their estimates of these measures.

DIFFERENTIATION

More able: encourage them to use a wider range of measurements.

Less able: suggest items that they could measure. Limit them to one set of units of measurement, eg length or weight measure to nearest 1cm or 10g.

PLENARY

Discuss units of measurement. Ask: *What units would you use to measure the distance from London to Birmingham?* Repeat for other units of measure.

LESSON 2

As Lesson 1, but for the **Oral and mental starter** count in 20s, 25s and 50s. In the **Main teaching activity** they find the actual measurements of the items on their list. For **Differentiation**, encourage the more able to record to a greater degree of accuracy; the less able may need help taking the measurements. In the **Plenary** compare measurements with the estimates and compare the accuracy of different measuring apparatus.

RESOURCES

Number fans; measure recordings from previous lesson; measurements chart; pencils.

PREPARATION

Prepare an A3 version of this chart, then photocopy, one per group:

Length					Weight				
Less than 0.1m	About 0.1m	About 0.25m	About 0.5m	More than 0.5m	Less than 100g	About 100g	About 250g	About 500g	More than 500g

LEARNING OUTCOMES

ORAL AND MENTAL STARTER
● **Use known number facts and place value to add or subtract mentally, including any pair of two-digit whole numbers.**

MAIN TEACHING ACTIVITY
● Know the equivalent of one-half, one-quarter and one-tenth of 1km, 1m, 1kg and 1l in m, cm, g, ml. Convert up to 1000 centimetres to metres, and vice versa.

VOCABULARY

Half; quarter; tenth; metre; centimetre; millimetre; gram; kilogram; litre; millilitre.

ORAL AND MENTAL STARTER

AT SPEED: Give addition and subtraction sums involving two-digit numbers, encouraging a quick response. The children show their answers on their number fans. Remind them to use doubles and near doubles.

MAIN TEACHING ACTIVITY

FRACTIONS OF A MEASURE: Write on the board 100cm = 1m. Ask: *How many centimetres in half a metre? ...in one-quarter of a metre? What about $\frac{1}{10}$ metre?* Record the answers on the board: 50cm = $\frac{1}{2}$ m; 25cm = $\frac{1}{4}$ m; 10cm = $\frac{1}{10}$ m. Point out that these can also be written as: 0.5m; 0.25m; 0.1m. Ask if anyone measured anything that was about half a metre; ask for other suggestions of items in the room that measure about $\frac{1}{2}$ m. Repeat for $\frac{1}{4}$ m and $\frac{1}{10}$ m. Then repeat the whole process for kg. In groups, children complete the weighing and measuring chart using the items that they measured in the previous lesson, recording the measurement in the appropriate column.

DIFFERENTIATION

The more able can help the less able with recording.

PLENARY

Recap on how to record measurements. Ask questions such as: *What is another way to write half a metre?* (50cm or 0.5m) *How many millimetres in a metre? ...half a metre?*

LESSON 4

RESOURCES	Number fans; prepared examples of measurements for the class to measure (flip chart and copies of pairs); range of measuring items such as ruler, thermometer, weighing scales and measuring cylinders; pencils.
LEARNING OUTCOMES	**ORAL AND MENTAL STARTER** ● **Use known number facts and place value to add or subtract mentally.** **MAIN TEACHING ACTIVITY** ● Record estimates and readings from scales to a suitable degree of accuracy.
ORAL AND MENTAL STARTER	DIGIT ADDITION: Repeat activity from Lesson 3, Unit 1, Term 2.
MAIN TEACHING ACTIVITY	READING SCALES: Show the children scales on a ruler, thermometer, weighing scales, measuring cylinder. Give them measurements for individual children to point out on the scale. Point out that when we read scales we often have to go to the nearest mark on the scales. Discuss suitable degrees of accuracy for each scale. Children then work independently or in pairs to complete your prepared examples. Suggested measurements: 250g; 6cms; 35kgs; 750mls; –15C; 15C; 12C; 3¼ kg (or 3kgs 250g)
DIFFERENTIATION	More able: encourage them to give more precise readings. Less able: work with this group initially, demonstrating and discussing examples, using practical apparatus.
PLENARY	Discuss rounding when reading scales, referring to examples from the photocopiable.

LESSON 5

RESOURCES	Copies of photocopiable page 104 ('Baking for the party'); pencils.
LEARNING OUTCOMES	**ORAL AND MENTAL STARTER** ● **Use known number facts and place value to add or subtract mentally.** **MAIN TEACHING ACTIVITY** ● Use all four operations to solve problems involving measures.
ORAL AND MENTAL STARTER	WHICH NUMBER?: Repeat activity from Lesson 5, Units 2–3, Term 2.
MAIN TEACHING ACTIVITY	PARTY TIME: Ask the children for examples of situations when we need to weigh. Give examples from cooking, explaining that often when we are baking we need to increase or decrease quantities given on the recipe. Go through the first example on the photocopiable sheet together before children work in pairs to complete it.
DIFFERENTIATION	More able: suggest other quantities for each item, such as what is needed for 10 cheese straws. Less able: just work out the first recipe.
PLENARY	Go through the answers and let children explain their calculations.

LESSON 6

RESOURCES

Number fans, one per child; prepared rectangle; cm squared paper; pencils and paper.

PREPARATION

On an enlarged sheet of squared paper draw a rectangle 4 × 3.

LEARNING OBJECTIVE

ORAL AND MENTAL STARTER

● Consolidate knowing by heart addition and subtraction facts for all numbers to 20.

MAIN TEACHING ACTIVITY

● Measure and calculate the perimeter and area of rectangles and other simple shapes, using counting methods and standard units (cm, cm²).

VOCABULARY

Perimeter; area; rectangle.

ORAL AND MENTAL STARTER

MAKE 20: Repeat activity from Lesson 3, Units 2–3, Term 2.

MAIN TEACHING ACTIVITY

COUNTING SQUARES: Remind the children that perimeter is the distance around the edge of a shape and is measured in linear units such as cm and that area is a measurement of a surface and is two dimensional, so is measured in square units such as cm^2. Show them the rectangle on your enlarged squared paper and tell them that each square represents $1cm^2$. Together count the perimeter. Now ask a child to count the squares in the rectangle putting a cross in each square as it is counted. Explain that this gives the area in square units. The children then draw a rectangle on their squared paper, using complete squares. They swap with their partner to work out the perimeter and area of each other's rectangle. They then repeat for other shapes, each time using whole squares. Point out that as they are working on cm squared paper the units will be cm and cm^2.

DIFFERENTIATION

More able: suggest more complex shapes. Ask them to think about how they could work out the area of shapes that did not just include whole squares.
Less able: limit them to simple shapes. Suggest that they write in a number in each square as they count the squares.

PLENARY

Let children show their examples. Draw a triangle on the squared grid and ask the children to work out an approximate area by counting the squares. Count the whole squares first, then examine each part square and decide if it is > or < a half. If it is greater than a half count it as one and if it is less than a half discount it. Draw some other simple shapes and encourage the children to work out the approximate area.

RESOURCES	Number cards; dotty paper; rulers; mirrors, one per child; copies of photocopiable page 105 ('Reflections'), one per child; pencils.
LEARNING OUTCOMES	**ORAL AND MENTAL STARTER** ● **Use known number facts and place value to add or subtract mentally.** **MAIN TEACHING ACTIVITY** ● Sketch the reflection of a simple pattern in a mirror line parallel to one side (all sides parallel or perpendicular to the mirror line).
ORAL AND MENTAL STARTER	WHICH NUMBER?: Repeat activity from Lesson 5, Units 2–3, Term 2.
MAIN TEACHING ACTIVITY	REFLECTIONS: Give out the photocopiable sheet, 'Reflections', and explain to the children that they should draw and colour in a reflection of each shape, in the mirror line. They can use a mirror to check what the pattern should look like. When they have finished they draw their own pattern and its reflection in the mirror line.
DIFFERENTIATION	More able: encourage them to draw more complex designs. Less able: work with this group giving support where it is needed.
PLENARY	Let children show their patterns and reflections. Encourage them to fold the paper along the mirror line and to use a mirror to check the reflections. If some children have not drawn correct reflections encourage others to try and explain what has 'gone wrong'.

RESOURCES

HTU number fans; enlarged sheets of grid paper; squared paper; pencils.

PREPARATION

Provide number fans prepared for Lesson 1, Unit 1, Term 1. Draw horizontal and vertical axes on 2 separate large sheets of grid paper.

LEARNING OUTCOMES

ORAL AND MENTAL STARTER
● Derive quickly: doubles of multiples of 10 to 500; doubles of multiples of 100 to 5000; and the corresponding halves.

MAIN TEACHING ACTIVITY
● Describe and find the position on a grid of squares where the lines are numbered.

VOCABULARY

Co-ordinates; position; grid; horizontal; vertical.

ORAL AND MENTAL STARTER

DOUBLING AND HALVING: Give a multiple of 10 (up to 500) or multiple of 100 (up to 5000) for children to double or halve and then show their answer on their HTU number fan.

MAIN TEACHING ACTIVITY

CO-ORDINATE PICTURES: On your prepared grid, label the point where the axes meet 0, 0 and then label both axes up to 10. Explain to the children that each point is defined by co-ordinates and that the horizontal or x co-ordinate comes first followed by the vertical or y co-ordinate. Stress that the co-ordinates mark the point where the lines cross. Demonstrate some points on the grid, asking children to locate different points from given co-ordinates and vice versa. Display the other grid sheet. Give the following instructions for a different child to carry out each time. The other children follow the same instruction on their individual grids.
● Find the point 1,1 and mark it with a small cross. Find the point 9,1 and draw a line joining these two points.
● Find 9,7 and draw a line to join it to the point 9,1.
● Find 5,10 and draw a line from 9,7 to that point.
● Then draw a line from 5,10 to 1,7, then back to 1,1.
Ask: *What shape has been drawn?* (house) In pairs, the children draw in and write down the co-ordinates for other features on the house: windows, doors and so on.

DIFFERENTIATION

More able: go on to design their own grid pictures and write out a list of instructions for their partner to follow, in order for them to draw that picture.
Less able: ask them to add one item and then work out the co-ordinates.

PLENARY

Children should share their work. The more able group could give instructions for children to follow and to draw on the class grid.

LESSON 9

RESOURCES	Compass; enlarged compass scale; copies of photocopiable page 106 ('Compass points'), one per child; pencils.
LEARNING OUTCOME	**ORAL AND MENTAL STARTER** ● Extend number sequences formed by counting from any number in steps of constant size. **MAIN TEACHING ACTIVITY** ● Recognise and use the eight compass directions.
ORAL AND MENTAL STARTER	NUMBER CHAINS: Repeat Lesson 2, Unit 1, Term 2, but this time count on and back in 2s, 4s, 5s, 20s, 25s, 50s.
MAIN TEACHING ACTIVITY	COMPASS DIRECTIONS: Talk to children about the compass points and explain that they are directions. Demonstrate on the board the eight compass directions. Explain, for example, that W is a 90-degree turn in an anticlockwise direction from N, that NW is in between N and W. Children then complete 'Compass points' (page 106), working on their own.
DIFFERENTIATION	More able: on squared paper design their own plan on a bigger scale, giving compass directions for a route around the plan. Less able: do just the first part of the activity.
PLENARY	Label directions in the classroom and ask children to give directions for another child to follow to get from one part of the classroom to another.

RESOURCES

Prepared shapes; sets of 2-D shapes, including regular and irregular polygons; mirrors; sorting rings and labels; paper and pencils.

PREPARATION

On a large sheet of paper, draw the following shapes exactly: an isosceles triangle; a square; a rectangle; a circle; a right-angled triangle. Have sets of shapes ready for children to classify. Provide sorting rings and prepare card labels 'symmetrical' and 'not symmetrical' for less able group.

LEARNING OUTCOMES

ORAL AND MENTAL STARTER
● **Use known number facts and place value to add or subtract mentally, including any pair of two-digit whole numbers.**

MAIN TEACHING ACTIVITY
● **Classify polygons using criteria such as symmetry properties.**

VOCABULARY

Shape; polygon; regular; irregular; line of symmetry; square; triangle; rectangle; pentagon; hexagon; isosceles triangle; right-angled triangle; circle; semicircle.

ORAL AND MENTAL STARTER

EQUATION GAME: See Term 2, Units 2–3, Lesson 10.

MAIN TEACHING ACTIVITY

SHAPE SORT: Recap previous work with 2-D shapes, including regular and irregular. Say that you are looking for shapes that are symmetrical. Take a square and fold it in half. Use a mirror to show that each half is a mirror image of the other. Explain that this is called a line of symmetry. Go through the shapes on your sheet, asking children to draw in the lines of symmetry. Encourage the children to find all four lines on the square:

Point out that some shapes have more than one line of symmetry. With the circle, keep inviting different children to draw a line of symmetry to show that it has an infinite number of lines of symmetry that all pass through the centre. When they are unable to find a line of symmetry on the right-angled triangle point out that this shape is not symmetrical. In groups, the children sort a set of shapes into those that are symmetrical and those that are not.

DIFFERENTIATION

More able: further sort the shapes by the number of lines of symmetry. Then define their own criteria for sorting. Record their work in an appropriate way.
Less able: give them a set of shapes that are easily sorted. Give them sorting rings and labels and let them complete the task practically.

PLENARY

Talk about how the children sorted the shapes. Discuss how many lines of symmetry different shapes have. *What did you notice about regular shapes?*

LESSON 11 +12 +13

RESOURCES

Number fans; 2-D and 3-D shapes; sets of 2-D shapes; bags; large sheets of paper for recording; pens; for Lessons 12 and 13: copies of photocopiables pages 107 and 108 ('Shape tree 1and 2'); sets of shapes; pencils.

PREPARATION

Put a selection of shapes in a bag, one bag per group. Photocopy 'Shape tree 1' (page 107) and 'Shape tree 2' (page 108), enlarged to A3 size, one of each per group. Provide sets of shapes according to ability level to sort on the shape trees.

LEARNING OUTCOMES
ORAL AND MENTAL STARTER
● Derive quickly all number pairs that total 100.

MAIN TEACHING ACTIVITY
● Describe and visualise 3-D and 2-D shapes. Recognise equilateral and isosceles triangles.
● Classify polygons using criteria.

VOCABULARY

Line; side; edge; face; surface; angle; vertex; vertices; square; circle; semicircle, triangle; equilateral triangle; isosceles triangle; quadrilateral; rectangle; oblong; pentagon; hexagon; heptagon; octagon; polygon; regular; irregular.

ORAL AND MENTAL STARTER

MAKE 100: Repeat activity from Lesson 3, Units 2–3, Term 2, but for number bonds for 100.

MAIN TEACHING ACTIVITY

GUESS MY SHAPE: Recap work on 2-D and 3-D shapes. Hold up a rectangle and ask the children to tell you some of its properties, eg a 2-D shape, with 4 sides, and 4 right angles, opposite sides are the same length. Repeat for a cylinder and then for other shapes. Next describe a shape and ask the children to identify it. For example: *It has three sides; two sides are the same length; two angles are the same size.* (Isosceles triangle). Invite a child to come and give clues about a shape. In mixed ability groups of five–six, the children take turns to choose a shape from the bag without showing the rest of the group. They then give at least three clues about the shape for the others to guess. A member of the group should record the clues on a chart and draw the shape.

DIFFERENTIATION

More able children can help any less able children in their group who need support.

PLENARY

Each group chooses one shape from their chart and reads out the clues for the class to guess the shape. Point out to the children that there may be several shapes that match the first clue, but as they are given more clues, fewer shapes match, until eventually at the final clue their is only one shape that fits.

LESSON 12

For the **Oral and mental starter** use the GUESS MY SHAPE game from the Main teaching activity in Lesson 11. In the **Main teaching activity** the children classify shapes using a question tree. Demonstrate with a shape first, before the children complete the photocopiable sheet 'Shape tree 1'. For **Differentiation** ask the more able children to add extra shapes to the tree, inserting extra questions to accommodate the new shapes. Let the less able use only those shapes on the photocopiable. In the **Plenary** go through the questions and compare answers.

LESSON 13

Repeat the **Oral and mental starter** from Lesson 12. In the **Main teaching activity** the children work in groups using the photocopiable sheet 'Shape tree 2' to devise their own question tree to classify a set of given shapes, between four and eight shapes for each group. For **Differentiation** include both regular and irregular shapes for the more able group and limit the less able group to basic contrasting shapes, eg cube, triangle, cylinder and pentagon. In the **Plenary** let the children discuss their shape trees.

Baking for the party

You are going to do some baking for a party.
You need 24 cakes, 50 cheese straws and at least 48 biscuits.

**Ingredients for
10 biscuits**
100g margarine
150g flour
100g sugar
ginger

**Ingredients for
6 cakes**
200g flour
150g margarine
100g sugar
50g currants
1 egg

**Ingredients for
20 cheese straws**
170g flour
80g margarine
120g cheese

Work out the ingredients you need to bake the food for your party.
Write out the quantities for each recipe.

Total the amounts of each ingredient that you need and write out your
shopping list.

I will need _____ of flour

I will need _____ of sugar

I will need _____ of currants

I will need _____ of cheese

I will need _____ of margarine

Reflections

Draw the reflections of each of these shapes. The first one has been done for you.

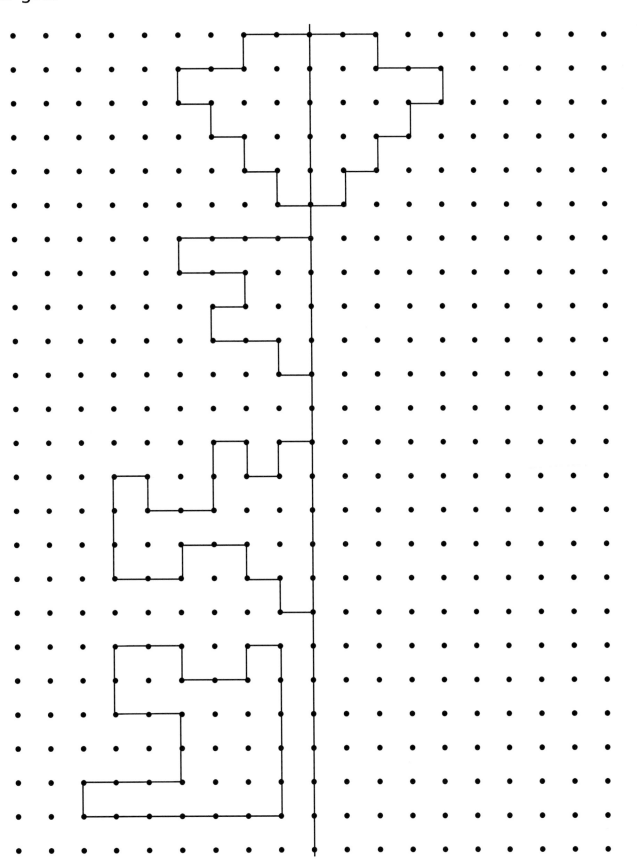

Compass points

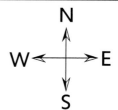

Use the information to label the buildings on this plan:

- Uptown Junior School is N from Sam's house
- Downtown Infants School is W from Sam's house.
- The Church is W of the Junior School and NW of Sam's house
- The supermarket is S of Sam's House
- The Post Office is SE of Sam's House
- The Newsagent's is SW of Sam's house
- The entrance to the park is W of Sam's house
- Ben is Sam's friend, his house is NE of Sam's House.

		Sam's house		

Draw some buildings on your own plan and give directions to find them:

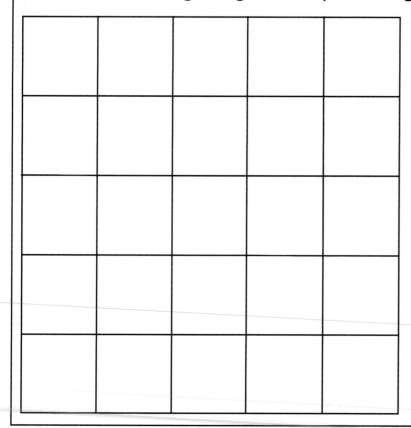

Shape tree 1

A set of three-dimensional shapes like these may help you:

    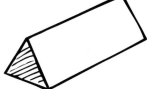 

Complete this tree diagram using each of these shapes in turn. Write the name of the shape in all of the appropriate places on the diagram.

Yes	Does the shape roll?	No

Does it have flat faces?

Yes	No

Does it have six faces?

Yes	No

Does it have two flat faces?

Yes	No

Are all the faces the same size and shape?

Yes	No

Choose another set of shapes and make up your own tree diagram.

Shape tree 2

Choose a set of different shapes. Write a question in the first circle, that will split the set of shapes into two. Follow the arrows and do the same again, writing a question in the circles to sort the shapes further.

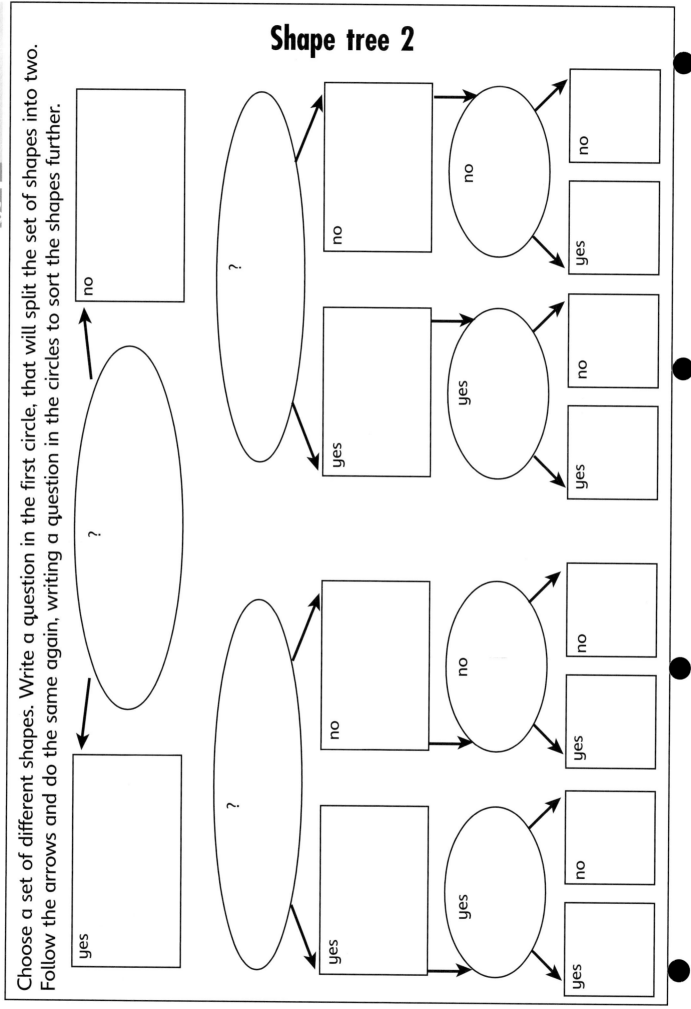

UNIT 7: Assess & Review

Choose from the following activities over the next two lessons. During the group activities, some of the children can complete assessment worksheets 3a and 3b. These assess skills in: using column addition and subtraction methods; checking results with equivalent calculations; choosing and using appropriate number operations and appropriate ways of calculating to solve problems; classifying polygons using different criteria; using the relationship between familiar units of length, mass, and capacity.

RESOURCES

Number fans; two-digit number cards; squared paper; rulers; measuring scales; items for weighing; pencils and paper.

ORAL AND MENTAL STARTER

ASSESSMENT

● Can the children: derive quickly all number pairs that total 100; **round any positive integer less than 1000 to the nearest 10 or 100; use known number facts and place value to add or subtract mentally, including any pair of two-digit whole numbers**?

MAKE 100: Given a two-digit number, the children, on the count of 3, show on their number fans the number that has to be added on to make 100. Repeat this several times, noting any children who are not ready with the answer or who give an incorrect one.

ROUNDING: Given a two-digit number, the children, on the count of 3, show on their number fans the number rounded to the nearest 10. Repeat several times then tell them that you want them to round to the nearest 100. Note the children who are hesitant with their answers.

HOW QUICK ARE YOU?: Call out addition and subtraction questions, such 37 + 39, 54 – 19, for children to calculate mentally then record their answers. Repeat each question once and allow children five seconds to answer.

GROUP ACTIVITIES

ASSESSMENT

● Can the children: **use symbols correctly, including less than (<), greater than (>), equals (=)**; measure and calculate the perimeter and area of rectangles and other simple shapes using counting methods and standard units (cm, cm^2); suggest suitable units and measuring equipment to estimate or measure mass; record estimates and readings from scales to a suitable degree of accuracy?

● Do the children: **know the relationship between familiar units of mass**?

USING SYMBOLS: Give each child two two-digit number cards for them to use to create a number sentence using the two numbers and adding any symbols, eg for cards 34, 17, write 17 < 34. Then give them another card and ask them to write a number sentence using all three cards, eg 34, 17, 21 (21 + 17) > 34. Use at least one set of cards where = can be used, eg 25, 52, 27. Question the children about their understanding of the symbols. Do they know when there is only one answer and when there are an infinite number of answers?

WHAT DOES IT WEIGH?: Ask the children to choose an item that they think weighs less than a kilogram and an item that weighs more than a kilogram. They should then weigh the items and record the results. Ask them to write their results in grams and then convert their answer to kilograms and grams. Repeat for other measures.

AREA AND PERIMETER: Ask the children to draw a rectangle on squared paper and then give it to their partners to measure and calculate the perimeter and area. Then ask them to draw shapes with particular perimeters and areas, eg *Draw a shape with an area of 12cm^2; Draw a shape with a perimeter of 12cm.*

Assessment 3a

Write your answers on the back of this sheet.

1. Write these sums in a column format and complete the calculations:

a. 327 + 362   b. 418 + 325   c. 302 + 409

d. 627 + 263   e. 538 + 262   f. 46 + 237 + 35

2. Now write these as column subtractions and calculate the answers:

a. 887-233   b. 928- 725   c. 404-272

d. 700 – 482   e. 820 – 387   f. 529 – 380

3. Do each of the following calculations in two different ways, record the methods you use then check that your answers are the same.

a. Find the difference between 639 and 818.

b. What is the total of 489 + 399 + 299?

c. Find the sum of 378 and 496.

d. Subtract 482 from 730.

e. Take 529 from 1000.

f. Total 392, 477 and 723.

4. Decide what numbers and operations you need to use to solve these problems. Record these, then calculate the answer.

a. The giant sunflower was 276cm when Sam measured it two weeks ago. Since then it has grown another 43cm. How tall is it now?

b. Ben's sunflower is 19cm shorter than Sam's. How tall is it?

● **Develop and refine written methods for column addition and subtraction for two whole numbers less than 1000, and addition of more than two such numbers.**
● Check results with equivalent calculations.

Assessment 3b

Put a cross in the shapes that are regular.
Put a tick in the shapes that have just two lines of symmetry.

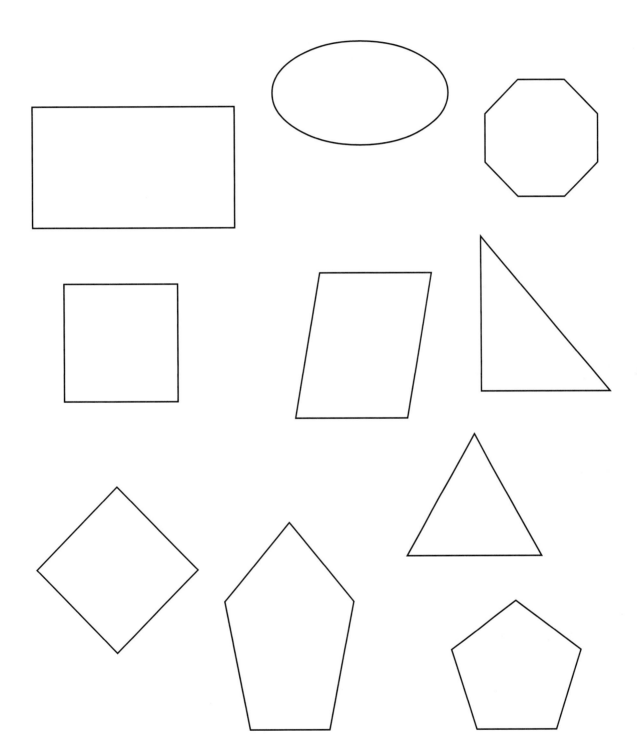

Which of the shapes has two or more right angles? Can you name them?

● Classify polygons using criteria such as number of right angles, whether or not they are regular, symmetry properties.

UNIT 8

ORGANISATION (5 LESSONS)

	LEARNING OUTCOMES	ORAL AND MENTAL STARTER	MAIN TEACHING ACTIVITY	PLENARY
LESSON 1 + 2	● Recognise and extend number sequences formed by counting from any number in steps of constant size, extending beyond zero when counting back.	TABLES BINGO: Use knowledge of 2, 3, 4, 5 and 10 times tables to play bingo.	FIND THE RULE: Identify rules for number sequences.	Count in number sequences. Discuss rules.
LESSON 3	● Recognise odd and even numbers up to 1000, and some of their properties, including the outcome of sums or differences of pairs of odd/ even numbers.	NUMBER CHAINS: Count on and back in 2s, 3s, 4s, 5s and 10s to 100.	ODD AND EVEN: Investigate odd and even numbers.	Share results of investigations and make conclusions.
LESSON 4 + 5	● Explain methods and reasoning about numbers orally and in writing. ● Solve mathematical problems or puzzles, recognise and explain patterns and relationships, generalise and predict. Suggest extensions by asking 'What if...?' ● Make and investigate a general statement about familiar numbers by finding examples that satisfy it.	EQUATION GAME: Give equivalent multiplications.	INVESTIGATIONS: Work through number investigations.	Report back on findings.

ORAL AND MENTAL SKILLS   Know by heart multiplication facts for 2, 3, 4, 5, and 10 times tables.

Lessons 1, 3 and 4 are shown in full. Lessons 2 and 5 are provided as developments of the previous lessons.

RESOURCES

Prepared bingo cards; number lines, both class and individual; pencils and paper; copies of photocopiable page 116 ('Continue the sequence').

PREPARATION

Prepare different bingo cards with numbers from the 2, 3, 4, 5 and 10 times tables, one per child, and write corresponding questions. Prepare the class number line from −500 to 500. Prepare a variety of number lines from photocopiable resource sheet A, according to the range of numbers that you want the different ability levels to cover. Photocopy 'Continue the sequence' (page 116), one per child for Lesson 2.

LEARNING OUTCOMES

ORAL AND MENTAL STARTER
● Know by heart multiplication facts for 2, 3, 4, 5, and 10 times tables.

MAIN TEACHING ACTIVITY
● Recognise and extend number sequences formed by counting from any number in steps of constant size, extending beyond zero when counting back.

VOCABULARY

Sequence;
forward;
backward;
digit; next;
consecutive;
continue; rule.

ORAL AND MENTAL STARTER

TABLES BINGO: Repeat the activity from Lesson 2, Unit 8, Term 1, but this time for the 2, 3, 4, 5 and 10 times tables.

MAIN TEACHING ACTIVITY

FIND THE RULE: Tell the children that you are going to start a number sequence and that you want them to identify the 'rule'. Ask a child to point to the numbers on the class number line as you count. Start: 10, 20, 30, 40, 50, then ask: *What is the rule?* (Add 10). Together continue the sequence to 200. Then start from 200 and give them the sequence 200, 175, 150, 125, 100.... *What is the rule?* (Subtract 25). Together continue the sequence beyond zero. Repeat for doubles or multiply by 2, and for other examples. Then try minus 10 with a starting number such as 53. Encourage them to count back beyond zero. The children use their number lines to devise number sequences, recording the first six numbers in a sequence and what the rule is. They then read out their sequences to challenge their partner to identify the rule each time.

DIFFERENTIATION

More able: devise more complex sequences involving two 'steps'.
Less able: devise sequences following given rules, eg add 2 starting at 5. Give them number lines with a limited span of numbers.

PLENARY

Let children read out their number sequences for others to guess the rule. Together count further to extend each number sequence.

LESSON 2

Repeat the **Oral and mental starter** from Lesson 2. In the **Main teaching activity** children complete 'Continue the sequence' (page 116). For **Differentiation**, encourage the more able to extend the sequences further; work with the less able group on sequences 6–10. Explain that a way to find out the rule is to find the 'differences' between successive numbers. In the **Plenary** go through their answers. Let individual children give their instructions for a sequence for the class to then chant the sequence.

RESOURCES

Class 100 square; 0–9 dice, one per group; pencils and paper.

PREPARATION

None.

LEARNING OUTCOMES

ORAL AND MENTAL STARTER

● Extend number sequences formed by counting from any number in steps of constant size.
● **Know by heart multiplication facts for 2, 3, 4, 5 and 10 times tables.**

MAIN TEACHING ACTIVITY

● Recognise odd and even numbers up to 1000, and some of their properties, including the outcome of sums or differences of pairs of odd/even numbers.

VOCABULARY

Sequence;
forward;
backward;
next; odd;
even; digit;
integer; sum;
add; total;
difference;
subtract; take
away; minus.

ORAL AND MENTAL STARTER

NUMBER CHAINS: Repeat the activity from Lesson 2, Unit 1, Term 2, but this time count on and back in 2s, 3s, 4s, 5s and 10s to 100.

MAIN TEACHING ACTIVITY

ODD AND EVEN: Write the numbers 1–10 on the board. Ask the children to say the even numbers then the odd numbers. Ask: *How do you know what is odd and what is even?* Explain that an even number can be divided by 2 to give a whole number and that its last digit is always 0, 2, 4, 6, or 8 while the last digit of an odd number is always 1, 3, 5, 7 or 9. Demonstrate on the class 100 square. Give some examples up to 999 and ask children to identify whether the number is odd or even. In groups, the children use their 0–9 dice to generate pairs of numbers to add together. As a group they should investigate what happens when you add two even numbers, two odd numbers, and an odd and an even number. They should investigate addition of numbers with one, two and then three digits.

DIFFERENTIATION

More able: investigate subtraction of odd and even numbers as well, particularly if they completed the addition investigation in Lesson 4, Unit 8, Term 1.
Less able: limit them to investigating addition of one-digit numbers.

PLENARY

Share the results of the investigation to conclude that addition of two odd numbers or two even numbers results in an even number but addition of odd plus even results in an odd number. With subtraction, even minus even gives even, odd minus odd gives even, but odd minus even or even minus odd gives odd.

RESOURCES

Photocopiable pages 117 and 118, 'Investigation cards'; pencils and paper.

PREPARATION

Photocopy onto card the two photocopiables 'Investigation cards...' (pages 117 and 118), then cut up the cards. Prepare about four copies of each one, as appropriate for the ability levels in your class. Investigations 1 and 2 are the easiest; 3 and 4 are the most difficult.

LEARNING OUTCOMES

ORAL AND MENTAL STARTER
● **Know by heart multiplication facts for 2, 3, 4, 5, and 10 times tables.**

MAIN TEACHING ACTIVITY
● Explain methods and reasoning about numbers orally and in writing.
● Solve mathematical problems or puzzles, recognise and explain patterns and relationships, generalise and predict. Suggest extensions by asking 'What if...?'
● Make and investigate a general statement about familiar numbers by finding examples that satisfy it.

VOCABULARY

Investigate; solve; sequence; consecutive; pattern; odd; even; digit; integer; sum; difference; Euler's square; palindrome.

ORAL AND MENTAL STARTER

EQUATION GAME: Repeat the activity from Lesson 10, Units 2–3, Term 2, but this time for multiplication.

MAIN TEACHING ACTIVITY

INVESTIGATIONS: Tell the children that they are going to do more work investigating statements about numbers by finding examples that make them work. This process of generalising and checking lays the foundation of later algebra work. Introduce this consecutive numbers investigation: *How many of the numbers between 1 and 100 can you make by adding together consecutive numbers? You may use as many numbers as you wish. What numbers can't you make? Do you notice anything about them?* Make sure they understand the term 'consecutive', then together try to find numbers to 20. Write on the board the numbers 1–20 vertically, each followed by an = sign. Start with the easy ones, such as 1 + 2 = 3, 1 + 2 + 3 = 6. Ask questions such as: *Are there numbers you cannot find?* (2, 4, 8, 16). Then in pairs or groups, set children to work on the investigation cards. Some children could continue the consecutive numbers investigation: *How many of the numbers to 100 can you make? What generalisations can you make?* (eg all odd numbers can be made by adding two consecutive numbers; find half of the odd number and add the two adjacent numbers, eg 57 = 28 + 29). *Do you notice anything about the numbers that you cannot make?*

Other children work on the investigation on the card you give them, according to their abilities.

Investigation 1: The children will find that adding two even numbers or two odd numbers glways gives an even answer – E + E or O + O = E – because the 'odd' 1s pair up to make an answer even. If there is an O + E, then there is an 'odd' 1 left over, giving an odd answer.

Investigation 2: An odd number is always bounded by even numbers and vice versa. O × O = O, E × E = E and O × E = E. Again, as in Investigation 1, this is due to the 'pairing up' of the 'odd' 1s of the odd number. For example, 3 × 2 can be expressed as:

Investigation 3: The Euler's square configures the numbers 1–64 in a unique way. Each row totals 260, as does each column. Each of the four quarters totals 520 (= 260 × 2, or 130 × 4), which means that the entire square totals 2080 (520 × 4, or 260 × 8, or 130 × 16). This investigation reinforces pattern seeking; the children should be able to establish that some of the answers to the sums are achievable through multiplication rather than adding up every number, because of the relationships within the square.

Investigation 4: This investigation is another exercise in reinforcing the concept of numerical patterns. The children should be able to conclude that when two-digit numbers are added to their reverse, a palindromic number results. However, this is not the case with three- or four-digit numbers.

DIFFERENTIATION

More able: create their own statement for investigation.
Less able: do Investigations 1 and/or 2.

PLENARY

Each group should explain their investigation to the class and discuss their generalisations.

LESSON 5

Repeat the **Oral and mental starter** from Lesson 4. In the **Main teaching activity** children either continue with the investigation from the previous lesson or attempt different ones. **Differentiation** is as per Lesson 4. In the **Plenary** ensure that each group reports back at least once.

Continue the sequence

Look carefully at each sequence and fill in the missing numbers. Then work out the rule.

30 50 70 _____ 110 _____ _____ _____ Rule _____

50 75 _____ _____ 200 _____ _____ Rule _____

70 120 170 _____ _____ Rule _____

450 420 390 _____ _____ _____ Rule _____

10 20 40 _____ _____ _____ Rule _____

7 12 17 _____ 27 _____ _____ Rule _____

48 41 34 _____ 20 _____ _____ Rule _____

$\frac{1}{4}$ $\frac{1}{2}$ $\frac{3}{4}$ 1 $1\frac{1}{4}$ $1\frac{1}{2}$ Rule _____

10 $9\frac{1}{2}$ 9 $8\frac{1}{2}$ _____ _____ Rule _____

3 $2\frac{1}{2}$ 2 $1\frac{1}{2}$ _____ _____ Rule _____

Investigations 1 and 2

1: Investigating odd and even numbers

+	2	4	6	8	10
2					
4					
6					
8					
10					

What do you notice when you add an even number to an even number?

+	1	3	5	7	9
1					
3					
5					
7					
9					

What do you notice when you add an odd number to an odd number?

+	1	3	5	7	9
2					
4					
6					
8					
10					

What do you notice when you add an odd number to an even number?

+	14	24	82	26	22
15					
27					
53					
33					
47					

What happens when you add two-digit odd and even numbers?

2: Odds and evens

Choose any odd number below 100.
What is the number immediately before that number? Is it odd or even?
What is the number immediately after that number? Is it odd or even?
Investigate some other odd numbers in this way. What do you notice?

Now investigate some even numbers. Look at the numbers immediately before and after each even number.

Investigate what happens when you multiply two odd numbers together. Can you discover a rule? Check to see if your rule works when you multiply other pairs of odd numbers.
What about when you multiply two even numbers? Can you discover a rule? Check to see if your rule works when you multiply other pairs of even numbers.

What happens when you multiply an odd and an even number together? Investigate some divisions with odd and even numbers. Do you notice any patterns?

Investigations 3 and 4

3: Euler's square

18	63	16	33	50	31	48	1
35	14	19	62	3	46	51	30
64	17	34	15	32	49	2	47
13	36	61	20	45	4	29	52
60	21	40	9	56	25	44	5
37	12	57	24	41	8	53	28
22	59	10	39	26	55	6	43
11	38	23	58	7	42	27	54

This is a special square. Investigate some totals and see what you can discover. Find the totals:

- for each row
- for each column
- of the four quarters
- of the entire square

4: Palindromes

Write a two-digit number, say   83
Then reverse the digits: 38.
Then add this to the original number: 83

$$\begin{array}{r} 83 \\ + 38 \\ \hline 121 \end{array}$$

The answer is a palindrome as it reads the same forwards as it does backwards.

Investigate for other two-digit numbers. If you add a two-digit number to its reverse does it always result in a palindrome?

Now write a three-digit number, say   825
Add the reverse of that answer: 825

$$\begin{array}{r} 825 \\ + 528 \end{array}$$

Add the reverse of that answer: 3531
                                 1353
                                 4884   is a palindrome.

Investigate other three-digit numbers. Do they all result in a palindrome? What about four-digit numbers?

ORGANISATION (10 LESSONS)

	LEARNING OUTCOMES	ORAL AND MENTAL STARTER	MAIN TEACHING ACTIVITY	PLENARY
LESSON 1	● Begin to know multiplication facts for 6, 7, 8 and 9 times tables.	NUMBER CHAINS: Count on and back in 2s, 3s 4s, 5s and 10s.	MULTIPLE PATTERNS: Look for multiplication patterns on 100 squares.	Discuss multiplication patterns and predictions about patterns.
LESSON 2	● Extend understanding of the operations of × and ÷, and their relationship to each other and to + and −. Understand the principles (not the names) of the commutative and associative laws as they apply to multiplication.	EQUATION GAME: Give equivalent sums.	COMMUTATIVE AND ASSOCIATIVE LAWS: Answer questions that involve using the associative law for multiplication.	Go through answers.
LESSON 3 +4	● Extend understanding of the operation of × and its relationship to +. Understand the principle (not the name) of the distributive law as it applies to multiplication. ● Partition. ● Approximate first. Use informal pencil and paper methods to support, record or explain multiplications and divisions.	TABLES BINGO: Use knowledge of 2, 3, 4, 5 and 10 times tables to play bingo.	PARTITION IT: Use partitioning in order to multiply.	Discuss methods.
LESSON 5	● Extend understanding of the operations of × and ÷ and their relationship to each other and to + and −. ● Develop and refine written methods for TU × U, TU ÷ U. ● Use doubling or halving, starting from known facts.	DIVISION SNAP: Play snap for 2, 3, 4, 5 and 10 times tables facts.	RUSSIAN MULTIPLICATION: Practise new method for multiplication.	Discuss how the method works.
LESSON 6 +7	● Develop and refine written methods for TU × U, TU ÷ U. ● Check with an equivalent calculation.	DIVISION SNAP: Play snap for 2, 3, 4, 5 and 10 times tables facts.	STANDARD METHODS: Use grid and column methods for multiplication.	Recap on both methods.
LESSON 8	● Develop and refine written methods for TU × U, TU ÷ U. ● Use the relationship between × and ÷. ● Check with inverse operation.	NUMBER CHAINS: Count on and back in 3s, 4s, 6s, 7s, 8s and 9s.	CHECK IT: Use different methods for multiplication and division; check using inverse operation.	Discuss choice of methods. Recap on inverse operations.
LESSON 9	● Use the relationship between × and ÷. ● **Find remainders after division.**	TABLES BINGO: Use knowledge of all times tables to play bingo.	REMAINDERS: Work out divisions with remainders.	Go through examples set in context.
LESSON 10	● Use all four operations to solve word problems involving numbers in 'real life' and money.	DIVISION SNAP: Play snap for 2, 3, 4, 5 and 10 times tables facts.	WHICH OPERATION?: Choose appropriate operations to solve number problems.	Discuss answers and choice of operations and methods.

ORAL AND MENTAL SKILLS **Know by heart multiplication facts for 2, 3, 4, 5 and 10 times tables.** Begin to know multiplication facts for 6, 7, 8 and 9 times tables. **Derive quickly division facts corresponding to 2, 3, 4, 5 and 10 times tables.** Extend number sequences formed by counting in steps of constant size.

Lessons 1, 2, 3, 6, 8 and 9 are shown in full. Lessons 4 and 7 are provided as developments of the previous lessons. Lessons 5 and 10 are an extension of what has already been taught so are shown in outline.

LESSON 1

RESOURCES

Class number line; enlarged 100 square from photocopiable resource sheet B; 100 squares; 0–100 number lines from photocopiable resource sheet A; crayons.

PREPARATION

Photocopy '1–100 square' (resource sheet B), one enlarged class version and nine A4 copies per child. Prepare 0–100 number lines from resource sheet A, for less able children.

LEARNING OUTCOMES

ORAL AND MENTAL STARTER
● **Know by heart multiplication facts for 2, 3, 4, 5 and 10 times tables.**

MAIN TEACHING ACTIVITY
● Begin to know multiplication facts for 6, 7, 8 and 9 times tables.

VOCABULARY
Times; multiply; multiplied by; product; multiple.

ORAL AND MENTAL STARTER

NUMBER CHAINS: Repeat Lesson 2, Unit 1, Term 2, but this time count on and back in 2s, 3s, 4s, 5s and 10s.

MAIN TEACHING ACTIVITY

MULTIPLE PATTERNS: Discuss the patterns the children created on their number squares for the 3 and 4 times tables last term (Lessons 2 and 3, Unit 8, Term 1). Using a 0–100 number line, count in 2s and tell the children that these numbers are called multiples of 2. On the enlarged 100 square colour in all multiples of 2, counting as you go. Then discuss the pattern that these make, an even pattern of alternate columns of numbers. The children then colour in the multiples for each of the times tables on a separate 100 square. Start with 2, then 3, 4, 5, 10; 6, 7, 8 and 9. Children should work with partners to discuss their work.

DIFFERENTIATION

More able: challenge them to predict the pattern before they colour in and discuss with their partner how the patterns will develop. They should then investigate numbers that are multiples of more than one of the numbers.
Less able: let them use a number line to help 'count on'.

PLENARY

Go through the grids showing the different patterns of multiples. Ask: *Which were the easiest to fill in? Why? Which ones could you predict without counting on? How soon were you able to recognise a pattern?*

LESSON 2

RESOURCES

Prepared multiplication questions; base 10 apparatus; Big base 10 apparatus; two sets of 0–9 digit cards per pair; calculators; pencils and paper.

PREPARATION

Prepare multiplication questions for the equation game. Give out paper for them to record multiplications and divisions.

LEARNING OUTCOMES

MENTAL AND ORAL STARTER
● **Know by heart multiplication facts for 2, 3, 4, 5 and 10 times tables.**

MAIN TEACHING ACTIVITY
● Extend understanding of the operations of × and ÷ and their relationship to each other and to + and –. Understand the principles (not the names) of the commutative and associative laws as they apply to multiplication.

<table>
<tr><td>

VOCABULARY

Times;
multiply;
multiplied by;
product;
multiple;
inverse.

</td></tr>
</table>

ORAL AND MENTAL STARTER

EQUATION GAME: Repeat activity from Lesson 10, Units 2–3, Term 2, but this time for multiplication facts, the children reply with an equivalent number phrase such as double 16.

MAIN TEACHING ACTIVITY

COMMUTATIVE AND ASSOCIATIVE LAWS: Ask the children: *What is 3 × 8?* Demonstrate using Big base 10 apparatus, showing three groups of eight. Point out that 3 × 8 is equal to 8 + 8 + 8, which is 24. Ask a child to rearrange the apparatus to make eight groups of three. Point out that 8 × 3 is equal to 3 + 3 + 3 + 3 + 3 + 3 + 3 + 3 and also makes 24 (commutative law 3 × 8 = 8 × 3). Go through this again recording:
3 × 8 = 8 + 8 + 8 = 8 × 3 = 3 + 3 + 3 + 3 + 3 + 3 + 3 + 3 = 24.

Go through other examples. Then ask the children if they think the same rule will apply to division. Give an example, such as *You have eight bars of chocolate to share or divide between two children. How many bars each? What if we have two bars of chocolate to share or divide between eight children? How much would they have each?* If necessary show a practical example using bars of chocolate for the children to realise that although 8 divided by 2 is 4, 2 divided by 8 is not 4 it is one-quarter. So this rule does not apply to division: 8 ÷ 2 does not equal 2 ÷ 8. Ask: *What is 3 × 4?* Write 3 × 4 = 12. Ask: *What is 12 × 2?* Write 12 × 2 = 24. Write on the board 3 × 8 and say: *What if we wrote the 8 as 4 × 2?* Write up the calculation 8 × 3 = 3 × 4 × 2. Ask: *What order shall be do the multiplication in?* First do (3 × 4) × 2 = 12 × 2 = 24. Then repeat for 3 × (4 × 2) = 3 × 8 = 24. Then record: 3 × 8 = (3 × 4) × 2 = 3 × (4 × 2) = 24 (associative law). Repeat for 5 × 9 to lead to the conclusion that 5 × 9 = 5 × (3 × 3) = (5 × 3) × 3 = 45.

Test for bigger numbers. Write 6 × 18 on the board and ask: *How could we break 18 down?* 9 × 2 or 3 × 6. Go through the process to lead to the conclusion that 6 × 18 = 6 × (9 × 2) = (6 × 9) × 2 = 108 and 6 × 18 = 6 × (3 × 6) = (6 × 3) × 6 = 108. Explain to the children that this means they can rearrange a multiplication problem in this way to find the easiest way to calculate the answer.

In pairs the children pick two numbers from their combined pack of 0–9 digit cards. They record and calculate the multiplication of two numbers (such as 4 × 7), and then the other way round (7 × 4). They repeat for other number pairs before doing the same for number trios, when they will be able to create six multiplications from the three numbers. Discuss what they notice about the answers.

DIFFERENTIATION

More able: Ask them to record and calculate the two divisions from the number pairs.
Less able: let them use base 10 materials to support their calculations.

PLENARY

Go through their answers to the photocopiable, reinforcing the main teaching points.

RESOURCES

Bingo cards; pencils and paper.

PREPARATION

Use the bingo cards prepared for Term 2, Unit 8, Lesson 1. Write different questions.

LEARNING OUTCOMES
MENTAL AND ORAL STARTER
● **Know by heart multiplication facts for 2, 3, 4, 5 and 10 times tables.**

MAIN TEACHING ACTIVITY
● Extend understanding of the operation of × and its relationship to +. Understand the principle (not the name) of the distributive law as it applies to multiplication.
● Partition.
● Approximate first. Use informal pencil and paper methods to support, record or explain multiplications and divisions.

ORAL AND MENTAL STARTER

TABLES BINGO: Repeat the activity from Lesson 2, Unit 8, Term 1, but include the 3 and 4 times tables as well.

MAIN TEACHING ACTIVITY

PARTITION IT: Tell the children they will be learning about another way to regroup numbers to make multiplication questions easier to answer. Write on the board 18×7 and ask if anyone knows the answer. Ask some children to make up seven lots of 18 using Big base 10 apparatus and count up the total (126). Explain that as $18 = 10 + 8$, 18×7 is the same as 10 lots of 7 plus 8 lots of 7, or $18 \times 7 = (10 \times 7) + (8 \times 7)$ (distributive law). Demonstrate by using Big base 10. Then calculate this together: $(10 \times 7) + (8 \times 7) = 70 + 56 = 126$. Then calculate 16×9, by partitioning and then multiplying. Remind them of the grid method used last term (Term 1, Units 9–10, Lesson 7) and set out the calculation as follows:

×	10	6	Total
9	90	54	144

Write up these multiplications for them to calculate on their own: 16×9, 14×6, 19×7, 17×4, 16×8, 18×8. Let them discuss methods with a partner. Give them time to complete at least two, then ask children to explain their calculations to the class. Next, write 17×5 on the board and ask them how they would calculate this. They will probably suggest:

×	10	7	Total
5	50	35	85

Explain that an alternative would be to say that 17×5 is half of 17×10, or $17 \times 5 = 17 \times (10 \div 2) = (17 \times 10) \div 2$. Then complete the calculation: $17 \times 10 = 170$ and half of 170 is 85. Write up other examples for children to work through, such as 18×5, 13×5, 19×5. Then bring the class together to ask children to explain their calculations. Finally, write 20×19 on the board and ask for suggestions as to how to calculate it. Accept any method that gives the correct answer. Then explain that: $20 \times 19 = (2 \times 10) \times 19 = 2 \times (10 \times 19) = 2 \times 190 = 380$. In pairs, the children then discuss the most appropriate way to calculate multiplications from the following: 15×8, 20×24, 5×24, 18×9, 20×18, 9×19, 5×26, 13×12, 20×35, 9×17, 27×20, 36×5. Write these up on the board.

DIFFERENTIATION

More able: calculate the answers.
Less able: use base 10 apparatus to work out the multiplications practically.

PLENARY

Ask children to explain which methods they chose for particular calculations. Ask: *Did anyone choose a different way?*

LESSON 4

In the **Oral and mental starter** play TABLES BINGO again. In the **Main teaching activity** children work through further examples, approximating an answer and then deciding which is the most appropriate calculation method to use. These questions could be taken from commercially produced materials. For **Differentiation** vary the level of questions given to each pair. In the **Plenary** children explain their choice of methods.

RESOURCES	Copies of photocopiable page 127 ('Russian multiplication'), one per child; prepared division questions for 2, 3, 4, 5 and 10 times tables with single-digit answers; sets of 0–9 digit cards (enough for four cards per child); calculators; pencils and paper.
LEARNING OUTCOMES	**ORAL AND MENTAL STARTER** ● **Derive quickly division facts corresponding to 2, 3, 4, 5 and 10 times tables.** **MAIN TEACHING ACTIVITY** ● Extend understanding of the operations of × and ÷ and their relationship to each other and to + and −. ● Develop and refine written methods for TU × U, TU ÷ U. ● Use doubling or halving, starting from known facts.
ORAL AND MENTAL STARTER	DIVISION SNAP: Deal about four digit cards to each child. Read out a question card, eg 36 divided by 9. The children who have an 'answer card' hold up their card and say 'snap'.
MAIN TEACHING ACTIVITY	RUSSIAN MULTIPLICATION: Go through the Russian multiplication method as shown on the photocopiable sheet. Remind children about doubling and halving. They then work on their own to answer the questions. They may want to check their answers on a calculator.
DIFFERENTIATION	More able: try out the method with larger numbers. Less able: children may need help working through the questions, as they progress in difficulty.
PLENARY	Discuss how and why this method works. Go through a few of the questions.

RESOURCES

Prepared division questions; sets of 0–9 digit cards; prepared multiplication questions; base 10 apparatus; pencils and paper.

PREPARATION

Prepare division questions for 2, 3, 4, 5 and 10 times tables with single-digit answers. Provide enough sets of 0–9 digit cards to give 4 cards per child. Provide multiplication questions differentiated for the three levels, either taken from commercially produced materials or prepared yourself.

LEARNING OUTCOMES

ORAL AND MENTAL STARTER
● **Derive quickly division facts corresponding to 2, 3, 4, 5 and 10 times tables.**

MAIN TEACHING ACTIVITY
● Develop and refine written methods for TU × U, TU ÷ U.
● Check with an equivalent calculation.

ORAL AND MENTAL STARTER

DIVISION SNAP: Repeat the activity from the previous lesson.

MAIN TEACHING ACTIVITY

STANDARD METHODS: Explain that although we can use a variety of mental strategies with informal jottings for multiplication sometimes we need written methods. Write 8 × 78 on the board. First work out an approximate answer: 78 rounded to the nearest ten is 80, so an approximate answer would be 8 × 80. Remind children that when we multiply numbers that are multiples of 10 we multiply the significant digits first (8 × 8) and then adjust for the tens. So 8 × 80 = (8 × 8) × 10 = 640. Then remind them of the grid method and use this to work out 8 × 78. Talk through the calculation as you record on the board:

×	70	8	Total
8	560	64	624

Now use a standard column method instead:

70 × 8:
8 × 8:

$$
\begin{array}{r}
78 \\
\times\ 8 \\
\hline
560 \\
64 \\
\hline
624 \\
\hline
\end{array}
$$
1

Go through other examples, approximating first and then demonstrating both methods. Select from: 7 × 56, 9 × 83, 4 × 93, 8 × 66. Children then work through your prepared examples, using first one method and then the other method to check the result. Remind them to approximate first.

DIFFERENTIATION

More able: ask them to look for 'short cuts' to reduce the number of stages in the column method.
Less able: use base 10 apparatus to aid calculations.

PLENARY

Using an example from the children's work go through the two methods once again, reinforcing the principal of approximating first.

LESSON 7

For the **Oral and mental starter** repeat DIVISION SNAP. In the **Main teaching activity** children continue working through the examples. Encourage children to reduce the number of stages in the column method when they are ready. For **Differentiation** vary the level of difficulty of questions you provide each group. In the **Plenary** ask more able children to demonstrate the reduced method of column multiplication.

RESOURCES

Prepared division and multiplication sums; base 10 apparatus; pencils and paper.

PREPARATION

Provide division and multiplication calculations differentiated for the three levels, either taken from commercially produced materials or prepared yourself.

LEARNING OUTCOMES

ORAL AND MENTAL STARTER
● Extend number sequences formed by counting from any number in steps of constant size.

MAIN TEACHING ACTIVITY
● Develop and refine written methods for TU × U, TU ÷ U.
● Use the relationship between multiplication and division.
● Check with the inverse operation.

Times;
multiply;
multiplied by;
product;
multiple;
inverse;
quotient;
share; share
equally;
divide; divided
by; divided
into; divisible
by.

ORAL AND MENTAL STARTER

NUMBER CHAINS: Repeat Lesson 2, Unit 1, Term 2, but this time count on and back in 3s, 4s, 6s, 7s, 8s and 9s.

MAIN TEACHING ACTIVITY

CHECK IT: Remind children about the informal methods for division that they have used. Point out that division is the inverse of multiplication and that each operation can be used to check its inverse. Stress the relationship between multiplication and division. Then write on the board 84 ÷ 7 and ask children to approximate the answer and explain their reasoning: *We know that 10 × 7 = 70 so 70 ÷ 7 = 10 and by adding on half of 70 (35) to 70 we can work out that 15 × 7 = 105. So 84 ÷ 7 lies between 70 ÷ 7 and 105 ÷ 7, so the answer must be >10 and <15.* Then ask them how they would work out the answer. Let them explain any informal methods that they may use, including knowledge of table facts. Then go through the method using multiples of the divisor:

$$84 ÷ 7 = (70 + 14) ÷ 7$$
$$= 10 + 2$$
$$= 12$$

Ask: *What calculation could we do to check this result?* (12 × 7). Invite a child to demonstrate this calculation; they may choose an informal method or a standard written method. Children then work through your prepared division and multiplication examples. Tell them to approximate first, then calculate, then use the inverse operation to check their answers.

DIFFERENTIATION

More able: investigate different methods of multiplication and division. Justify their reasoning as to which is the best method to use.
Less able: use base 10 apparatus to aid calculations.

PLENARY

Ask children to explain their choice of methods and how they carried out the calculations. Recap on the inverse operation.

RESOURCES

Bingo cards; copies of photocopiable resource sheet C ('Times tables square'); 0–9 dice; digit cards; prepared recording chart; pencils.

PREPARATION

Prepare different bingo cards with numbers from all the times tables, one per child, and write corresponding questions. Prepare sets of 1–10 digit cards; for the low ability group include several each of the 2, 5 and 10 cards only and for the more able group provide more of the 3, 4, 6, 8 and 9 digit cards. Provide one set per ability group of 4–6 along with one 0–9 dice. Copy this chart onto A4 paper, then photocopy, one per child:

The two-digit number I divided	The number I divided by	My estimate	How many times	Remainder
37	5	< 10	7	2

VOCABULARY

Times;
multiply;
multiplied by;
product;
multiple;
share; divide;
divided by;
divided into;
divisible by;
remainder.

LEARNING OUTCOMES
ORAL AND MENTAL STARTER
● **Know by heart multiplication facts for 2, 3, 4, 5 and 10 times tables.**
● **Begin to know multiplication facts for 6, 7, 8 and 9 times tables.**

MAIN TEACHING ACTIVITY
● Use the relationship between multiplication and division.
● **Find remainders after division.**

ORAL AND MENTAL STARTER

TABLES BINGO: Repeat the activity from Lesson 2, Unit 8, Term 1, but for all the times tables.

MAIN TEACHING ACTIVITY

REMAINDERS: Remind the children about previous work on remainders. Give an example: *You have a bag of 22 cherries to share between 4 children.* Then go through the working out: *Look at the multiplication square to find the column with 4 at the beginning. Look across at the multiples of four: 4, 8, 12, 16, 20, 24. We can see that 20 is a multiple of 4 so will divide exactly by four, the next multiple of four is 24. We know that 4 × 5 is 20 so 20 divided by 4 is 5 each with two cherries left as the remainder. We can say 22 divided by 4 is 5 remainder 2.* Repeat for other examples, asking individual children to explain how to work them out. In ability groups of four–six, each child rolls the dice twice to generate a two-digit number. They then take a digit card from the pile and divide their two-digit number by that single digit. Tell them to approximate the answer first and then use the multiplication square to help them solve it. They record their calculations on the chart you have prepared.

DIFFERENTIATION

More able: devise a 'real-life' context for each division calculation, eg for 30 divided by 4, 'put 30 crayons into 4 boxes'.
Less able: use the digit cards to limit them to division problems involving the 2, 5 and 10 times tables.

PLENARY

Go through some of the examples, asking the children to explain their workings out. Ask the more able to give their contexts, and each time calculate the answer together.

RESOURCES	Prepared division questions for 2, 3, 4, 5 and 10 times tables with single-digit answers; sets of 0–9 digit cards (enough for four cards per child); copies of photocopiable 128 ('Fresh Farm'); pencils.
LEARNING OUTCOMES	**ORAL AND MENTAL STARTER** ● **Derive quickly division facts corresponding to 2, 3, 4, 5 and 10 times tables.** **MAIN TEACHING ACTIVITY** ● Use all four operations to solve word problems involving numbers in 'real life' and money.
ORAL AND MENTAL STARTER	DIVISION SNAP: Repeat the activity from Lesson 5.
MAIN TEACHING ACTIVITY	WHICH OPERATION?: Give out the photocopiable sheets 'Fresh Farm', and together go through the first example. Ask: *Which operation must we use? Why?* Then ask the children to suggest the most appropriate method to use. Discuss their responses. Remind them of how they have checked results in previous work by using an alternative method. Ask them to suggest an alternative method in this case. They then work individually to answer the remaining questions.
DIFFERENTIATION	More able: make up different quantities of eggs and milk for their partner to calculate the cartons and churns required. Less able: give help with the more difficult questions.
PLENARY	Go through the questions and discuss which operations and methods were used and why.

Russian multiplication

Russian multiplication is a clever way to work out difficult multiplication questions. It involves using doubling and halving.
Here is how it works, starting with an easy multiplication 9 × 15:

● Write 9 and 15 at the top of two columns:

● halve the number on the left and ignore the remainder

● halve the number on the left

9	×	15
4		30
2		60
1		120

● double the number on the right

● double the number on the right

● halve the number on the left   ● double the number on the right

● Stop when you get to 1 in the left-hand column. Then cross out the even numbers in the left-hand column and the numbers opposite them in the right-hand column, including the numbers from the original multiplication:

9	×	15
4		30
2		60
1		120

Total the remaining numbers on the right to get the answer
15 + 120 = 135, so 9 × 15 = 135.

Here is a more difficult one:

● halve the number on the left
● halve the number on the left, ignore the remainder
● halve the number on the left
● halve the number on the left, ignore the remainder

26	×	54
13		108
6		216
3		432
1		864

● double the number on the right
● double the number on the right,
● double the number on the right
● double the number on the right

Cross out the even numbers in the left-hand column and the numbers opposite them in the right-hand column:
This gives 108 + 432 + 864 = 1404 as the answer.

26	×	54
13		108
3		432
1		864

Now work out the answers to these multiplication sums using this method. Sometimes it is easier to change the order – think about it!

12 × 12	13 × 22	42 × 21	12 × 19	14 × 65	54 × 17
36 × 83	45 × 78	33 × 25	76 × 24	84 × 37	96 × 48

Fresh Farm

On Fresh Farm eggs have to be packed into cartons each day. Each carton can hold six eggs. The table shows how many eggs were laid for each day of one week. Complete the table to show how many cartons can be filled each day and how many eggs will be left over.

Day of week	Number of eggs	Number of cartons filled	Number of eggs left over
Monday	30		
Tuesday	24		
Wednesday	31		
Thursday	50		
Friday	41		
Saturday	19		
Sunday	52		

The hens each need 50g of feed each day. The farmer has 50 hens. How much feed does he need for each day? How much for each week?

The milk is put into churns that can hold 10 litres. Complete the table to show how many churns are filled each day and how much milk is left over.

Day of week	Litres of milk	Number of churns filled	Litres of milk left over
Monday	60		
Tuesday	55		
Wednesday	58		
Thursday	64		
Friday	71		
Saturday	59		
Sunday	75		

The farmer is paid £2 for each full churn of milk. How much is he paid for this week's milk?

He is paid 25p for each carton of six eggs. How much was he paid for his eggs this week?

He has just bought some pigs at market. There is only room for four pigs in each enclosure. He has bought 50 pigs and has 20 enclosures. How many more pigs has he got room for?

ORGANISATION (5 LESSONS)

LEARNING OUTCOMES	ORAL AND MENTAL STARTER	MAIN TEACHING ACTIVITY	PLENARY
LESSON 1 + 2 ● Use fraction notation. **Recognise simple fractions that are several parts of a whole; recognise the equivalence of simple fractions.**	TABLES BINGO: Use knowledge of 2, 3, 4, 5 and 10 times tables to play bingo.	EQUAL PARTS: Give fractions of shapes and record equivalent fractions.	Demonstrate equivalent fractions.
LESSON 3 ● Identify two simple fractions with a total of 1. ● Order simple fractions: for example, decide whether fractions such as $3/8$ or $7/10$ are greater or less than $1/2$. ● Find fractions such as $2/3$, $3/4$, $3/5$, $7/10$... of shapes.	FRACTION NUMBER CHAINS: Count on and back in $1/2$ s and $1/4$ s up to 20.	FRACTION PAIRS: Identify pairs of fractions that make 1.	Colour in given fractions of squares.
LESSON 4 + 5 ● Begin to relate fractions to division and find simple exact fractions such as $1/2$, $1/3$... of numbers or quantities.	DIVISION SNAP: Play snap for 2, 3, 4, 5 and 10 times tables facts.	FRACTION GAME: Find fractions of numbers.	Answer quick-fire questions – target individual children at appropriate level.

ORAL AND MENTAL SKILLS Know by heart multiplication facts for **2, 3, 4, 5 and 10 times tables. Recognise simple fractions that are several parts of a whole; recognise the equivalence of simple fractions.** Begin to know multiplication facts for 6, 7, 8 and 9 times tables. **Derive quickly division facts corresponding to 2, 3, 4, 5 and 10 times tables.**

Lessons 1 and 3 are shown in full. Lessons 2 and 5 are developments of the previous lessons. Lesson 4 is an extension of what has already been taught so is shown in outline.

RESOURCES

Bingo cards; paper circles; enlarged paper circle; squared paper; felt-tipped pens; prepared coloured squares; for Lesson 2: coloured pieces of card; adhesive tape; metre stick; 1m strips of coloured card; Blu-Tack; elastic bands; large sheet of squared paper; copies of blank strips for labelling fractions (see below).

PREPARATION

Use the bingo cards prepared for Lesson 1, Unit 8, Term 2. Write different corresponding questions. Prepare one large circle for display purposes and smaller paper circles, one per child. Prepare four equal-sized squares. Divide the first into two and colour in $1/2$. Divide the second into four and colour in two adjacent segments to show $2/4$. Use the same method to show $4/8$ on the third square and $8/16$ on the fourth. Attach eight different coloured pieces of card around a metre stick to divide it into eight equal segments. On a sheet of A4 paper, draw seven strips of equal length, then split them into equal parts for the children to label: $1/2$, $1/3$, $1/4$, $1/5$, $1/6$, $1/8$ and $1/10$. Photocopy, one per child.

LEARNING OUTCOMES

ORAL AND MENTAL STARTER
● **Know by heart multiplication facts for 2, 3, 4, 5 and 10 times tables.**

MAIN TEACHING ACTIVITY
● Use fraction notation. **Recognise simple fractions that are several parts of a whole; recognise the equivalence of simple fractions.**

VOCABULARY

Fraction; part; equal parts; one whole; half; halves; quarter; eighth; third; sixth; fifth; tenth; twentieth.

ORAL AND MENTAL STARTER

TABLES BINGO: Repeat the activity from Lesson 2, Unit 8, Term 1 but include the 3 and 4 times tables as well.

MAIN TEACHING ACTIVITY

EQUAL PARTS: Ask the children to fold their paper circle in half. Ask: *How many halves?* Point out that these are two equal parts and that two halves make a whole one. Write on the board $1 = \frac{1}{2} + \frac{1}{2}$. Point out that the whole has been divided into 2 which is why 2 is on the bottom (denominator) and that for each section there is just one half so the 1 is written on the top of the fraction (numerator). Fold the shape in half again and repeat the process. Then ask: *How do you think we write two-quarters?* Ask a child to demonstrate on the board: four on the bottom because there are four equal parts (or quarters) in a whole and the number on top tells us how many quarters in that section. Repeat for four-quarters and two halves. Ask the children to show you $^2/_4$ of their circle. Say: *What is this the same as?* Continue the discussion until the children discover that $^2/_2 = ^4/_4 = 1$ whole. Extend this to include eighths. Then, in pairs, the children draw some 4×4 squares on squared paper and find as many ways as possible to show half by colouring in the individual squares in two different colours. Repeat for one-quarter and then for one-eighth.

DIFFERENTIATION

More able: repeat for other fractions and using different sized rectangles.
Less able: together count the number of individual squares (16) and ask for half 16 (8). They then colour 8 squares in each colour to create different 4×4 squares.

PLENARY

Display your prepared coloured squares to demonstrate equivalent fractions $^1/_2 = ^2/_4 = ^4/_8 = ^8/_{16}$. Children display coloured squares for other fractions, for the rest of the class to identify the fraction shown.

LESSON 2

Repeat the **Oral and mental starter** from Lesson 1. For the **Main teaching activity** hold up the coloured metre stick and ask a child to position an elastic band to divide the stick into two halves. Point out that halving is the same as dividing by two. Repeat for other fractions. Point to $^1/_2$ and ask for other fractions the same. Repeat for $^1/_4$ and then $^1/_4$. Then attach one of the strips of coloured card to the board. Take another colour and ask a child to fold it and make two halves. Mark the fold with a felt-tipped pen and ask the child to label each of the two halves as 'one half'. Then Blu-Tack it below the whole strip. Repeat to make quarters and eighths. Then children work in pairs to colour in and label the fractions on your prepared strips. For **Differentiation** let the less able use strips of card to complete the task practically. The more able children include thirds, sixths, fifths, tenths and twentieths. In the **Plenary** draw a square on a large sheet of squared paper and shade in a fraction of it for the children to identify the fraction. Then let individual children challenge the rest of the class in the same way.

RESOURCES

Prepared rectangles; squared paper; felt-tipped pens.

PREPARATION

On a large sheet of squared paper draw several 3×4 rectangles.

LEARNING OUTCOMES

ORAL AND MENTAL STARTER
● **Recognise simple fractions that are several parts of a whole; recognise the equivalence of simple fractions.**

MAIN TEACHING ACTIVITY
● Identify two simple fractions with a total of 1.
● Order simple fractions: for example, decide whether fractions such as $^3/_8$ or $^7/_{10}$ are greater or less than one-half.
● Find fractions such as $^2/_3$, $^3/_4$, $^3/_5$, $^7/_{10}$... of shapes.

VOCABULARY
Fraction; part; equal parts; one whole; half; halves; quarter; eighth; third; sixth; fifth; tenth; twentieth.

ORAL AND MENTAL STARTER

FRACTION NUMBER CHAINS: Repeat the activity from Term 2, Unit 1, Lesson 2, but this time count in halves, then quarters, up to 20. If the children say $^2/_4$ remind them that $^2/_4$ is the same as $^1/_2$.

MAIN TEACHING ACTIVITY

FRACTION PAIRS: Tell the children to draw a 3 × 4 rectangle on squared paper and use two different colours to colour in the individual squares in any order. Invite children to colour in one of the rectangles on your large sheet to show how they coloured their rectangle. Each time work out the fractions, eg $^5/_{12}$ in red and $^7/_{12}$ in blue. Point out that these two fractions make 1 whole one. Then, in pairs, the children each create more 3 × 4 rectangles in the same way. They then work together to work out and record the fractions. Next they make a list of the fractions that are $> ^1/_2$ and a list of those that are $< ^1/_2$. They then put the fractions in order of size.

DIFFERENTIATION

More able: encourage them to use more complex shapes.
Less able: give help with listing and ordering the fractions.

PLENARY

Share some of the children's work. Ask for volunteers to colour in one of your blank 3 × 4 rectangles to show $^1/_3$, then $^1/_3$, then $^1/_4$. Draw a 4 × 4 square and ask: *Who can colour in $^3/_8$? What fraction is left?* Repeat for other fractions.

LESSON 4 +5

RESOURCES	Prepared division questions; sets of 0–9 digit cards (enough for four cards per child); for each group of six, set of integer cards and set of fraction cards within ranges appropriate for different ability levels; commercially produced fraction games such as fraction dominoes.
LEARNING OUTCOMES	**ORAL AND MENTAL STARTER** ● **Derive quickly division facts corresponding to 2, 3, 4, 5 and 10 times tables.** **MAIN TEACHING ACTIVITY** ● Begin to relate fractions to division and find simple exact fractions such as $^1/_2$, $^1/_3$... of numbers or quantities.
ORAL AND MENTAL STARTER	DIVISION SNAP: Repeat activity from Lesson 5, Units 9–10, Term 2.
MAIN TEACHING ACTIVITY	FRACTION GAME: Talk to the children about sharing. Say: *If we have half each we divide by two.* Then ask questions such as, *If there are 16 sweets and you are given half, how many will you get? What about $^1/_4$?* In groups of six, children play the Fraction game. They take turns to take one card from the top of the integers pile and one card from the fractions pile. If they can complete the calculation they score a point. Children check each other's calculations.
DIFFERENTIATION	More able: introduce a wider range of integers and fraction cards. Less able: limit to finding halves and quarters of multiples of 4.
PLENARY	Ask quick-fire questions to test understanding, eg *If we want a quarter what do we divide by?* Include 'What is $^1/_4$ of, $^3/_4$ of' type questions.

LESSON 5

Repeat the **Oral and mental starter** from Lesson 4. In the **Main teaching activity** introduce other commercially-produced fraction games such as fraction dominoes. For the **Plenary** ask quick-fire questions as in Lesson 4.

UNIT 12

ORGANISATION (5 LESSONS)

LEARNING OUTCOMES	ORAL AND MENTAL STARTER	MAIN TEACHING ACTIVITY	PLENARY
LESSON 1 + 2 ● Solve a problem by collecting quickly, organising and representing data in tally charts and pictograms – symbol representing 2, 5, 10 or 20 units.	NUMBER CHAINS: Count on and back in 6s, 7s, 8s and 9s to 100. TABLES BINGO: Use knowledge of all times tables to 10 to play bingo.	PET PICTOGRAM: Use and create tally charts and pictograms.	Discuss how to represent 1 unit. Interpret data.
LESSON 3 ● Solve a problem by collecting quickly, organising and representing data in pictograms – symbol representing 2, 5, 10 or 20 units; bar charts – intervals labelled in 2s, 5s, 10s or 20s.	TABLES PAIRS: Give equivalent times tables sum.	PETS: Use data to produce a pictogram and a bar chart.	Discuss pictograms where symbols represent different numbers of units.
LESSON 4 + 5 ● Solve a problem by collecting quickly, organising and representing data in tables, charts, graphs and diagrams, for example: tally charts; bar charts – intervals labelled in 2s, 5s, 10s or 20s.	DIVISION SNAP: Play snap for 2, 3, 4, 5 and 10 times tables facts.	BOOK COUNT: Collect data and use it to produce a pictogram and a bar chart.	Present data. Discuss graphs.

ORAL AND MENTAL SKILLS Extend number sequences formed by counting from any number in steps of constant size. Begin to know multiplication facts for 6, 7, 8 and 9 times tables. **Know by heart multiplication facts for 2, 3, 4, 5 and 10 times tables. Derive quickly division facts corresponding to 2, 3, 4, 5 and 10 times tables.**

Lessons 1 and 4 are shown in full. Lessons 2 and 5 are developments of the previous lessons. Lesson 3 is an extension of what has already been taught so is shown in outline.

RESOURCES

Prepared division questions; sets of 0–9 digit cards (enough for four cards per child); bingo cards; OHP copy of photocopiable page 135 ('Pet data 1'); overhead projector and markers; grid paper; pencils and paper.

PREPARATION

Use the bingo cards prepared for Lesson 1, Unit 8, Term 2. Write different corresponding questions. Photocopy 'Pet data 1' (page 135) onto acetate.

LEARNING OUTCOMES

VOCABULARY

Vote; survey; data; count; tally; sort; set; represent; pictogram; most/least common; most/least popular; axis; axes; title.

ORAL AND MENTAL STARTER
● Extend number sequences formed by counting from any number in steps of constant size.
● Begin to know multiplication facts for 6, 7, 8 and 9 times tables.

MAIN TEACHING ACTIVITY
● Solve a problem by collecting quickly, organising and representing data in tally charts and pictograms – symbol representing 2, 5, 10 or 20 units.

ORAL AND MENTAL STARTER

NUMBER CHAINS: Repeat the activity from Lesson 2, Unit 1, Term 2 but this time count on and back in 6s, 7s, 8s and 9 up to 100.

MAIN TEACHING ACTIVITY

PET PICTOGRAM: Remind the children of the pictograms that they produced last term. Display the pets data on the OHP but just with the tally chart on view. Explain that some children from two classes have been finding out about their pets. Any children with more than one pet have just given their favourite. Remind children about tally charts, then ask: *How many children had cats?* 'There are 2 bundles of 5 plus another 2, so there are 12.' Write the total at the end of the row. Repeat for the other pets. When you get to 'Others', explain that you will add all these together as there is only a few of each. Now show them how the information has been displayed in a pictogram. Ask: *How many pets does each picture represent?* (2). Then ask questions about the data such as: *Which is the most popular pet? How many children do not have a pet? How many children were questioned? How many more dogs are there than rabbits?* In groups, the children then collect their own data with which to make a pictogram. Suggest topics that they could use, such as eye colour; favourite fruit. Tell them to think up their question, draw a tally chart, then collect and record the data. Next, they draw the pictogram on grid paper with each symbol representing two units.

DIFFERENTIATION

Children can work in mixed ability groups for this task.

PLENARY

Discuss the children's data and the symbols used on their pictograms. Ask them how they represented 1 unit (most will have used half of a symbol).

LESSON 2

Repeat the **Oral and mental starter** from Lesson 1. In the **Main teaching activity** each group devises a list of questions related to their data. Groups then swap their pictograms and list of questions. Each group should record their answers for the different sets of data. In the **Plenary** children present the results of another group's data.

RESOURCES	OHP copy of photocopiable page 136 ('Pet data 2') and one copy per child; OHP and markers; delete the animal pictures from the pictogram on photocopiable page 135 ('Pet data 1') then photocopy to provide blank pictogram grids, one enlarged version and one A4 version per pair; use the illustrations on 'Pet data 1' to provide a sheet of animal pictures, then photocopy, one per child; felt-tipped pens; scissors; glue.
LEARNING OUTCOMES	**ORAL AND MENTAL STARTER** ● **Know by heart multiplication facts for 2, 3, 4, 5 and 10 times tables.** ● Begin to know multiplication facts for 6, 7, 8 and 9 times tables. **MAIN TEACHING ACTIVITY** ● Solve a problem by collecting quickly, organising and representing data in pictograms and bar charts.
ORAL AND MENTAL STARTER	TABLES PAIRS: Given a tables question, eg 6×4, the children have to answer with an equivalent tables sum, eg 3×8.
MAIN TEACHING ACTIVITY	PETS: Display 'Pet data 2' on the OHP and tell the children that they are going to produce a pictogram and then a bar chart for this data. Point out that there are only 10 spaces in each column and ask for suggestions as to how many each 'picture' should represent. *Which is going to be the biggest number?* 48. *If each picture represents 2 how many squares would we need?* 24. *There isn't room for that. What if each picture represents 5, how many squares would we need?* About 10. Then together work out how many pictures of cats would be needed (nine whole ones and part of another). Show them the blank bar chart on the OHP and point out the scale in 5s. Hand out the pictogram grids, animal pictures and blank bar charts. In pairs, the children complete the two diagrams. Tell them that on their pictograms each 'picture' or symbol equals 5 units. If there are not exact multiples of 5 they should cut out a part of a picture for the remaining pets.
DIFFERENTIATION	More able: use the data to produce a range of pictograms. Draw pictograms where one symbol = 2 units and where one symbol = 10 units. Less able: just use data for two classes added together, using one symbol to represent 2 on the pictogram.
PLENARY	Reinforce the concept of using symbols for multiple numbers of units.

RESOURCES

Prepared division questions; sets of 0–9 digit cards (enough for four cards per child); OHP copy of page 137 ('Book count'); OHP and markers; blank bar charts; marker pens; felt-tipped pens; pencils; paper; copies of prepared class data collection sheet.

PREPARATION

Photocopy 'Book count' (page 134) onto acetate. Photocopy the blank bar chart from the photocopiable sheet, one per child. While the children collate their tally charts, draw up a class data collection sheet including all the categories you have decided on. At the end of the lesson photocopy the completed sheet, one per child, ready for Lesson 5.

LEARNING OBJECTIVE

ORAL AND MENTAL STARTER
● Derive quickly division facts corresponding to 2, 3, 4, 5 and 10 times tables.

MAIN TEACHING ACTIVITY
● Solve a problem by collecting quickly, organising and representing data in tables, charts, graphs and diagrams, for example: tally charts; bar charts – intervals labelled in 2s, 5s, 10s or 20s.

VOCABULARY

Vote; survey; data; count; tally; sort; set; represent; pictogram; most/least common; most/least popular; axis; axes; title.

ORAL AND MENTAL STARTER

DIVISION SNAP: Repeat activity from Term 2, Units 9–10, Lesson 5.

MAIN TEACHING ACTIVITY

BOOK COUNT: Tell the children that you want to carry out a survey of books in the class library. Show the 'Book count' pictogram (page 137) on the OHP and explain that this is how one class showed the data for their school library. Discuss the scale used (one symbol represents 10 books). Explain that this data could be used to produce a bar chart. Then show them the blank bar chart. Label the intervals along the vertical axis. Discuss what the title should be eg, 'Favourite types of books in Class 4'. Then for each book category ask children to come out and show how many boxes should be coloured in, using the data from the pictogram. Discuss how they will sort the books in their class library. *By author, type, publisher?* Then decide on the categories. Each group then audits a box of books or a section of the library, recording the data on a tally chart. Explain that you will want them to put their group's data onto a 'class data collection sheet' at the end of the lesson.

DIFFERENTIATION

Children work in mixed ability groups.

PLENARY

Individual groups should present the data they have collected, recording it on your class data collection sheet.

LESSON 5

Repeat the **Oral and mental starter** from Lesson 4. In the **Main teaching activity** discuss the collated data for the book audit. Children then produce a bar chart showing the class data. Discuss what intervals may be suitable for the bar chart. For **Differentiation** let the less able children use just the data collected by their own group (and maybe one other group) and tell them which intervals to use. More able children could produce further bar charts or pictograms using different intervals and selecting different ways to sort the data. In the **Plenary** discuss the graphs the children have produced, revising the main points.

Pet data 1

Tally chart

Pet	Tally	Total
Cat	⊬⊬⊬ ⊬⊬⊬ ||	
Dog	⊬⊬⊬ ⊬⊬⊬ ||||	
Rabbit	⊬⊬⊬ |||	
Bird	⊬⊬⊬ |	
Fish	||||	
No pet	⊬⊬⊬ ⊬⊬⊬	
Others: Mouse Tortoise Guinea pig	 || | |||	

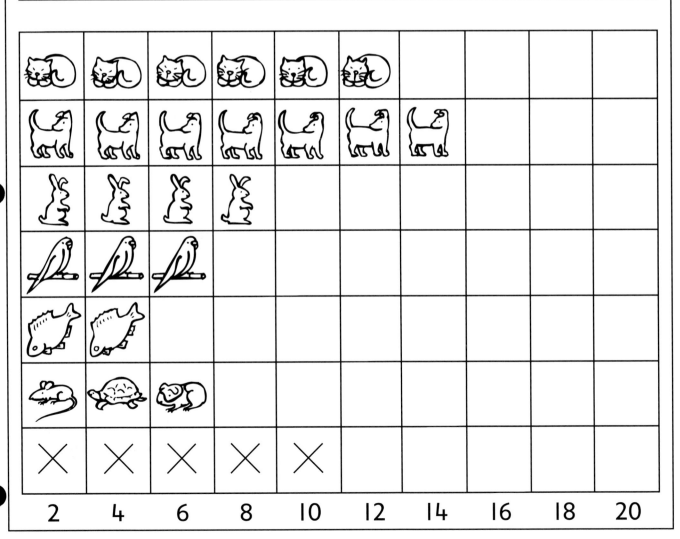

| | 2 | 4 | 6 | 8 | 10 | 12 | 14 | 16 | 18 | 20 |

Pet data 2

Data from the whole school about pets

Class	1	2	3	4	5	6	7	Total
Cat	6	4	8	5	9	9	7	**48**
Dog	7	4	3	6	6	3	4	**33**
Rabbit	4	2	4	3	2	5	2	**22**
Bird	3	3	2	4	2	3	1	**18**
Fish	2	2	3	5	5	2	3	**22**
No pet	5	6	4	3	2	8	9	**37**
Other	3	3	2	4	5	1	5	**23**
Total	**30**	**24**	**26**	**30**	**31**	**31**	**31**	

Pet bar chart

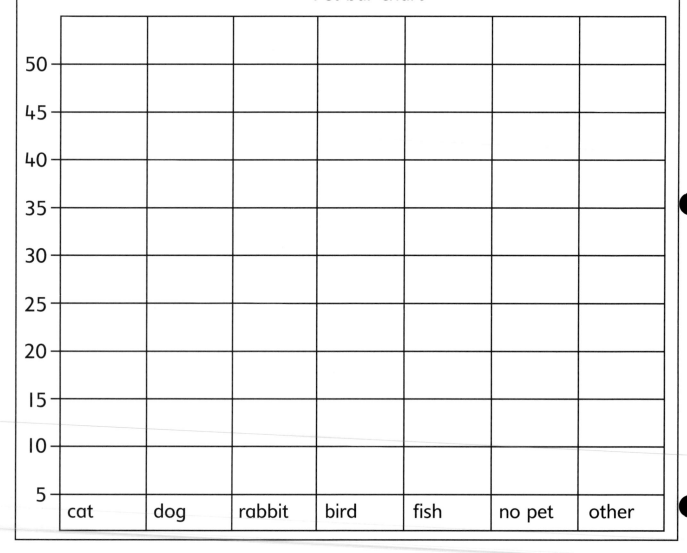

Book count

$\square$ = less than 10 $\square$ = 10

Poetry	📖	📖	📖	📖		
Animal stories	📖	📖	📖	📖	📖	
Historical stories	📖	📖	📖	📖	📖	
Adventure stories	📖	📖	📖	📖	📖	📖
Myths and legends	📖	📖	📖	📖	📖	📖
Favourite authors	📖	📖	📖	📖	📖	📖
Science fiction	📖	📖	📖	📖	📖	

UNIT 13: Assess & Review

Choose from the following activities over the two lessons. During the group activities, some children can complete Assessment worksheets 4a and 4b, which assess their skills in: approximating first and using informal pencil and paper methods for multiplication and division; using written methods for TU × U and TU ÷ U; recognising simple fractions that are part of a whole; identifying two simple fractions with a total of 1; recognising the equivalence of simple fractions. The specific assessment criteria for the assessment sheets can be found at the bottom of each sheet.

RESOURCES

Prepared bingo cards with numbers from the 2, 3, 4, 5, and 10 times tables, one per child; prepared division questions; sets of 0–9 digit cards (enough for 4 cards per child); 0–9 digit cards or dice; chart prepared for Term 2, Units 9–10, Lesson 9; pencils and paper.

ORAL AND MENTAL STARTER

ASSESSMENT
● Do the children: **know by heart: multiplication facts for 2, 3, 4, 5 and 10 times tables?**
● Can the children: **derive quickly division facts corresponding to 2, 3, 4, 5 and 10 times tables?**

TABLES BINGO: Repeat the activity from Lesson 2, Unit 8, Term 1, but this time for the 2, 3, 4, 5, and 10 times tables. When somebody has 'won', go through the questions asked and see which children had not 'marked off' the numbers.
DIVISION SNAP: Repeat the activity from Lesson 5, Units 9–10, Term 2. Carry on with the game until all the children have used up their digit cards; this will help you to identify children who are least able to derive quickly the division facts.

GROUP ACTIVITIES

ASSESSMENT
● Can the children: recognise and extend number sequences formed by counting from any number in steps of constant size, extending beyond zero when counting back; use doubling or halving starting, from known facts; **find remainders after division?**

FIND THE RULE: Using the activity from Lesson 1, Unit 8, Term 2, give the children a number sequence such as 25, 50, 75, ask them to find the rule and then continue the sequence. Give several examples including extending beyond zero when counting back, eg 12, 9, 6, 3, ?, ?. Check that the children can identify the 'rule' and can then implement it.
DOUBLES: Write the following calculations on the board:
a) 13 × 4; b) 39 × 5; c) ½ of 460; d) 14 × 5; e) ¼ of 28; f) 8 × 15.
Ask the children to calculate the answers using doubling and halving and then explain their reasoning.
REMAINDERS: Each player in the group throws the 0–9 dice twice to generate a two-digit number. They then select a digit card and divide their two-digit number by that single digit. They record their calculations on the chart you prepared for Lesson 9, Units 9–10, Term 2.

Assessment 2a

Calculate the answers to the following. Approximate first and then show how you worked it out.

25 × 4	89 × 9
73 × 8	49 × 10
49 − 2	73 − 7
86 − 3	130 − 10

Complete these calculations:

Multiply 43 × 7

$$\begin{array}{r} 43 \\ \times\ 7 \\ \hline \end{array}$$

40 × 7 _____

3 × 7 _____

Ans: _____

Divide 84 − 7

$$7\overline{)84}$$

10 × 7 _____

? × 7 _____

Ans: _____

● Approximate first. Use informal pencil and paper methods to support, record or explain multiplication and divisions. Develop and refine written methods for TU × U, TU ÷ U.

Assessment 2b

What fraction of each shape has been shaded?

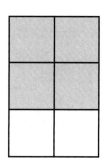 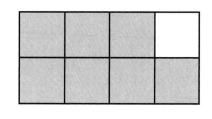 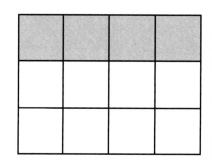

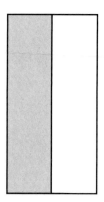 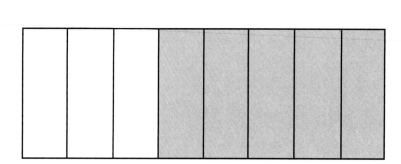 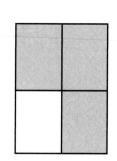

Draw a line to link pairs of fractions that total 1:

$\frac{2}{3}$ $\frac{2}{5}$ $\frac{3}{5}$ $\frac{7}{10}$ $\frac{6}{8}$ $\frac{1}{3}$ $\frac{1}{4}$

$\frac{5}{8}$ $\frac{2}{8}$ $\frac{3}{10}$ $\frac{3}{4}$ $\frac{1}{5}$ $\frac{4}{5}$ $\frac{3}{8}$

Draw a line matching a fraction from the first box to its equivalent in the second box:

$\frac{2}{4}$ $\frac{4}{8}$ $\frac{1}{3}$ $\frac{4}{10}$		$\frac{6}{10}$ $\frac{2}{6}$ $\frac{3}{6}$ $\frac{6}{8}$
$\frac{3}{4}$ $\frac{5}{10}$ $\frac{4}{6}$ $\frac{3}{5}$		$\frac{50}{100}$ $\frac{2}{5}$ $\frac{2}{3}$ $\frac{1}{2}$

● **Recognise simple fractions that are part of a whole; recognise the equivalence of simple fractions.** Identify two simple fractions with a total of 1.

TERM 3

Term 3 revises mental calculation strategies and rounding and further develops informal and written methods for the four operations. Children order numbers up to 100 000. Familiarity with multiples of 2, 3, 4, 5 and 10 is reinforced and knowledge of the 6, 8 and 9 times tables is developed further. In measurement, children learn how to choose suitable units and equipment to estimate and measure capacity and how to read scales accurately. They also start to measure angles. Work in fractions begins to use the idea of simple proportion and develops understanding of the links between simple fractions and their decimal equivalents. When time is revisited timetables and calendars are studied. Handling data features the way in which information can be interpreted by using Venn and Carroll diagrams. There is the opportunity to incorporate ICT.

ENLARGE THIS SHEET TO A3 AND USE IT AS YOUR MEDIUM-TERM PLANNING GRID.

Oral and mental: Read and write whole numbers to at least 10 000 in figures and words. Begin to multiply by 100. Find a small difference by counting up. Consolidate knowing by heart addition and subtraction facts for all numbers to 20. Derive quickly all number pairs that total 100; all pairs of multiples of 50 with a total of 1000. Count on or back in repeated steps of 1, 10 or 100. Partition into tens and units, adding the tens first. Identify near doubles, using known doubles. Add three or four small numbers, finding pairs totalling 10, or 9 or 11. Add the nearest multiple of 100, then adjust. Consolidate understanding of the relationship between + and −. Check with the inverse operation. Recognise odd and even numbers up to 1000. Estimate and check by approximating.

UNIT	TOPIC	OBJECTIVES: CHILDREN WILL BE TAUGHT TO...
1	Place value, ordering and rounding	● Begin to multiply by 100. ● Read and write the vocabulary of comparing and ordering numbers. **Use symbols correctly, including less than (<), greater than (>), equals (=).** Give one or more numbers lying between two given whole numbers and order a set of whole numbers less than 10000. ● **Round any positive integer less than 1000 to the nearest 10 or 100.**
2–3	Understanding + and − Mental calculation strategies (+ and −) Pencil and paper procedures (+ and −) Money and 'real life' problems Making decisions	● Understand the principles (not the names) of the commutative and associative laws as they apply or not to addition and subtraction. ● Add three two-digit multiples of 10. ● Add or subtract the nearest multiple of 10, then adjust. ● **Use known number facts to add or subtract mentally.** ● **Develop and refine written methods for column addition and subtraction**, money calculations. ● Use addition and subtraction to solve word problems involving numbers in 'real life'. ● **Choose and use appropriate number operations and ways of calculating to solve problems.**
4–6	Measures, including problems Shape and space Reasoning about shapes	● Suggest suitable units and measuring equipment to estimate or measure capacity. ● **Know and use the relationships between familiar units of capacity.** ● Record estimates and readings from scales to a suitable degree of accuracy. ● Use all four operations to solve word problems involving numbers in measures. ● Sketch the reflection of a simple shape. ● Recognise positions and directions. Recognise simple examples of horizontal and vertical lines. ● Make and measure clockwise and anticlockwise turns. ● Use the eight compass directions. ● Begin to know that angles are measured in degrees. Start to order a set of angles less than 180°.
7	Assess and review	See the key objectives listed on the relevant pages.

Oral and mental: Consolidate knowing by heart addition and subtraction facts for all numbers to 20. Derive quickly all number pairs that total 100; all pairs of multiples of 50 with a total of 1000. **Derive quickly: division facts corresponding to 2, 3, 4, 5 and 10 times tables**; doubles of all whole numbers to 50, of multiples of 10 to 500, of multiples of 100 to 5000, and the corresponding halves. **Know by heart multiplication facts for 2, 3, 4, 5 and 10 times tables.** Begin to know multiplication facts for 6, 7, 8 and 9 times tables.

UNIT	TOPIC	OBJECTIVES: CHILDREN WILL BE TAUGHT TO...
8	Properties of numbers Reasoning about numbers	● Recognise and extend number sequences formed by counting in steps of constant size. ● Recognise multiples of 2, 3, 4, 5 and 10 up to the tenth multiple. ● Use halving. ● Explain methods and reasoning about numbers orally and in writing. ● Solve mathematical problems or puzzles, recognise and explain patterns and relationships, generalise and predict. Suggest extensions by asking 'What if...?'.
9–10	Understanding × and ÷ Mental calculation strategies (× and ÷) Pencil and paper procedures (× and ÷) Money and 'real life' problems Making decisions and checking results	● Use the relationship between multiplication and division. ● Use closely related facts. ● Use doubling and halving, starting from known facts. ● Derive quickly doubles of multiples of 10 to 500, and of 100 to 5000, and the corresponding halves. ● **Find remainders after division.** Divide a whole number of pounds by 2, 4, 5 or 10 to give £.p. ● Approximate first. Use informal pencil and paper methods to support, record or explain multiplications and divisions. Develop and refine written methods for TU × U. ● Use all four operations to solve word problems involving numbers in 'real life' and money.
11	Fractions and decimals	● Understand decimal notation and place value for tenths and hundredths, and use it in context. ● Recognise the equivalence between decimal and fraction forms of one-half, one-quarter, and tenths. ● Begin to use ideas of simple proportion.
12	Understanding + and − Mental calculation strategies, pencil and paper procedures Time, including problems	● **Develop and refine written methods for: column addition and subtraction of two whole numbers less than 1000 and addition of more than two such numbers;** for money calculations. ● Use, read and write the vocabulary related to time. Estimate/check times using seconds, minutes, hours. Use am and pm. Read simple timetables and use this year's calendar. ● Use all four operations to use word problems involving time.
13	Handling data	● Solve a problem by collecting quickly, organising and interpreting data in tables, charts, graphs and diagrams, including those generated by a computer.
14	Assess and review	See the key objectives listed on the relevant pages.

ORGANISATION (3 LESSONS)

	LEARNING OUTCOMES	ORAL AND MENTAL STARTER	MAIN TEACHING ACTIVITY	PLENARY
LESSON 1	● Begin to multiply by 100.	PUT UP THE NUMBER: Show given numbers in figures and in words.	MULTIPLY BY 100: Multiply and divide by 10 then multiply by 100.	Revise rules for multiplying and dividing by 10 and multiplying by 100.
LESSON 2	● Read and write the vocabulary of comparing and ordering numbers. **Use symbols correctly, including less than (<), greater than (>), equals (=).** Give one or more numbers lying between two given numbers and order a set of whole numbers less than 10 000.	TIMES 100: Multiply numbers by 100.	LARGER OR SMALLER?: Order pairs then groups of numbers. Fill in the gaps on number lines. Use <, >, = symbols.	Complete number lines and number statements.
LESSON 3	● **Round any positive integer less than 1000 to the nearest 10 or 100.**	IT'S CLOSE: Find differences by counting up.	ROUNDING: Round to the nearest 10 and nearest 100.	Revise rules for rounding off to nearest 10 or 100.

ORAL AND MENTAL SKILLS Read and write whole numbers to at least 10 000 in figures and words, and know what each digit represents. Begin to multiply by 100. Find a small difference by counting up.

Lessons 1 and 2 are shown in full. Lesson 3 is an extension of what has already been taught so is shown in outline.

RESOURCES

Number fans prepared for Lesson 1, Unit 1, Term 1; Multibase equipment; copies of photocopiable page 146 ('Bigger and bigger'); prepared grid; pencils.

PREPARATION

Photocopy 'Bigger and bigger' (page 146), one per child. Write this grid on the board:

	1	2	3	4	5	6	7	8	9
× 10	10	20	30	40					
× 10 again or × 100	100	200	300	400					

LEARNING OUTCOMES

ORAL AND MENTAL STARTER
● Read and write whole numbers to at least 10 000 in figures and words, and know what each digit represents.

MAIN TEACHING ACTIVITY
● Begin to multiply by 100.

VOCABULARY

Units; tens;
hundreds;
thousands;
multiply;
divide; digit;
place value.

ORAL AND MENTAL STARTER

PUT UP THE NUMBER: Give the children a two-digit number for them to show you on their number fans. Then show them a number on your number fan for them to say in words. After a few turns, repeat for three-digit numbers, then for four-digit numbers. Ask questions such as: *Show me the number that is 1 more than 99. Show me the number that is 2 less than 400. Show the number that is 10 more than 3120. Show the number that is 10 less than 6857.*

MAIN TEACHING ACTIVITY

MULTIPLY BY 100: Remind the children that when a whole number is multiplied by 10 the digits move one place to the left, so $23 \times 10 = 230$ and $68 \times 10 = 680$. Similarly, when a whole number ending in zero is divided by 10 the digits move one place to the right, so $450 \div 10 = 45$ and $730 \div 10 = 73$. Try other examples. Then introduce multiplying whole numbers by 100. Explain that this time the digits will move two places to the left to correspond with the number of zeros. So $5 \times 100 = 500$ and $92 \times 100 = 9200$. Point out that multiplying by 100 is the same as multiplying by 10 and then by 10 again. Then together fill in the grid you started on the board. Children then work through 'Bigger and bigger' (page 146) on their own.

DIFFERENTIATION

More able: investigate what will happen when numbers are divided by 100.
Less able: initially let them use structured equipment to help them.

PLENARY

Go through their answers. Revise rules for multiplying and dividing by 10 and multiplying by 100. Get the children to recite them.

LESSON 2

RESOURCES

Number fans prepared for Lesson 1, Unit 1, Term 1; copies of photocopiable page 147 ('Plug the gaps'); pencils.

PREPARATION

Photocopy 'Plug the gaps' (page 147), one per child. Prepare a revised version of the photocopiable page for the less able group (see **Differentiation**).

LEARNING OUTCOMES

ORAL AND MENTAL STARTER
● Begin to multiply whole numbers by 100.

VOCABULARY

More than;
fewer than;
greater than;
less than;
bigger than;
smaller than;
larger than;
most; least;
largest;
smallest; first;
second; third;
fourth...;
order; before;
after; next;
between; <, >,
and = signs.

MAIN TEACHING ACTIVITY
● Read and write the vocabulary of comparing and ordering numbers.
● **Use symbols correctly, including less than (<), greater than (>), equals (=).**
● Give one or more numbers lying between two given numbers and order a set of whole numbers less than 10000.

ORAL AND MENTAL STARTER

TIMES 100: This starter activity reinforces the work done in the **Main Teaching Activity** of the previous lesson. Ask the children to tell you the rule for multiplying by 100 (move the digits two places to the left). Then give them numbers to multiply by 100 and ask them to show you the answers on their number fans. Start with single-digit numbers, for example 4×100, then progress to two-digit numbers, for example 53×100. Focus on vocabulary by asking questions such as: *Make 7 a hundred times bigger, 12 multiplied by 100, 34 times 100*. Check that children can also work out the answers by multiplying by 10 and then by 10 again, such as $19 \times 10 \times 10 = 1900$.

MAIN TEACHING ACTIVITY

LARGER OR SMALLER?: Write on the board pairs of numbers for the children to say which one is the larger. Start with two-digit numbers, such as 78 and 87, then extend to three-digit numbers, such as 105 and 150 then to four-digit numbers, 1522 and 1255. Repeat, but this time ask for the smaller number. Then write up a series of four numbers and ask the children to put them in order of size, smallest first. Include at least one digit that is common to all four numbers, such as 1215, 5211, 5121, 5125. Write up part of a number line and ask children to fill in the missing numbers. For example:

495   498 499   504 505   509

Remind the children of the < and > signs. Write on the board a pair of two-digit numbers and ask the children which sign should go between them and why, such as 21 and 12; 37 and 73. Remind them that the open part of the sign always faces towards the larger number. Repeat using three-digit numbers. Children now work on their own to complete 'Plug the gaps' (page 147).

DIFFERENTIATION

More able: make up their own number statements using the signs.
Less able: work on a revised version of the photocopiable sheet with number lines with one step gaps only, and smaller numbers when using the signs.

PLENARY

Draw on the board several number lines with missing numbers for children to complete. Then ask one child to write up a pair of numbers and invite another child out to complete the statement with the correct sign, < or >. They should say the statement aloud once they have completed it using phrases such as 'bigger than'/'smaller than'.

RESOURCES	Class 0–100 number line with 10s marked in different colour; 0–100, 0–1000 number lines prepared from resource sheet A for the less able group; 0–9 dice or 0–9 digit cards per pair; pencils and paper.
LEARNING OUTCOMES	**ORAL AND MENTAL STARTER** ● Find a small difference by counting up. **MAIN TEACHING ACTIVITY** ● **Round any positive integer less than 1000 to the nearest 10 or 100.**
ORAL AND MENTAL STARTER	IT'S CLOSE: Repeat the whole class activity from the Main teaching activity in Lesson 3, Units 2–3, Term 1. Include questions when the larger number is given first, eg *Find the difference between 4002 and 3995.*
MAIN TEACHING ACTIVITY	ROUNDING: Display the class 0–100 number line then revise rounding to the nearest ten, eg 52 rounded down to 50, 79 rounded up to 80 and 35 rounded up to 40. Remind the children that when rounding numbers to the nearest hundred, the numbers up to 50 go back to the previous hundred while numbers of 50 or more go on to the next hundred. Work through some examples, eg 247 goes back to 200, 586 goes up to 600 and 450 goes up to 500. In pairs, the children use dice or digit cards to generate their own two-digit numbers then three-digit numbers for rounding. Tell them to round the three-digit numbers to the nearest ten first and then to the nearest hundred, eg 576 rounded to the nearest ten would be 580 and to the nearest hundred, 600.
DIFFERENTIATION	More able: use their ability to round off numbers to find approximate answers to addition sums, eg 49 + 73 rounds off to 50 + 70, so an approximate answer would be 120. Less able: check they are working confidently with two-digit numbers before they move on to larger numbers. Give them number lines for support.
PLENARY	Work through examples of rounding off which the children have generated through their dice/digit cards. Revise counting up and back in tens and up and back in hundreds. Check rules for rounding off to the nearest 10 and nearest 100. Check through the approximated answers from the more able group.

LESSON 3

Bigger and bigger

1. Fill in the missing numbers:

	1	2	3	4	5	6	7	8	9
× 10	10			40			70		
× 10 again or × 100		200				600			900

2. Circle the number on the right that is <u>10 times bigger</u> than the number on the left:

8	18	80	800	88	8
17	117	77	170	70	700
36	360	63	136	630	60
128	821	138	120	800	1280
653	600	500	6500	6530	65000

3. Circle the number on the right that is <u>100 times bigger</u> than the number on the left:

3	30	31	300	33	1300	103
9	900	99	9000	190	910	119
16	160	600	6100	1600	100	60
25	250	520	2000	5000	52	2500
72	7200	7200	2700	27	700	7000

4. Circle the number on the right that is <u>10 times smaller</u> than the number on the left:

50	15	51	5	25	500	105
100	12	10	21	1000	101	11
190	109	1119	91	9000	1000	19
2100	21	210	2000	1000	1200	2021
7400	74	740	470	4000	7000	4700

UNIT 1

Plug the gaps

1. Fill in the missing numbers on these number lines:

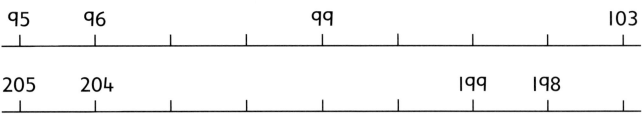

95   96   99   103

205   204   199   198

426   428   432   434

994   999   1005

9984   9990   9999

2. Put the correct < or > sign between these number pairs:

| 76   67 | 121   112 | 210   120 |

| 752   725 | 1500   5100 |

| 2001   1200 | 7435   7543 | 9990   9999 |

3. Put in the missing signs <, >, = in these questions:

| 34 + 26   70 | 76 + 39   115 | 110 + 23   131 |

| 524 + 47   715 | 50   75 – 20 |

| 64   100 – 38 | 100   159 – 64 | 77   292 – 215 |

4. Complete these sentences using your own numbers:

| 50 + 27 < | > 72 – 20 | 94 + 19 > |

| 42 + 69 > 100 – | = 16 + 5 + 12 | 39 – 6 – 14 < |

UNITS 2-3

ORGANISATION (10 LESSONS)

	LEARNING OUTCOMES	ORAL AND MENTAL STARTER	MAIN TEACHING ACTIVITY	PLENARY
LESSON 1	● Understand the principles (not the names) of the commutative and associative laws as they apply or not to addition and subtraction. ● Add three two-digit multiples of 10.	TOP TWENTY: Answer quick-fire questions on addition using numbers up to 20.	IN ANY ORDER: Produce own numbers to check out commutative and associative laws.	Check through examples. Revise the two laws.
LESSON 2	● Add or subtract the nearest multiple of 10, then adjust.	TOP TWENTY: Answer quick-fire questions on subtraction using numbers up to 20.	FUNCTION MACHINES: Add and subtract using function machines.	Review function machine tasks.
LESSON 3	● **Use known number facts to add or subtract mentally.**	MAKE 100: Give the other number in the pair to make 100.	UP TO THE NEXT 100: Make up numbers to the next 100 or 1000.	Discuss methods used.
LESSON 4 +5	● **Develop and refine written methods for column addition.** ● Use knowledge of sums or differences of pairs of odd/ even numbers.	THOUSAND UP: Give the other number in the pair to make 1000.	COLUMN ADDITION: Calculate HTU + HTU sums using column addition.	Reinforce teaching points from methods used.
LESSON 6 +7	● **Develop and refine written methods for column subtraction.** ● Use knowledge of sums or differences of pairs of odd/ even numbers.	CLAP COUNTER: Count on and back in steps of 1, 10 and 100.	COLUMN SUBTRACTION: Calculate HTU – TU using the decomposition method.	Reinforce teaching points from methods used.
LESSON 8	● **Develop and refine written methods for column addition and subtraction;** money calculations.	MAKE 100: Give the other number in the pair to make 100, in the context of money.	MONEY CALCULATIONS: Calculate money problems.	Work through examples on the board.
LESSON 9	● Use addition and subtraction to solve word problems involving numbers in 'real life'.	CLAP COUNTER: Count on and back in steps of 100.	ON THE FARM: Solve 'real life' word problems.	Discuss methods and strategies used.
LESSON 10	● **Choose and use appropriate number operations and appropriate ways of calculating to solve problems.**	IT'S CLOSE: Find differences by counting up.	WHICH OPERATION?: Choose the correct operation to answer questions.	Discuss methods and strategies used.

ORAL AND MENTAL SKILLS Consolidate knowing by heart addition and subtraction facts for all numbers to 20. Derive quickly all number pairs that total 100; all pairs of multiples of 50 with a total of 1000. Count on or back in repeated steps of 1, 10 or 100. Find a small difference by counting up.

Lessons 1, 2, 8, and 9 are shown in full. Lessons 3, 4, 6 and 10 are shown in outline. Lessons 5 and 7 are shown as developments of the previous lessons.

LESSON 1

RESOURCES

0–9 dice or 0–9 digit cards per pair; pencils and paper.

PREPARATION

None.

LEARNING OUTCOMES

ORAL AND MENTAL STARTER

● Consolidate knowing by heart addition and subtraction facts for all numbers to 20.

MAIN TEACHING ACTIVITY

● Understand the principles (not the names) of the commutative and associative laws as they apply or not to addition and subtraction.
● Add three two-digit multiples of 10.

ORAL AND MENTAL STARTER

TOP TWENTY: Repeat the activity from Lesson 3, Unit 1, Term 1, but focusing just on addition and using different vocabulary to ask the questions.

MAIN TEACHING ACTIVITY

IN ANY ORDER: First revise the commutative law for addition (see Lesson 1, Units 2–3, Term 1). Ask children to add 56 and 74, then 74 and 56. Ask: *What do you notice about the answers?* Repeat for 3 two-digit multiples of 10, such as 40 + 30 + 10, now try 30 + 40 + 10 and 10 + 30 + 40. Repeat for any 3 two-digit numbers, eg 25, 36 and 82. Ask: *Does this work for subtraction?* Check with a calculation such as 87 – 53 is 34 but 53 – 87 does not give the same answer. Remind the children of when they regrouped numbers in additions to help with calculations (the associative law). For example, 74 + 36 + 29 can be added as 74 + (36 + 29) = 74 + 65 = 139 or (74 + 36) + 29 = 110 + 29 = 139. Again, give an example to remind that the same method does not work for subtraction.

In pairs, children use the dice or digit cards to generate 10 pairs of three-digit numbers, which they add in the two different orders. They then repeat for 10 sets of three two-digit numbers, recording different ways of grouping them to obtain the same answer.

DIFFERENTIATION

More able: remind children to check their answers by using the inverse operation – that is to say, the answers to addition questions can be checked using subtraction.
Less able: restrict to two-digit multiples of 10 until they are confident enough to move on.

PLENARY

Write up some of the children's examples on the board for the class to check. Reinforce the two laws (but do not mention them by name).

RESOURCES

Copies of photocopiable page 155 ('Function machines'); pencils.

PREPARATION

Photocopy 'Function machines' (page 155), one per child.

LEARNING OUTCOMES

ORAL AND MENTAL STARTER

● Consolidate knowing by heart addition and subtraction facts for all numbers to 20.

MAIN TEACHING ACTIVITY

● Add or subtract the nearest multiple of 10, then adjust.

ORAL AND MENTAL STARTER

TOP TWENTY: Repeat the activity from Lesson 3, Unit 1, Term 1, but focusing just on subtraction and using different vocabulary to ask the questions.

VOCABULARY

More; add; sum; total; altogether; equals; inverse; plus; take away; subtract; difference between; minus

VOCABULARY

More; add; sum; total; altogether; equals; plus; take away; subtract; minus; function machine.

MAIN TEACHING ACTIVITY

FUNCTION MACHINES: Remind the children how function machines work: a number is put into the machine in the 'in' column, it goes through a stated process to produce a new number for the 'out' column. Show them examples of a single and double process function machine:

single
process: (+5)

in	out
6	11
12	17
19	24
32	37
68	73

double
process: (+7   −3)

in	middle	out
9	16	13
14	21	18
27	34	31
39	46	43
50	57	54

Remind the children that an easier way to add or subtract some numbers is to use the nearest multiple of 10 and then adjust. Use 9 and 11 as examples. Write on the board these function machines to show the processes:

add 9: (+10 − 1)

in	middle	out
74	84	83

subtract 9: (−10 + 1)

in	middle	out
84	74	75

Repeat for adding and subtracting 99, for example 59 + 99 = 59 + 100 − 1 = 158. Children now work on their own to complete 'Function machines' (page 155).

DIFFERENTIATION

More able: investigate ways of adding and taking away numbers linked to other near multiples of 10 such as 31 and 39.
Less able: consolidate work on adding and subtracting 9 and 11 before progressing to other multiples of 10 on the photocopiable.

PLENARY

Write some function machines on the board to complete with the children's help. Discuss in what ways these methods make addition and subtraction easier.

LESSON 3

RESOURCES	Number fans prepared for Lesson 1, Unit 1, Term 1; 0–9 dice or 0–9 digit cards per pair; pencils and paper.
LEARNING OUTCOMES	**ORAL AND MENTAL STARTER** ● Derive quickly all number pairs that total 100. **MAIN TEACHING ACTIVITY** ● Use known number facts to add or subtract mentally.
ORAL AND MENTAL STARTER	MAKE 100: Repeat the activity from Lesson 1, Units 4–6, Term 1, but just for pairs that make 100.
MAIN TEACHING ACTIVITY	UP TO THE NEXT 100: Write on the board 163 and ask: *What needs to be added to this number to make 200?* (37). Give other three-digit numbers for them to make up to the next hundred. Repeat for four-digit multiples of 100 to make the next thousand, eg you say 1400 and they respond with 600. In pairs, the children use the dice or digit cards to generate ten three-digit numbers. They then work on their own to make each number up to the next hundred. They repeat for ten four-digit multiples of 100, which they then make up to the next thousand. Ask them to check each other's answers.
DIFFERENTIATION	More able: repeat for four-digit multiples of 50, eg 3450 (answer 550). Less able: use three-digit numbers only to make up to the next hundred. Use number lines to support counting in hundreds.
PLENARY	Discuss strategies used to make the total up to the next 100 or 1000.

LESSON 4 + 5

RESOURCES	Base 10 equipment; prepared three-digit number sums written horizontally on the board, including examples that involve carrying, a different set for each ability group; squared paper; rulers; pencils; sets of three-digit numbers written on the board, a different set for each ability group.
LEARNING OUTCOMES	**ORAL AND MENTAL STARTER** ● Derive quickly all pairs of multiples of 50 with a total of 1000. **MAIN TEACHING ACTIVITY** ● Develop and refine written methods for column addition.
ORAL AND MENTAL STARTER	THOUSAND UP: Repeat the activity from Lesson 1, Units 4–6, Term 1 but this time for number bonds for 1000 and counting on/back in steps of 50.
MAIN TEACHING ACTIVITY 356 + 412 ――― 8 60 700 ――― 768 356 + 412 ――― 768 268 + 617 ――― 15 70 800 ――― 885 268 + 617 ――― 885 1	COLUMN ADDITION: Remind the children of the method of column addition introduced in Lessons 6 and 7, Units 2–3, Term 2. Write on the board 356 + 412 and look at the place value of each of the digits in the numbers: *356 is 3 hundreds, 5 tens and 6 units. 412 is 4 hundreds, 1 ten and 2 units.* Write the sum vertically, reminding the children that the units must be directly under each other in the units column and similarly for the tens and hundreds. As before, add the units first, then the tens, then the hundreds, discussing each stage as you go: Use Big base 10 equipment to illustrate this if necessary. Work through other examples of this type then explain that we can reduce the number of lines by just writing: Talk through this process starting with the least significant digits (the units). Then give an example that involves carrying, say 268 + 617. First work it out in the long way, adding first the units, then the tens and finally the hundreds: Then repeat using the short way, explaining the processes as you record (see Lesson 6, Units 2–3, Term 2): Invite children out to the board to work through further examples of these. Then tell the children to work on their own through the examples you have written on the board. Recording on squared paper helps them to keep the digits in the correct columns.
DIFFERENTIATION	More able: give them questions that include numbers with zero and three-digit numbers that will take answers into four digits, eg 674 + 458. Less able: let them use equipment when carrying is involved to work practically.
PLENARY	Use the method to add three integers less than 1000 to show that the process is exactly the same. Include examples where more than one ten is carried into the hundreds column, eg 379 + 283 + 153 = 815.

LESSON 5

Repeat the **Oral and mental starter** from Lesson 4. In the **Main teaching activity** revise the column addition method then tell the children to write their own questions using combinations of the numbers on the board and then calculate the answers. **Differentiation** is achieved by providing each ability group with an appropriate set of numbers. In the **Plenary** go through some of the children's examples.

LESSON 6 + 7

RESOURCES	Prepared HTU – TU subtractions written on the board, and sets of three-digit and two-digit numbers written on the board, a different set for each ability group; squared paper; rulers; base 10 apparatus; pencils.
LEARNING OUTCOMES	**ORAL AND MENTAL STARTER** ● Count on or back in repeated steps of 1 or 10. **MAIN TEACHING ACTIVITY** ● **Develop and refine written methods for column subtraction.** ● Use knowledge of sums or differences of pairs of odd/even numbers.
ORAL AND MENTAL STARTER	CLAP COUNTER: Repeat the activity from the first part of the Main teaching activity in Lesson 2, Units 2–3, Term 1 to find answers to questions such as 2,003 + 6, the difference between 672 and 622, add together 371 and 400 (by counting on in hundreds).
MAIN TEACHING ACTIVITY	COLUMN SUBTRACTION: Remind the children of the method of column addition introduced in Lessons 8 and 9, Units 2–3, Term 2. Go through examples (see Lesson 8 for the method), eg 453 – 78 and 647 – 98. Invite children to write up given subtractions vertically on the board and then work through them. Remind them to start at the right with the least significant digits (the units) and work towards the left. Use apparatus to back up explanation. The children then work on their own through the examples you have written on the board.
DIFFERENTIATION	More able: tell them to check their answers by using the inverse operation. Less able: start with subtraction sums that do not involve decomposition. Use base 10 apparatus to support written work.
PLENARY	Invite children out to demonstrate their own calculations to the class. Reinforce teaching points, especially placing of digits in the correct columns.

LESSON 8

RESOURCES

Sets of plastic coins; copies of photocopiable page 156 ('School fête'); squared paper; rulers; pencils.

PREPARATION

Photocopy 'School fête' (page 156), one per child.
Have sets of coins available for less able groups.

LEARNING OUTCOMES

ORAL AND MENTAL STARTER
● Derive quickly all number pairs that total 100.

MAIN TEACHING ACTIVITY
● **Develop and refine written methods for column addition and subtraction**; money calculations.

ORAL AND MENTAL STARTER

MAKE 100: Repeat the activity from Lesson 1, Units 4–6, Term 1, but just for pairs that make 100 and this time in the context of money. Revise how many of each of the coins are needed to make up £1.

MAIN TEACHING ACTIVITY

MONEY CALCULATIONS: Write these questions horizontally first and then show how to write them down in columns. Stress the numbers must go into the correct columns and the decimal points, which mark off pounds from pence, must line up under each other. Tell the children that the answer should be clearly labelled with a £ sign to indicate a money calculation.

1. £3.27 + £2.15

```
  £3.27
+  2.15
  ‾‾‾‾‾
  £ .
```

2. £4.20 + 57p

```
  £4.20
+  0.57
  ‾‾‾‾‾
  £ .
```

3. £2.58 + 73p + £1.25

```
  £2.58
+  0.73
   1.25
  ‾‾‾‾‾
  £ .
```

Together calculate the answers, then repeat for money subtraction calculations.

1. £4.56 – £2.34

```
  £4.56
–  2.34
  ‾‾‾‾‾
  £ .
```

2. £3.78 – 52p

```
  £3.78
–  0.52
  ‾‾‾‾‾
  £ .
```

3. £5.00 – £3.25

```
  £5.00
–  3.25
  ‾‾‾‾‾
  £ .
```

The children then work on their own to complete 'School fête' (page 156). Let them record their calculations on squared paper.

DIFFERENTIATION

More able: encourage children to set their own questions using the amounts given where totals get larger and change is required from £10, £15 or £20.
Less able: check early calculations are correct before children proceed to more difficult problems as the questions progress. Use sets of coins for support.

PLENARY

Ask children to pick out items they would like to buy themselves. Some can say how much they will spend, while others work out how much change they would have from given amounts. Ask children to show their workings on the board.

RESOURCES

Copies of photocopiable page 157 ('Down on the farm'); squared paper; rulers; prepared word problems; pencils.

PREPARATION

Photocopy 'Down on the farm' (page 157), one per child. Write word problems on the board, starting with single step operations of the type 'If a gardener collects 15 flowers from one bed, 23 from another and 19 from a third, how many flowers have been gathered in total?' and 'John has 45 comics in his collection but he loses 27 of them, how many are left?' Then include problems involving more than one step, such as 'If 12p was spent on a notepad and 25p on a pencil, how much change would be left from 50p?'

LEARNING OUTCOMES

ORAL AND MENTAL STARTER
● Count on or back in repeated steps of 100.

MAIN TEACHING ACTIVITY
● Use addition and subtraction to solve word problems involving numbers in 'real life'.

VOCABULARY

Calculate; calculation; method; jotting; answer; right; correct; wrong; what could we try next?; number sentence; sign; operation.

ORAL AND MENTAL STARTER

CLAP COUNTER: Repeat the activity from the first part of the **Main teaching activity** in Lesson 2, Units 2–3, Term 1, focusing mainly on 100s.

MAIN TEACHING ACTIVITY

ON THE FARM: Go through the word problems that you have written on the board and ask children to explain how numbers, signs and symbols can be used to solve the problems. For example, for the problem 'Twelve apples are put into a box. Twenty-three more are added. How many apples are there altogether?' they should respond $12 + 23 = 35$; for the problem 'A teacher collects 15 books from one class and 19 books from another to mark. There should be 58 books altogether. How many children have not handed in their book?' they should respond $58 - (19 + 15) = 24$ or $19 + 15 = 34$ then $58 - 34 = 24$. The children then work on their own to complete 'Down on the farm' (page 157).

DIFFERENTIATION

More able: go on to generate their own questions using the same setting.
Less able: check early calculations are correct before children proceed to more difficult problems as the questions progress.

PLENARY

Invite children out to write on the board the numbers, signs and symbols needed to solve each of the problems. Then invite other children to work out the solutions. Discuss strategies and examine other suggested methods.

RESOURCES	Number lines; times tables square; copies of photocopiable page 158 ('You choose'), one per child; pencils.
LEARNING OUTCOMES	**ORAL AND MENTAL STARTER** ● Find a small difference by counting up. **MAIN TEACHING ACTIVITY** ● **Choose and use appropriate number operations and appropriate ways of calculating to solve problems.**
ORAL AND MENTAL STARTER	IT'S CLOSE: Repeat the whole class activity from the **Main teaching activity** in Lesson 3, Units 2–3, Term 1, moving up to counting through the next multiple of a thousand.
MAIN TEACHING ACTIVITY	WHICH OPERATION?: Write on the board number statements that have the operation sign missing for the children to fill in the gaps. For example, $12 ? 9 = 21$, $35 ? 24 = 11$, $9 ? 3 = 27$ and $30 ? 10 = 3$. Repeat for larger numbers, mixing up the order in which you use the operations. Children then work on their own to complete 'You choose' (page 158).
DIFFERENTIATION	Less able: check they have answered the addition and subtraction questions correctly before they move on to multiplication and division. Use multiples of 10 and 5 to make numbers easier to work with. More able: go on to make up similar questions for their partner to answer.
PLENARY	Go through the questions and discuss methods and strategies as well as answers. Ask: *How did you check you had the correct answer?*

LESSON 5

Repeat the **Oral and mental starter** from Lesson 4. In the **Main teaching activity** revise the column addition method then tell the children to write their own questions using combinations of the numbers on the board and then calculate the answers. **Differentiation** is achieved by providing each ability group with an appropriate set of numbers. In the **Plenary** go through some of the children's examples.

RESOURCES	Prepared HTU – TU subtractions written on the board, and sets of three-digit and two-digit numbers written on the board, a different set for each ability group; squared paper; rulers; base 10 apparatus; pencils.
LEARNING OUTCOMES	**ORAL AND MENTAL STARTER** ● Count on or back in repeated steps of 1 or 10. **MAIN TEACHING ACTIVITY** ● **Develop and refine written methods for column subtraction.** ● Use knowledge of sums or differences of pairs of odd/even numbers.
ORAL AND MENTAL STARTER	CLAP COUNTER: Repeat the activity from the first part of the Main teaching activity in Lesson 2, Units 2–3, Term 1 to find answers to questions such as 2,003 + 6, the difference between 672 and 622, add together 371 and 400 (by counting on in hundreds).
MAIN TEACHING ACTIVITY	COLUMN SUBTRACTION: Remind the children of the method of column addition introduced in Lessons 8 and 9, Units 2–3, Term 2. Go through examples (see Lesson 8 for the method), eg 453 – 78 and 647 – 98. Invite children to write up given subtractions vertically on the board and then work through them. Remind them to start at the right with the least significant digits (the units) and work towards the left. Use apparatus to back up explanation. The children then work on their own through the examples you have written on the board.
DIFFERENTIATION	More able: tell them to check their answers by using the inverse operation. Less able: start with subtraction sums that do not involve decomposition. Use base 10 apparatus to support written work.
PLENARY	Invite children out to demonstrate their own calculations to the class. Reinforce teaching points, especially placing of digits in the correct columns.

LESSON 6 + 7

RESOURCES

Sets of plastic coins; copies of photocopiable page 156 ('School fête'); squared paper; rulers; pencils.

PREPARATION

Photocopy 'School fête' (page 156), one per child.
Have sets of coins available for less able groups.

LEARNING OUTCOMES

ORAL AND MENTAL STARTER
● Derive quickly all number pairs that total 100.

MAIN TEACHING ACTIVITY
● **Develop and refine written methods for column addition and subtraction**; money calculations.

ORAL AND MENTAL STARTER

MAKE 100: Repeat the activity from Lesson 1, Units 4–6, Term 1, but just for pairs that make 100 and this time in the context of money. Revise how many of each of the coins are needed to make up £1.

LESSON 8

VOCABULARY

Money; coin; pound; £; pence; note; price; cost; cheaper; more/most expensive; pay; change; total; value; amount.

RESOURCES	Number fans prepared for Lesson 1, Unit 1, Term 1; 0–9 dice or 0–9 digit cards per pair; pencils and paper.
LEARNING OUTCOMES	**ORAL AND MENTAL STARTER** ● Derive quickly all number pairs that total 100. **MAIN TEACHING ACTIVITY** ● Use known number facts to add or subtract mentally.
ORAL AND MENTAL STARTER	MAKE 100: Repeat the activity from Lesson 1, Units 4–6, Term 1, but just for pairs that make 100.
MAIN TEACHING ACTIVITY	UP TO THE NEXT 100: Write on the board 163 and ask: *What needs to be added to this number to make 200?* (37). Give other three-digit numbers for them to make up to the next hundred. Repeat for four-digit multiples of 100 to make the next thousand, eg you say 1400 and they respond with 600. In pairs, the children use the dice or digit cards to generate ten three-digit numbers. They then work on their own to make each number up to the next hundred. They repeat for ten four-digit multiples of 100, which they then make up to the next thousand. Ask them to check each other's answers.
DIFFERENTIATION	More able: repeat for four-digit multiples of 50, eg 3450 (answer 550). Less able: use three-digit numbers only to make up to the next hundred. Use number lines to support counting in hundreds.
PLENARY	Discuss strategies used to make the total up to the next 100 or 1000.

RESOURCES	Base 10 equipment; prepared three-digit number sums written horizontally on the board, including examples that involve carrying, a different set for each ability group; squared paper; rulers; pencils; sets of three-digit numbers written on the board, a different set for each ability group.
LEARNING OUTCOMES	**ORAL AND MENTAL STARTER** ● Derive quickly all pairs of multiples of 50 with a total of 1000. **MAIN TEACHING ACTIVITY** ● Develop and refine written methods for column addition.
ORAL AND MENTAL STARTER	THOUSAND UP: Repeat the activity from Lesson 1, Units 4–6, Term 1 but this time for number bonds for 1000 and counting on/back in steps of 50.
MAIN TEACHING ACTIVITY $\begin{array}{r} 356 \\ +\ 412 \\ \hline 8 \\ 60 \\ 700 \\ \hline 768 \end{array}$ $\begin{array}{r} 356 \\ +\ 412 \\ \hline 768 \end{array}$ $\begin{array}{r} 268 \\ +\ 617 \\ \hline 15 \\ 70 \\ 800 \\ \hline 885 \end{array}$ $\begin{array}{r} 268 \\ +\ 617 \\ \hline 885 \\ \hline {\scriptstyle 1} \end{array}$	COLUMN ADDITION: Remind the children of the method of column addition introduced in Lessons 6 and 7, Units 2–3, Term 2. Write on the board 356 + 412 and look at the place value of each of the digits in the numbers: *356 is 3 hundreds, 5 tens and 6 units. 412 is 4 hundreds, 1 ten and 2 units.* Write the sum vertically, reminding the children that the units must be directly under each other in the units column and similarly for the tens and hundreds. As before, add the units first, then the tens, then the hundreds, discussing each stage as you go: Use Big base 10 equipment to illustrate this if necessary. Work through other examples of this type then explain that we can reduce the number of lines by just writing: Talk through this process starting with the least significant digits (the units). Then give an example that involves carrying, say 268 + 617. First work it out in the long way, adding first the units, then the tens and finally the hundreds: Then repeat using the short way, explaining the processes as you record (see Lesson 6, Units 2–3, Term 2): Invite children out to the board to work through further examples of these. Then tell the children to work on their own through the examples you have written on the board. Recording on squared paper helps them to keep the digits in the correct columns.
DIFFERENTIATION	More able: give them questions that include numbers with zero and three-digit numbers that will take answers into four digits, eg 674 + 458. Less able: let them use equipment when carrying is involved to work practically.
PLENARY	Use the method to add three integers less than 1000 to show that the process is exactly the same. Include examples where more than one ten is carried into the hundreds column, eg 379 + 283 + 153 = 815.

Function machines $\longrightarrow$

Use the function machine to add 9.

$$(+10 \longrightarrow -1)$$

in	middle	out
5		
12		
35		
42		
69		

Use the function machine to subtract 9.

$$(-10 \longrightarrow +1)$$

in	middle	out
15		
24		
53		
78		
93		

Use the function machine to add 11.

$$(+10 \longrightarrow +1)$$

in	middle	out
10		
27		
61		
78		
105		

Use the function machine to subtract 11.

$$(-10 \longrightarrow -1)$$

in	middle	out
19		
35		
65		
84		
112		

Use the function machine to add 19.

$$(+20 \longrightarrow -1)$$

in	middle	out
17		
36		
	52	
	70	
		45

Use the function machine to subtract 19.

$$(-20 \longrightarrow +1)$$

in	middle	out
23		
48		
	72	
	96	
		124

Complete your own function machines to add and subtract 21 and add and subtract 29.

School fête

bookmarks 35p

T-shirts £3.50

mugs 60p

posters £1.20

small toys £1.15

PE bags £4.25

compact discs £1.75

books £2.40

birthday cards 80p

badges £1.10

1. Find the cost of:

a. a bookmark and a mug _____

b. the cards and a toy _____

c. a poster and compact disc _____

d. a T-shirt and a book _____

2. How much change from £5 would you have after buying:

a. a badge?

b. a T-shirt?

c. a PE bag?

_____

_____

_____

d. a book and a mug?

e. a poster?

f. a badge and a small toy?

_____

_____

_____

3a. Which item is the most expensive? _____

b. Which item is the cheapest? _____

c. Which two items cost exactly £2? _____

d. Which two items cost exactly £3? _____

e. Which three items cost exactly £8.40? _____

4. Look at each statement and say whether it is true or false.

a. You could buy a mug and a badge with £2. _____

b. You could buy four posters with £5. _____

c. Four items cost less than £1. _____

d. Five badges would cost £6.50. _____

e. PE bags are £2 more than T-shirts. _____

Make up some of your own questions using the items and prices above.
Ask a partner to work out the answers.

Down on the farm

Farmer Bell and Farmer Price own farms next to each other. Help them solve these problems. Underneath each question write down the numbers and the operations you use. Then calculate the answer, recording how you worked it out.

1. Farmer Bell has 75 cows and Farmer Price has 139. How many cows do they have altogether?

_____

2. Farmer Bell did have 147 sheep, but he sold 55 at market. How many does he have now?

_____

3. Farmer Price keeps 27 pigs in one field, 35 in another and 19 in another. What is the total number of pigs he keeps?

_____

4. Farmer Price planted 356 potatoes in one field and 128 fewer in another field. How many did he plant in the other field?

_____

5. Farmer Bell had 200 hens. At market he sold 43 and bought 36. How many hens does he have now?

_____

6. It normally takes Farmer Price every day in July and August to cut his wheat. If he loses 19 days because of bad weather, how many days is he able to work?

_____

7. Of Farmer Bell's 200 hens, one-half were black and one-quarter were white. The rest were brown. How many brown hens did he have?

_____

8. Farmer Bell, Farmer Price and another farmer, Farmer Barn, decide to put all their apple harvests together. Farmer Bell picks 252 apples, Farmer Price 169 apples and Farmer Barn 307 apples. If 85 of the apples turn out to be rotten, how many do they have to sell between them?

_____

You choose

In these number sentences all of the operation symbols have been used. The four choices are given next to the number sentence. Ring what you think is the correct operation and check to make sure the answer is right.

a) 15 ? 17 = 32   15 – 17   15 + 17   15 × 17   15 ÷ 17

b) 7 ? 3 = 21   7 × 3   7 + 3   7 ÷ 3   7 – 3

c) 46 ? 19 = 27   46 × 19   46 ÷ 19   46 – 19   46 + 19

d) 13 = 39 ? 3   39 + 3   39 – 3   39 × 3   39 ÷ 3

e) 239 ? 76 = 315   239 × 76   239 ÷ 76   239 + 76   239 – 76

f) 20 = 80 ? 4   80 ÷ 4   80 + 4   80 × 4   80 – 4

g) 15 ? 5 = 75   15 + 5   15 × 5   15 – 5   15 ÷ 5

h) 53 = 214 ? 161   214 – 161   214 × 161   214 ÷ 16   214+ 161

i) $\frac{1}{2}$ of 70 = 35   70 + $\frac{1}{2}$ 70 – $\frac{1}{2}$ 70 × 2   70 ÷ 2

j) $\frac{1}{4}$ of 48 = 12   48 + 12   48 ÷ 4   48 × 4   48 – $\frac{1}{4}$

Make up some questions with the operation signs missing for your partner to work out.

UNITS 4–6

ORGANISATION (13 LESSONS)

	LEARNING OUTCOMES	ORAL AND MENTAL STARTER	MAIN TEACHING ACTIVITY	PLENARY
LESSON 1	● Suggest suitable units and measuring equipment to estimate or measure capacity. ● **Know and use the relationships between familiar units of capacity.**	NUMBER SPLITS: Add two numbers by adding the tens first.	CAPACITY: Convert millilitres to litres and vice versa.	Write capacity measurements in different ways.
LESSON 2	● Record estimates and readings from scales to a suitable degree of accuracy.	NEAR DOUBLES: Use near doubles to add two two-digit numbers.	READING SCALES: Read amounts shown on measuring cylinders.	Discuss strategies used.
LESSON 3 + 4	● Record estimates and readings from scales to a suitable degree of accuracy. ● **Know and use the relationships between familiar units of capacity.**	MAKE TEN: Use pairs that total 10, 9 or 11 to add three or four single-digit numbers. Repeat for two-digit numbers.	CONTAINER LOAD: Carry out practical capacity measuring tasks.	Check the choice of equipment, estimating and measuring skills.
LESSON 5	● Use all four operations to solve word problems involving numbers in measures. ● **Know and use the relationships between familiar units of capacity.**	CLEVER ONE: Add numbers close to multiples of ten.	SANJAY'S PARTY: Answer word problems related to capacity.	Review operations and strategies used.
LESSON 6	● Sketch the reflection of a simple shape.	IT'S CLOSE: Find differences by counting up.	GRID PATTERNS: Create a symmetrical pattern using grid co-ordinates.	Discuss patterns. Use mirrors to show they are symmetrical.
LESSON 7 + 8	● Recognise positions and directions.	IN THE FAMILY: Use the relationship between addition and subtraction facts.	PLOTTING SHAPES: Make 2-D shapes using co-ordinates.	Review the shapes made.
LESSON 9 + 10	● Make and measure clockwise and anticlockwise turns. ● Use the eight compass directions.	QUICK CHECK: Use the inverse operation to check calculations.	COMPASS POINTS: Make a compass and calculate turns.	Children provide their own movement questions.
LESSON 11 + 12	● Begin to know that angles are measured in degrees. ● Start to order a set of angles less than 180°.	ODD AND EVEN: Answer quick-fire additions of odd/even numbers.	COMPASS ANGLES: Calculate turns in right angles and degrees.	Record answers on a large chart. Revise key vocabulary.
LESSON 13	● Recognise positions and directions. Recognise simple examples of horizontal and vertical lines.	ROUNDING: Use rounding to give approximate answers.	ROUTES: Solve route tasks based on right angles and compass directions.	Check through solutions.

ORAL AND MENTAL SKILLS Partition into tens and units, adding the tens first. Identify near doubles, using known doubles. Add three or four small numbers, finding pairs totalling 10, or 9 or 11. Add the nearest multiple of 100, then adjust. Find a small difference by counting up. Consolidate understanding of the relationship between + and –. Check with the inverse operation. Recognise odd and even numbers up to 1000. Estimate and check by approximating (round to nearest 10 or 100).

Lessons 1, 3, 7, 9 and 11 are shown in full. Lessons 2, 5, 6 and 13 are extensions of what has already been taught so are shown in outline. Lessons 4, 8, 10 and 12 are shown as developments of the previous lessons.

Use Roamer and/or other computer programs (such as Logo and Superlogo) to support and enrich the activities in Lessons 9–13.

RESOURCES

Measuring containers; copies of photocopiable page 167 ('Metric capacity'); pencils.

PREPARATION

Photocopy 'Metric capacity' (page 167), one per child.

LEARNING OUTCOMES

ORAL AND MENTAL STARTER
● Partition into tens and units, adding the tens first.

MAIN TEACHING ACTIVITY
● Suggest suitable units and measuring equipment to estimate or measure capacity.
● **Know and use the relationships between familiar units of capacity.**

VOCABULARY

Metric unit; litre (l); millilitre (ml); capacity; full; half full; empty; holds; contains; container; measuring cylinder.

ORAL AND MENTAL STARTER

NUMBER SPLITS 1: Repeat the activity from Lesson 4, Units 2–3, Term 1, then use the partition method for subtraction, such as 76 − 35 = (76 − 5) − 30 = 71 − 30 = 41.

MAIN TEACHING ACTIVITY

CAPACITY: Revise key units used already to measure length and mass: in length 10mm = 1cm, 100cm = 1m and 1000m = 1km; in mass 1000g = 1kg. Then introduce capacity as the amount something holds. Explain that when containers are filled up with liquids the measurement is carried out in litres and millilitres.

Write these words on the board then show the children the measuring containers. Ask: *How many millilitres do you think there are in a litre?* Write 1000ml = 1l. Ask questions that require them to convert from one to the other, such as *How many litres in 6000ml? 9000ml makes how many litres?* Show how 3450ml equals 3l 450ml. Introduce children to the key fractional parts of a litre:

½l = 500ml, ¼l = 250ml, ¾l = 750ml, ¹/₁₀l = 100ml.

Write their decimal equivalents:

500ml = 0.5l, 250ml = 0.25l, 750ml = 0.75l, 100ml = 0.1l.

Children then work on their own to complete 'Metric capacity' (page 167).

DIFFERENTIATION

More able: extend to addition of capacity amounts using different units and when conversions are required – for example, 3½l + 300ml = ?.
Less able: ensure they are confident with easier conversions, such as 3000ml = ?l before using fractional amounts.

PLENARY

Reinforce the conversion of capacities from one format to another. Write some capacity measurements on the board and ask children to come out and write the same measurement in a different way. Start with examples of the type 4l 350ml = ?ml. Move on to more difficult ones, such as 3½l = ?ml and then try some decimal numbers, such as 0.65l = ?ml.

Use examples of each type until the children are used to dealing with the different formats. Try and relate these to real-life examples of capacity that will be familiar to the children – for example, using different capacities of container of milk, fruit juice and so on.

RESOURCES	Prepared near doubles questions of the type 29 + 26; 120 + 130; collection of measuring cylinders showing different scales; prepared large version of scales drawn on A1 size paper, including ones that go up in 100ml, 50ml, 20ml and 25ml divisions; copies of photocopiable page 168 ('Liquid measures'), one per child; prepared additional questions of the type on the photocopiable sheet but for 20ml and 25ml divisions; pencils.
LEARNING OUTCOMES	**ORAL AND MENTAL STARTER** ● Identify near doubles, using known doubles. **MAIN TEACHING ACTIVITY** ● Record estimates and readings from scales to a suitable degree of accuracy.
ORAL AND MENTAL STARTER	NEAR DOUBLES: Repeat the activity from Lesson 6, Units 2–3, Terms 1, extending to three-digit numbers.
MAIN TEACHING ACTIVITY	READING SCALES: Show the children how scales are marked on the side of measuring cylinders. Display the enlarged versions of the scales. Illustrate how the scales can vary, not only in the amount they measure altogether but also how they are divided up. Point out that when we are measuring we sometimes have to read and record to the nearest mark. Fill one of the cylinders with water as an example, say to just below 25ml. Ask different children to read the scale. Children then work on their own to complete 'Liquid measures' (page 168).
DIFFERENTIATION	More able: work on the prepared 20ml and 25ml division examples. Less able: consolidate reading off to nearest 100ml and 50ml initially. Encourage them to write in the 50ml division amounts where levels of multiples of 50 have to be marked.
PLENARY	Go through their readings. Discuss strategies used and how they decided which was the nearest 100ml/50ml.

RESOURCES

Range of containers; measuring cylinders; supply of water; trays of sand; 5ml spoons; 1 litre and 2 litre empty drinks bottles; prepared recording charts; pouring jugs; pencils.

PREPARATION

Organise groups of three or four to start with one of the four tasks. For Task 1 use felt-tipped pens to mark levels on the side of 1l and 2l drink bottles, a different level on each one. For Task 2 provide sets of containers that include some that hold less than a litre, some that hold about a litre, some that hold more than a litre. For Task 3 provide a collection of small containers, a tray of sand and a 5ml spoon, for each group. For Task 4 provide a collection of containers of different sizes and a choice of measuring cylinders. For each task use letters to label the containers. Prepare the following recording charts, then photocopy, one per group:

Container	Estimate (l/ml)	Measure (l/ml)	Spoonfuls	ml

Less than a litre	About a litre	More than a litre

LEARNING OUTCOMES

ORAL AND MENTAL STARTER
● Add three or four small numbers, finding pairs totalling 10, or 9 or 11.

MAIN TEACHING ACTIVITY
● Record estimates and readings from scales to a suitable degree of accuracy.
● **Know and use the relationships between familiar units of capacity.**

ORAL AND MENTAL STARTER

MAKE TEN: Repeat the activity from Lesson 1, Units 2–3, Term 1. Then repeat for sets of small two-digit numbers to find pairs that total 100.

VOCABULARY

Measure; measurement; compare; measuring scale (division); guess; estimate; holds; contains; container; measuring cylinder; litre; millilitre; enough; not enough; too much; too little; nearly; roughly; approximately; about; close to; about the same as; just over; just under.

MAIN TEACHING ACTIVITY

CONTAINER LOAD: Explain to the children that during the next two lessons they are going to find out how much a variety of containers will hold. Tell them to estimate first and then choose carefully which container and which measuring cylinder to use to measure the amount. They record their results on the prepared charts. Discuss measuring units, eg l and ml and possibly some fractional quantities, eg ½l, ¼l and so on. In groups of three or four the children then start work on one of the following tasks:

Task 1: Estimate how much water would be needed to fill to this level. Use measuring jugs to check estimates.

Task 2: Group the containers into three sets: those that hold less than a litre, those that hold about a litre and those that hold more than a litre.

Task 3: Estimate how many 5ml spoonfuls of sand it will take to fill up each of the small containers. Then use the spoon to check how good the estimates were.

Task 4: Estimate how much the containers will hold to the nearest 100ml or 50ml. Fill them up with water and then check results using a measuring cylinder. Check addition and subtraction of capacity amounts practically using measuring cylinders. Do the amounts 300ml and 250ml reach the 550ml level when poured into the same empty cylinder? If 400ml is poured out of a measuring cylinder holding ½l, is 100ml left? Tell the children to work carefully to avoid spillages.

DIFFERENTIATION

More able: encourage them to record answers numerically as well as in box form, eg 20 5ml spoonfuls to fill up a small container recorded as 20 × 5ml = 100ml.

Less able: start on Task 1. Ensure that their estimates of less than a litre, about a litre, more than a litre are sound.

PLENARY

Record some of their results on the board for discussion. *Did you choose the right equipment? Were scales easy to read? How close were your estimates?*

LESSON 4

Repeat the **Oral and mental starter** from Lesson 3. In the **Main teaching activity** children continue working through the measuring tasks. See Lesson 3 for **Differentiation**. In the **Plenary** continue discussion of results, asking questions such as: *Did your estimating improve with practice? Did spillage of water cause inaccurate results? How could this be overcome?*

LESSON 5

RESOURCES	Copies of photocopiable page 169 ('Sanjay's party'), one per child; pencils.
LEARNING OUTCOMES	**ORAL AND MENTAL STARTER** ● Add the nearest multiple of 100, then adjust. **MAIN TEACHING ACTIVITY** ● Use all four operations to solve word problems involving measures. ● **Know and use the relationships between familiar units of capacity.**
ORAL AND MENTAL STARTER	CLEVER ONE: Repeat the activity from the Main teaching activity in Lesson 5, Units 2–3, Term 1, but this time using the strategy to add 99.
MAIN TEACHING ACTIVITY	SANJAY'S PARTY: Write on the board some capacity related addition sums using all four operations, eg 239ml + 100ml + 900ml (answer recorded as 1,239ml or 1l 239ml or 1.239l); *If 645ml is poured out of a litre bottle of lemonade, how much is left? How much cola is there in 12 200ml tins? How many 50ml cups can be filled from a litre bottle?*. Go through these together. Then in pairs, children complete 'Sanjay's party' (page 169).
DIFFERENTIATION	More able: make up their own capacity related questions either in a party context or a different context of their choice. Less able: use number lines and table squares for support. Concentrate on addition and subtraction first.
PLENARY	Go through the questions on the photocopiable. Ask: *How did you decide which operation to use?* Check strategies used and the accuracy of conversion of units.

RESOURCES	Large grid paper with big squares showing x and y axes; cm squared paper; rulers; pencils; felt-tipped pens or crayons; mirrors.
LEARNING OUTCOMES	**ORAL AND MENTAL STARTER** ● Find a small difference by counting up. **MAIN TEACHING ACTIVITY** ● Sketch the reflection of a simple shape.
ORAL AND MENTAL STARTER	IT'S CLOSE: Repeat the whole class activity from the Main teaching activity in Term 1, Units 2–3, Lesson 3, giving the higher number first, eg *Find the difference between 74 and 68.* Progress to counting through the next multiple of a thousand.
MAIN TEACHING ACTIVITY	GRID PATTERNS: Revise the work done in Term 2, Units 4–6, Lessons 7 and 8. Then display the grid paper and show the children how to mark the axes. This also revises work with the minus/negative number line. Explain that the horizontal and vertical lines that form the grid cross at (0,0). Point out that the grid intervals are between the squares and not on the grid lines themselves. This is so co-ordinates will give squares rather than points. Remind them that when using co-ordinates the horizontal numbers always come first. Tell them that the vertical line is the mirror line, then begin a pattern by colouring in corresponding squares on either side of the line. Show them how to plot corresponding squares, eg if (5, 3) is coloured, they must also colour (–5, 3), if (10, 5) is coloured so must (–10, 5) and so on. Children then work individually to create their own symmetry patterns.
DIFFERENTIATION	More able: write down co-ordinates as they make their pattern, then give these numbers to another child to see if they can plot the pattern. Less able: give them squared paper with the grid already drawn.
PLENARY	Display their patterns. Use large mirrors to show they are symmetrical. Revise how positions were plotted.

RESOURCES

Squared paper; large grid paper showing x and y axes; rulers; copies of photocopiable page 170 ('Plotting shapes'); pencils; prepared shape co-ordinates.

PREPARATION

Photocopy 'Plotting shapes' (page 170), one per child. On the large grid paper draw a vertical and horizontal line intersecting at their midway point to create x and y axes, then attach it to the board. Prepare other examples of shape co-ordinates in the form of the questions on the photocopiable, for the less able group to plot in Lesson 8.

LEARNING OUTCOMES

ORAL AND MENTAL STARTER
● Consolidate understanding of the relationship between + and –.

MAIN TEACHING ACTIVITY
● Recognise positions and directions.

VOCABULARY
Position; grid; row; column; co-ordinates.

ORAL AND MENTAL STARTER

IN THE FAMILY: Repeat the activity from Lesson 9, Units 2–3, Term 1, extending to three-digit numbers.

MAIN TEACHING ACTIVITY

PLOTTING SHAPES: Remind the children of the work in the previous lesson and explain that this time they are going to plot positions where two lines on the grid cross. Using the large piece of grid paper, show children how to locate different positions, eg (6,3), (2,1), (5,4) and (3,2). Remind them again that horizontal numbers are always written and plotted first. Mark the point where the two lines cross with a dot or small cross. Give them 'Plotting shapes' (page 170). Stress that they should mark the points in the order given, joining them up with straight lines using their ruler.

DIFFERENTIATION

More able: go on to draw other shapes in the same way including other members of the quadrilateral family, hexagons and octagons.
Less able: give help with plotting the points and ensure that they join them correctly.

PLENARY

Go through the shapes on the photocopiable. Then ask individual children for the grid references for the shapes they have made themselves, for another child to plot on the large grid paper to see if they work.

LESSON 8

Repeat the **Oral and mental starter** from Lesson 7. In the **Main teaching activity** children continue creating different shapes, swapping grid references with a partner to create each other's shapes. For **Differentiation** encourage the more able to increase the complexity of their shapes, including irregular ones. The less able group can plot the shapes you have prepared. In the **Plenary** revise the main teaching points and then let individual children give grid references for one of their shapes, for the class to plot.

RESOURCES

Large circle; circles of coloured paper; copies of photocopiable page 171 ('Take it in turns'); pencils; felt-tipped pens; prepared blank compasses; prepared compass turn questions; Roamer and/or ICT software.

PREPARATION

Draw a circle on a piece of large paper, then attach to the board. Provide enough paper circles for one per child. Photocopy 'Take it in turns' (page 171), one per child. Delete the turns shown on the sheet, then photocopy to provide one sheet of blank compass circles for each child. On one of the sheets draw in other turns as per the photocopiable, then photocopy, one for each child in the less able group. Write a series of questions of the type: 'What is the amount of turn between NW and NE clockwise? …between NW and SE anticlockwise? If you start at SW and make a ¼ turn anticlockwise where will you be?', then photocopy, one per child.

LEARNING OUTCOMES

ORAL AND MENTAL STARTER
● Check with the inverse operation.

MAIN TEACHING ACTIVITY
● Make and measure clockwise and anticlockwise turns.
● Use the eight compass directions.

VOCABULARY

Clockwise;
anticlockwise;
north; south;
east; west;
north-east;
north-west;
south-east;
south-west;
compass
point;
movement;
direction;
whole turn;
half turn;
quarter turn;
rotate.

ORAL AND MENTAL STARTER

QUICK CHECK: Remind children that addition questions can be checked by subtracting and subtraction questions can be checked by adding. Start with some simple examples, such as 9 + 4 = ? so 13 – 9 = ?, then repeat for larger numbers. Then reverse the process.

MAIN TEACHING ACTIVITY

COMPASS POINTS: Divide your large circle into four quadrants. With the children's help mark on the four main points of the compass. Add two diagonal lines to divide the circle into eighths and, again with the children's help, add the other four directions to complete an eight-point compass rose. With a coloured pen, mark the clockwise turn from north to east. Tell the children that this is a quarter of a turn. Use a different colour to mark the turn from north to south, again clockwise. Explain that this is half a turn. Repeat the process with north to west clockwise (three-quarters of a turn) and from north all the way back to north (one complete turn). Children then make their own eight-point compass rose using circles of coloured paper. They should fold to make a right angle and then fold again to make eighths. They then use their compass to work on 'Take it in turns' (page 171). Throughout Lessons 9–12, let pairs of children take turns to use Roamer and/or ICT software to create different turns.

DIFFERENTIATION

More able: on the blank compasses, create and record their own turns where movement does not start from north and where some movements go anticlockwise.
Less able: give help with labelling the compass. Check they have completed the early questions on the photocopiable sheet successfully before they progress.

PLENARY

Invite the more able children to draw their turns on the board for others to solve.

LESSON 10

Repeat the **Oral and mental starter** from Lesson 9, giving addition and subtraction examples at random. In the **Main teaching activity** children continue working through 'Take it in turns' (page 171). They then use blank compasses to record turns, this time using all eight points of the compass to answer the questions you have set, eg *What is the amount of turn between NW and NE clockwise?* For **Differentiation** provide the more able with more questions that include anticlockwise turns and turns not starting from north; prepare more examples of turns for the less able to complete. In the **Plenary** revise the eight points of the compass by random checking and revise the terms clockwise and anticlockwise.

RESOURCES

Photocopiable page 172 ('Compass angles'); rulers; paper (A3 and A4); pencils; prepared blank compasses and compass turn questions; Roamer and/or ICT software.

LESSON 11 +12

PREPARATION

Draw a circle on a piece of large paper, then attach to the board. Photocopy 'Compass angles' (page 172), one per child. Delete the arrows shown on the photocopiable sheet, then photocopy to provide one sheet of blank compass circles for each child. Draw a recording chart with these headings, then photocopy, one per child

Compass	Turn	Right angles	Degrees	Rotation
1	¼	1	90°	Clockwise

Write a series of questions of the type: 'What is the angle between N and NE clockwise? ...between N and SE clockwise? ...between SW and N anticlockwise?' and at the bottom of the sheet write 'record the angles in order of size', then photocopy, one per child.

LEARNING OUTCOMES

ORAL AND MENTAL STARTER
● Recognise odd and even numbers up to 1000, including the outcome of sums or differences of pairs of odd/even numbers.

MAIN TEACHING ACTIVITY
● Begin to know that angles are measured in degrees.
● Start to order a set of angles less than 180º.

ORAL AND MENTAL STARTER

ODD AND EVEN: Ask: *What do even/odd numbers always end with?* (0, 2, 4, 6, 8) and (1, 3, 5, 7, 9) respectively. Give the children some even number sequences and ask them to say the next two numbers, eg 24, 26, 28, 30, ?, ?; 306, 304, 302, ?, ?. Repeat for odd

Clockwise;
anticlockwise;
north; south;
east; west;
north-east;
north-west;
south-east;
south-west;
compass
point;
movement;
direction;
whole turn;
half turn;
quarter turn;
rotate; angle;
right angle;
degrees;
rotation.

numbers. Ask the children to suggest what type of answer you get when two even numbers are added (the answer is always even). Check this out with quick-fire addition questions, such as 12 + 16, 54 + 28. Repeat for adding two odd numbers, to discover that the answer is always even, then for adding an odd and an even number (answer is always odd).

MAIN TEACHING ACTIVITY

COMPASS ANGLES: Check the children understand the meaning of quarter turn, half turn, three-quarter turn and whole turn, and of clockwise and anticlockwise. Divide your circle into four quadrants with a vertical and horizontal line through the centre. Mark in a quarter turn clockwise with a coloured pen. Tell the children this turn is one right angle or 90 degrees. Repeat for a half turn (two right angles or 180 degrees), then for a three-quarter turn (three right angles or 270 degrees) and finally for a complete turn (four right angles or 360 degrees). Children then work on their own to complete 'Compass angles' (page 172). Ask them to record their results in the prepared chart.

DIFFERENTIATION

More able: make up their own similar questions for their partner to answer.
Less able: the task increases in difficulty so the children should concentrate on the first group of questions.

PLENARY

Draw up a large version of the chart on the board and use it to check answers.

LESSON 12

Repeat the **Oral and mental starter** from Lesson 11. In the **Main teaching activity** children continue working through the sheet. Once complete, they use the blank compasses to create turns to answer the questions you have set, such as *What is the angle between N and NE clockwise?* They then write the angles in order of size. For **Differentiation** the more able can give their partner a starting point followed by a series of turns to check they end at the same finishing point. Work with the less able group to give support in creating the turns. In the **Plenary** revise quarter, half, three-quarter and full turns and what each one measures in degrees. Revise the terms clockwise and anticlockwise.

LESSON 13

RESOURCES	Large grid paper for flip chart; rulers; copies of photocopiable page 173 ('Right angle routes'), one per child; the first diagram on the sheet copied onto squared paper; enlarged copy the of bird and nest diagram; pencils.
LEARNING OUTCOMES	**ORAL AND MENTAL STARTER** ● Estimate and check by approximating (round to nearest 10 or 100). **MAIN TEACHING ACTIVITY** ● Recognise positions and directions. Recognise simple examples of horizontal and vertical lines.
ORAL AND MENTAL STARTER	ROUNDING: Give the children addition and subtraction questions and tell them to use rounding to find an approximate answer that is a multiple of 10, eg 9 + 18 rounded off to 10 + 20 gives an answer of about 30. Progress to three-digit numbers then use the same method for subtraction.
MAIN TEACHING ACTIVITY	ROUTES: Display the prepared diagram and explain to the children that the route from A to B involves five right angles. Mark the right angles and count them as you go. Then show them the enlarged bird and nest diagram. Explain that the bird has to get from its starting position to the nest, but it can only move south or east and can only take five steps in total. Demonstrate that this is just one solution. They then work on their own to complete 'Right angle routes' (page 173), the last task of which involves finding as many routes as possible for the bird and the nest activity.
DIFFERENTIATION	More able: invent their own set of movement rules for the bird and the nest activity, eg vary compass points used and/or number of steps allowed. Less able: provide them with ready-drawn grids for the bird and nest task.
PLENARY	Invite children to draw up a solution on the large grid paper. Give each child a different coloured pen to mark his or her route.

Metric capacity

Fill in the gaps:

Remember 1000 millilitres = 1 litre

$\frac{1}{2}$ $\frac{1}{4}$ $\frac{3}{4}$ $\frac{1}{10}$

1 litre _____ ml _____ ml _____ ml _____ ml

Fill in the missing amounts:

4l = _____ ml   2000ml = _____ l

7l = _____ ml   6000ml = _____ l

3l = _____ ml   1000ml = _____ l

9l = _____ ml   8000ml = _____ l

12l = _____ ml   15000ml = _____ l

If 1l 254ml = 1254ml and 2l 721ml = 2721ml, fill in these missing amounts:

1750ml = _____ l _____ ml   4l 178ml = _____ ml

3164ml = _____ l _____ ml   5l 679ml = _____ ml

5563ml = _____ l _____ ml   3.2l = _____ ml

7419ml = _____ l _____ ml   5.3l = _____ ml

9004ml = _____ l _____ ml   8.1l = _____ ml

Name

Liquid measures

Read off these levels to the nearest 100ml:

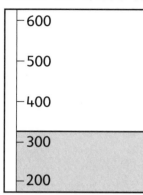 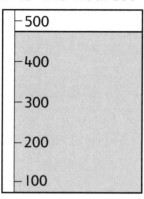 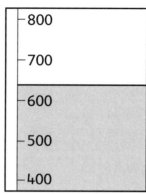 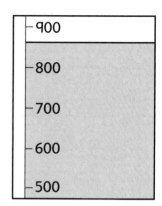

Read off these levels to the nearest 50ml:

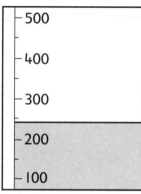 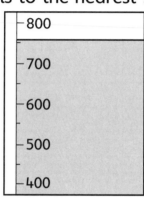 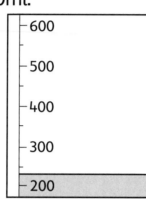 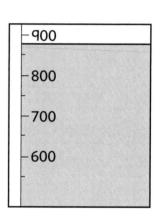

Show the amounts written underneath and colour them in:

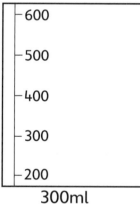 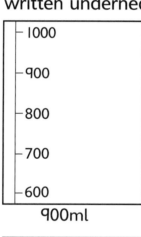 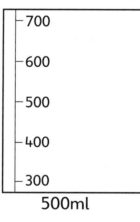 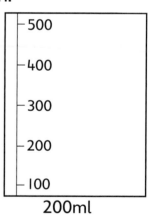

300ml　　900ml　　500ml　　200ml

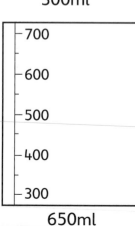 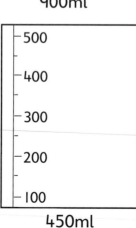 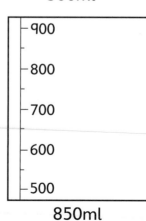 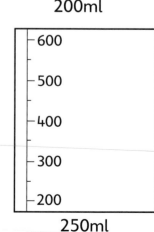

650ml　　450ml　　850ml　　250ml

Sanjay's party

Sanjay is organising the drinks at his party. Here are some containers with drinks in them and the amounts some children at the party have been given already. As you work the problems out, write the numbers you use and the operations underneath the questions.

Quantities already had	
Nina	200ml cola
Claire	50ml lemonade
Sita	125ml fruit juice
Ahmed	300ml water

How much liquid do Claire and Sita have together?

_____

How much more liquid does Ahmed have than Nina?

_____

How much more liquid does Nina have then Sita?

_____

How much fruit juice is left after Sita has taken her drink?

_____

How much water is left after Ahmed has taken his drink?

_____

Nina is the only person at the party drinking cola. Her glass holds 200ml. How many full glasses can she have from one bottle?

_____

Claire is the only person at the party drinking lemonade. Her glass holds 50ml. How many full glasses can she have before the bottle is empty?

_____

Ahmed has a container that holds 300ml when full. How much would it hold when:

half full? _____

quarter full? _____

Plotting shapes

For each grid, plot the points then join them together in the order in which they are written.

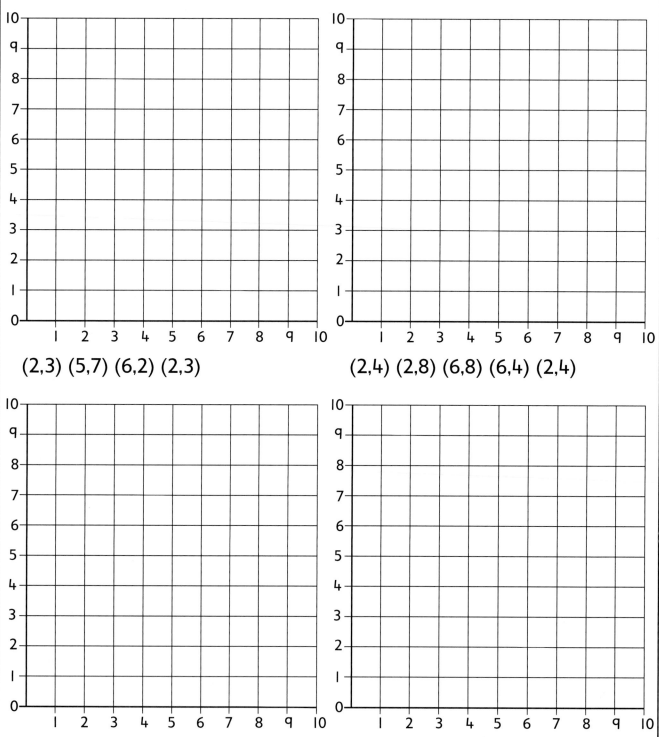

(2,3) (5,7) (6,2) (2,3)

(2,4) (2,8) (6,8) (6,4) (2,4)

(1,2) (1,9) (5,9) (5,2) (1,2)

(1,5) (2,9) (6,8) (7,4) (2,1) (1,5)

On squared paper draw these same 2-D shapes but in different positions. You could also vary their size. For each shape that you create, record the grid points in the order in which they should be joined.

Name

Take it in turns

Use the eight-point compass rose you have made to help you with these questions.

Write underneath each diagram the type of turn that is being made ($\frac{1}{4}$ turn, $\frac{1}{2}$ turn, $\frac{3}{4}$ turn, full turn) and whether the movement is being made clockwise or anticlockwise.

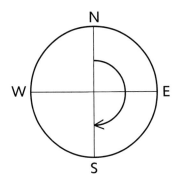

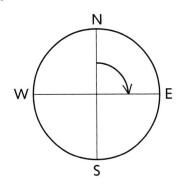

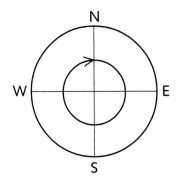

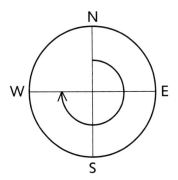

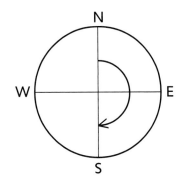

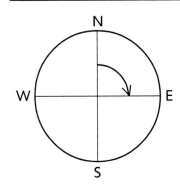

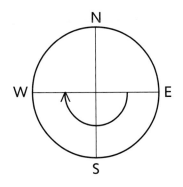

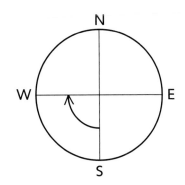

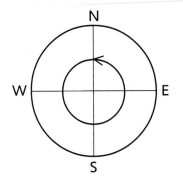

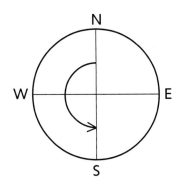

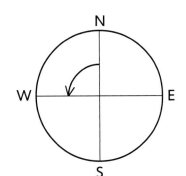

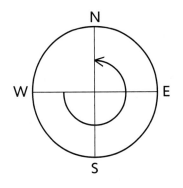

Compass angles

For each of these compass diagrams record the amount of turn in right angles and in degrees, then say whether the rotation is clockwise or anticlockwise. Record your results on the separate chart.

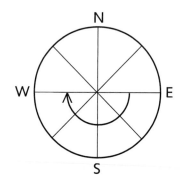

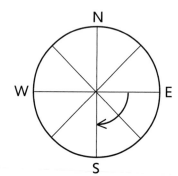

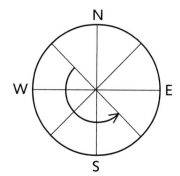

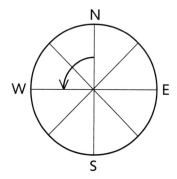

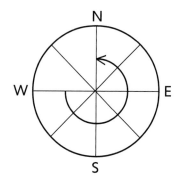

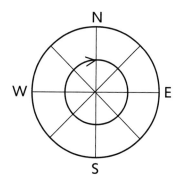

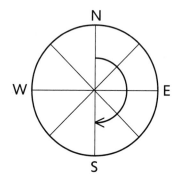

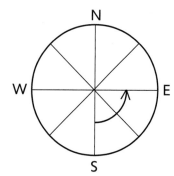

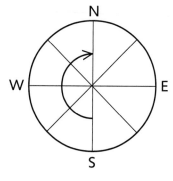

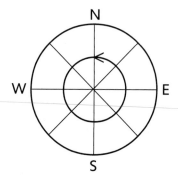

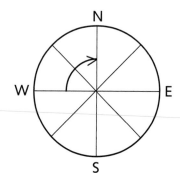

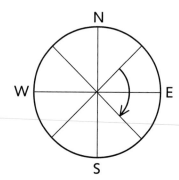

Right angle routes

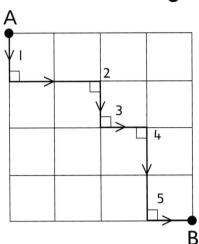

The path from A to B in this diagram moves through five right angles and along 8 sides of squares.

Count the number of right angles and the number of steps needed to get from A to B in these diagrams. Using the same 4 × 4 grid of squares, make up some of your own right angle turns.

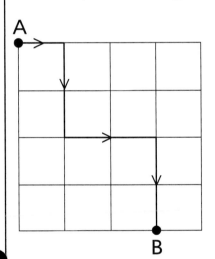

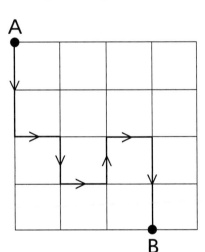

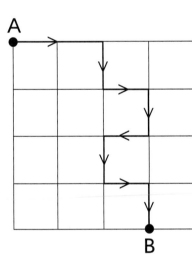

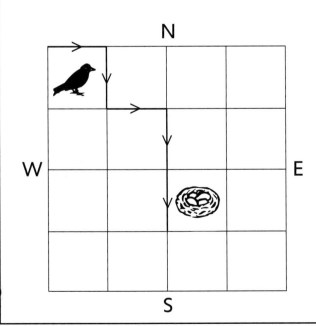

The bird can only move south or east and is only allowed to take five steps to get from its starting position to the nest. The solution shown here could be recorded ESESS. Record on squared paper all the other solutions you can find.

UNIT 7: Assess & Review

Choose from the following activities over the two lessons. During the group activities, some children can complete Assessment worksheets 5a and 5b, which assess their skills in: adding or subtracting to the nearest multiple of 10 and then adjusting, using written methods for column addition and subtraction and using all four operations to solve word problems. The specific assessment criteria for the assessment sheets are given at the bottom of each sheet.

RESOURCES

Unmarked plastic containers with amounts of water in them, labelled with letters; measuring cylinders; large cardboard circle marked with the four compass points N, S, E, W, with a large arrow pointer attached to the centre with a paper fastener; pencils and paper.

ORAL AND MENTAL STARTER

ASSESSMENT

● Can the children: **round any positive integer less than 1000 to the nearest 10 or 100?** Consolidate understanding of the relationship between + and –; **use known number facts to add or subtract mentally?**

ROUNDING: Call out numbers for the children to round to the nearest 10 or nearest 100, as directed by you. Then call out addition and subtraction questions and tell them to use rounding to find an approximate answer.

IN THE FAMILY: Give the children some two-digit and three-digit addition questions and ask them for the other three numbers statements that can be made with these numbers, for example, for 36 + 49 = 85, they respond 49 + 36 = 85; 85 – 49 = 36 and 85 – 36 = 49. Repeat for two-digit subtraction questions. Remind them of the different calculation strategies used during the term, including looking for pairs that make 9, 10, 11, 100, near doubles, adding the tens and units separately. Then give addition and subtraction questions for them to say what strategies they would use, before calculating the answer.

GROUP ACTIVITIES

ASSESSMENT

● Can the children: **choose and use appropriate number operations and appropriate ways of calculating to solve problems;** record estimates and readings from scales with a suitable degree of accuracy; **use symbols correctly, including less than (<), greater than (>), equals (=)?**
● Do the children: **know and use the relationships between familiar units of capacity;** begin to know that angles are measured in degrees?

USING NUMBER FACTS: Write up word problems for all four operations, of the type used in Units 2–3, Lesson 9 of this term, for the children to solve. Tell them to show their workings out clearly.
CAPACITY MEASURES: Ask the children first to estimate the amounts of water in each container, then to measure the actual amount, recording this in millilitres and then in litres. Then ask them to record number statements to show the relationship between the capacities of the containers, eg 500ml > 467ml; 250ml = ¼l; 9l 30ml < 9l 60ml. Ask questions such as: *What fraction of a litre is 500ml?*
TURNS AND ANGLES: Using different starting points move the pointer on your prepared compass from one position to another. Ask different children to tell you the amount of turn (¼, ½, ¾ or full), the angle turned through in degrees (90°, 180°, 270° or 360°) and the direction of rotation (clockwise or anticlockwise). Then ask questions such as: *What is the amount of turn going from N to W in a clockwise direction?*

Assessment 5a

Join the word money problem to the correct calculation. Then work out the answer carefully.

Mary and Ranjit have £5.50 between them. They share it equally. How much will they have each?	£2.75 × 6
Alan pays £6.25 into his savings account one week, £5.75 the next week and £4.07 the week after. How much has he saved altogether?	£5.50 ÷ 2
Sita had £5 in her purse but she lost £3.17. How much does she have left?	£7.20 ÷ 50p
If posters cost £2.75 each, how much would six cost?	£5 – £3.17
How many 50p tickets could you buy for £7.20? What would you have left over?	£6.25 + £5.75 + £4.07

Make up a word problem that has these metric measurements as the answer.

30m _____

_____

$4\frac{1}{2}$ litres _____

_____

8kg _____

_____

- Use all four operations to solve word problems in 'real life', money and measures.
- Choose and use appropriate number operations and appropriate ways of calculating to solve problems.

Assessment 5b

Use these function machines to show how you would add or subtract using a multiple of 10 and then adjusting.

1a. add 19

in	middle	out
12		
29		
78		
126		

b. subtract 19

in	middle	out
35		
59		
82		
191		

c. add 21

in	middle	out
53		
74		
131		
214		

d. subtract 21

in	middle	out
67		
88		
172		
325		

2. Fill in the missing digits in these calculations.

```
    5  □              1  □  5           3  2  □
  + 1  6            + 2  8  □         + 5  □  6
  ─────────         ─────────         ─────────
  □     1            3  9  2          □     0  0
```

```
  □     3            □  3  7           5  □  8
  - 1  9            -  □  9          -  □  0  9
  ─────────         ─────────         ─────────
  3  □               8  8            3  2  □
```

● Add or subtract the nearest multiple of 10, then adjust.
● **Develop and refine written methods for column addition and subtraction.**

UNIT 8

ORGANISATION (5 LESSONS)

LEARNING OUTCOMES	ORAL AND MENTAL STARTER	MAIN TEACHING ACTIVITY	PLENARY
LESSON 1 +2 +3 ● Recognise and extend number sequences formed by counting from any number in steps of constant size. ● Recognise multiples of 2, 3, 4, 5 and 10 up to the tenth multiple. ● Use halving.	TOP TWENTY: Answer quick-fire questions on addition and subtraction using numbers up to 20.	MULTIPLE TRICKS: Investigate the rule for multiples of 4, then for multiples of 3.	Look for rules for integers that are a multiple of more than one number.
LESSON 4 +5 ● Explain methods and reasoning about numbers orally and in writing, ● Solve mathematical problems or puzzles, recognise and explain patterns and relationships, generalise and predict. Suggest extensions by asking 'What if...?'	MAKE 100: Give the other number in the pair to make 100 or 1000.	WORK IT OUT: Complete number investigations.	Share methods and explain reasoning.

ORAL AND MENTAL SKILLS   Consolidate knowing by heart addition and subtraction facts for all numbers to 20. Derive quickly all number pairs that total 100; all pairs of multiples of 50 with a total of 1000.

Lesson 1 is shown in full. Lessons 2, 3 and 5 are given as developments of the previous lessons. Lesson 4 is an extension of what has already been taught so is shown in outline.

LESSON 1 +2 +3

RESOURCES

Copies of photocopiable resource sheet C ('Times tables square'); 0–9 dice; pencils and paper; prepared multiples chart.

PREPARATION

Photocopy 'Times tables square' (resource sheet C), one per pair. Provide enough dice for one per pair. Prepare the following chart with numbers up to 50, then photocopy, one per child:

	Multiple of 2	Multiple of 3	Multiple of 4	Multiple of 5	Multiple of 10
1					
2					
3					
4					
5					
6					
7					
8					
9					
10					
11					

Prepare a similar chart but with numbers up to 100 for the more able, and another one with numbers up to 30 for the less able children.

LEARNING OUTCOMES

ORAL AND MENTAL STARTER
● Consolidate knowing by heart addition and subtraction facts for all numbers to 20.

MAIN TEACHING ACTIVITY
● Recognise and extend number sequences formed by counting from any number in steps of constant size.
● Recognise multiples of 2, 3, 4, 5 and 10 up to the tenth multiple.
● Use halving.

VOCABULARY

Next; predict; sequence; consecutive; rule; relationship; factor; product.

ORAL AND MENTAL STARTER

TOP TWENTY: Repeat the activity from Lesson 3, Unit 1, Term 1.

MAIN TEACHING ACTIVITY

MULTIPLE TRICKS: Ask questions to remind the children that they already know that any integer multiplied by 10 will always have 0 as the last digit, any integer multiple of 5 will end in 5 or 0, all even numbers are multiples of 2, even numbers have final digits of 0, 2, 4, 6 or 8. Then ask: *Do you think 36 is a multiple of 4?* They may say yes because they know the 4 times table, but explain that if they halve a number and the result is even then the original number is a multiple of 4. Give other examples, such as 24, 44. Then try 42. Point out that when you halve 42 the result is 21 which is odd so 42 is not a multiple of 4.

In pairs, the children take turns to throw the dice twice to generate a two-digit number. They decide whether that number is a multiple of 2, 4, 5 and/or 10, then check using the tables square to see if they are correct.

DIFFERENTIATION

More able: generate three-digit numbers and then check whether the 'rule' still applies. Less able: test the multiple of 4 rule for the multiples of 2, 5 or 10, then check by referring to their coloured number squares from Lessons 2 and 3, Unit 8, Term 1, and Lesson 1, Units 9–10, Term 2.

PLENARY

Ask the children for any numbers they discovered that were multiples of more than one of the numbers. *Is there a pattern?* They may say that all multiples of 10 are also multiples of 2 and 5; all multiples of 4 are also multiples of 2. Write on the board four columns, headed 'Multiple of 2, …4, …5, …10'. Call out a number and the children have to tell you whether it can be added to any of the columns on your chart.

LESSON 2

Repeat the **Oral and mental starter** from Lesson 1. In the **Main teaching activity** ask the children to tell you the multiples of 3 in sequence. List them in a column on the board. Then ask them to work out the sum of the digits for each number. List these in an adjacent column. Ask: *Can you see a pattern?* The sum of the digits for numbers in the 3 times table follows the pattern 3, 6, 9, 3, 6, 9. Say: *Let's test for other numbers to see if this is always true.* Try 63. Ask children to demonstrate their methods for dividing 63 by 3 to give the answer 21 with no remainder. Then add the digits: 6 + 3 = 9, so the rule works for this number. In pairs of the same ability level, children use dice to generate two-digit numbers. For each number, they sum its digits and then decide whether they think it is a multiple of 3. They check by then dividing by 3 and record their results in two lists: those that are multiples of three and those that are not. For **Differentiation** the more able children can generate three-digit numbers and the less able can use 1–6 dice instead. Repeat the **Plenary** from Lesson 1, this time including multiples of 3.

LESSON 3

Repeat the **Oral and mental starter** from Lesson 1. In the **Main teaching activity** go through the main tests for recognising multiples of 2, 3, 4, 5 and 10 by demonstrating some examples on the board. Then give the children your prepared chart to fill in. They tick the boxes to record which numbers are multiples of 2, 3, 4, 5, or 10. For **Differentiation** provide the more able with a chart with numbers to 100 and the less able with a chart with numbers just to 30. In the **Plenary** talk about which numbers are multiples of more than one other number. Use the term 'factor'.

LESSON 4 +5

RESOURCES	Enlarged copies of investigation cards from photocopiable pages 180 and 181 ('Investigations 1 and 2'); digit cards; pencils and paper.
LEARNING OUTCOMES	**ORAL AND MENTAL STARTER** ● Derive quickly: all number pairs that total 100; all pairs of multiples of 50 with a total of 1000. **MAIN TEACHING ACTIVITY** ● Explain methods and reasoning about numbers orally and in writing. ● **Solve mathematical problems or puzzles, recognise and explain patterns and relationships, generalise and predict. Suggest extensions by asking 'What if...?'**
ORAL AND MENTAL STARTER	MAKE 100: Repeat the activity from Lesson 1, Units 4–6, Term 1.
MAIN TEACHING ACTIVITY	WORK IT OUT: Go through the investigation cards in turn to explain what is involved. Then give appropriate cards for children to attempt in pairs or small groups of similar ability level. Tell them to discuss methods that they could use then record their workings informally. Answers to page 180: Q1. 1; 4,9; 1,3; 5,2; 4,9; 7,8. Q2. A:3, B:5, C:1, D:7, E:0, F:2, G:6, H:9, I:4, J:8. Q3. 7; 4; 2,4; 0,2; 9,6. Answers to page 181: 3. 123 – 45 – 67 + 89 = 100 *or* 123 + 45 – 67 + 8 – 9 = 100; 4. $(1 + 2 + 3 + 4) \times 5 + (6 \times 7) + 8 = 100$.
DIFFERENTIATION	More able: work on investigation 2 from page 180 and investigations 3 and 4 from page 181. Less able: work on investigation 1 from 180 and investigation 5 from page 181.
PLENARY	Children explain their methods and reasoning..

LESSON 5

Repeat the **Oral and mental starter** from Lesson 4. In the **Main teaching activity** the children continue working through the investigations, sharing methods in the **Plenary**.

Investigations 1

1. Missing numbers – additions
Fill in the missing numbers to complete these additions:

```
  2 8        3 □        □ 6        3 6        5 □        □ □
+ 3 □      + 6 5      + 5        + □ □      + 2 6      + 3 4
-----      -----      -----      -----      -----      -----
  5 9        □ 9        □ 9        8 8        □ 3        8 3
```

2. Numbers for letters
Substitute numbers for letters to solve these additions:

```
  A B        I D        B C        G G        I J D        C I B
+ C I      + F J      + A H      + D F      + F E G      + D C B
-----      -----      -----      -----      -----        -----
  I H        D B        H E        C A J      G H A        J G E
```

3. Missing numbers – subtractions
Fill in the missing numbers to complete these subtractions:

```
  7 □        8 □        □ 8        9 4
- 4 5      - 6        - □ 7      - 2 6
-----      -----      -----      -----
  3 2        1 7        2 2        □ 4
```

Investigations 2

1. Making numbers
You can only use the digit cards 1, 2, 3 and 4.
The aim is to make as many numbers up to 50 using all four digit cards with any operation and brackets.
For example: $19 = 12 + 3 + 4$
$21 = (2+1) \times (3+4)$ Now try for numbers beyond 50.

2. Using 9s
You need four 9 digit cards.
The aim is to make as many numbers up to 50 using all four 9s with any operation and brackets. For example: $1 = \dfrac{9}{9} \times \dfrac{9}{9}$

3. Make 100 with + and −
Use the digit cards 1 to 9 placed in order. Then use + or − signs to make this sentence correct:

$$1 \quad 2 \quad 3 \quad 4 \quad 5 \quad 6 \quad 7 \quad 8 \quad 9 \ = 100$$

4. Make 100 with +, −, x, ÷
Use the digit cards 1 to 8 and the signs +, −, ×, ÷ to make this correct:

$$1 \quad 2 \quad 3 \quad 4 \quad 5 \quad 6 \quad 7 \quad 8 \ = 100$$

5. Investigating number bonds
Choose any number and try to think of all the number bonds that make that number.
For example, number bonds that make 6 are:
$1+2+3$ $1+1+1+1+1+1$ $2+2+2$ $3+3$

$1+1+2+2$ $1+1+1+3$ $1+1+4$ $1+5$ $1+1+1+1+2$

Then work out the product that each of these number bonds gives:
$1 \times 2 \times 3 = 6$, $1 \times 1 \times 1 \times 1 \times 1 \times 1 = 1$ and so on.
Which gives the greatest product? Answer: $3 \times 3 = 9$
Investigate to find the greatest products for numbers 1 to 20.
Do you notice any patterns?

UNITS 9–10

ORGANISATION (10 LESSONS)

	LEARNING OUTCOMES	ORAL AND MENTAL STARTER	MAIN TEACHING ACTIVITY	PLENARY
LESSON 1 +2	● Use the relationship between multiplication and division. ● Use closely related facts. ● Use doubling and halving, starting from known facts. For example: to multiply by 4, double, then double again; find the 8 times table facts by doubling the 4 times table.	TABLES BINGO: Use knowledge of all times tables to play bingo.	TIMES TABLES SQUARE: Complete a times tables square using a range of strategies.	Use a times tables square to solve division problems. Explain methods used to complete a jigsaw.
LESSON 3	● Derive quickly: doubles of multiples of 10 to 500, and of 100 to 5000, and the corresponding halves. ● Use doubling and halving.	NUMBER CHAINS: Count on and back in 10s, 100s and 1000s.	DOUBLE MULTIPLES OF 10: Use strategy to double and halve multiples of 10.	Answer quick-fire doubling and halving questions.
LESSON 4	● Use doubling and halving, starting from known facts. For example: double/halve two-digit numbers by doubling/halving the tens first; to multiply by 4, double, then double again; find the 8 times table facts by doubling the 4 times table.	DOUBLE/HALVE NUMBER CHAINS: Chant number sequences for doubling and halving.	CLEVER MULTIPLES: Use strategies for multiplying by 4, 5, 8 and 20.	Recap on strategies used. Answer multiplication and division questions.
LESSON 5	● Develop and refine written methods for TU × U. ● Approximate first. Use informal pencil and paper methods to support, record or explain multiplications and divisions.	DOUBLING AND HALVING: Double and halve three-digit numbers.	COLUMN MULTIPLICATION: Use the standard method for short multiplication.	Explain choices of method.
LESSON 6 +7 +8	● Develop and refine written methods for TU × U and TU ÷ U. ● Approximate first. Use informal pencil and paper methods to support, record or explain multiplications and divisions. ● **Find remainders after division.**	DIVISION SNAP: Play snap for 2, 3, 4, 5 and 10 times tables facts.	COLUMN DIVISION: Use the standard method for short division.	Share calculations.
LESSON 9	● **Find remainders after division.** Divide a whole number of pounds by 2, 4, 5 or 10 to give £.p. ● Approximate first. Develop and refine written methods for TU × U and TU ÷ U.	EQUATION GAME: Give equivalent number facts.	DIVIDING MONEY: Play a game to divide pounds to give pounds and pence.	Mentally calculate money divisions.
LESSON 10	● Use all four operations to solve word problems involving numbers in 'real life' and money, using one or more steps, including converting pounds to pence and vice versa.	TABLES BINGO: Use knowledge of all times tables to play bingo.	AT THE FAIR: Solve problems in the context of money.	Children explain their methods.

ORAL AND MENTAL SKILLS   Know by heart multiplication facts for 2, 3, 4, 5 and 10 times tables.
Begin to know multiplication facts for 6, 7, 8 and 9 times tables. **Derive quickly division facts corresponding to 2, 3, 4, 5 and 10 times tables.** Count on or back in repeated steps of 1, 10 or 100. Derive quickly doubles of all whole numbers to 50; doubles of multiples of 10 to 500; doubles of multiples of 100 to 5000 and the corresponding halves.

Lessons 1, 4, 5, 6 and 9 are shown in full. Lessons 2, 7 and 8 are given as developments of the previous lesson. Lessons 3 and 10 are extensions of what has already been taught so are shown in outline.

RESOURCES

Prepared bingo cards; prepared blank multiplication grids; 0–9 dice; enlarged copy of photocopiable resource sheet C ('Times tables square'); class and individual number lines; pencils and paper; card; envelopes; prepared multiplication and division questions.

PREPARATION

Prepare different bingo cards with numbers from all the times tables, one per child, and write corresponding questions. Draw a large blank version of the times tables square with just the row and column heading numbers. Photocopy one per child and prepare an enlarged version for demonstration purposes. Photocopy 'Times tables square' (resource sheet C) onto card, then cut up into sections to create a jigsaw. Create various jigsaws in this way, storing the pieces for each one in a separate envelope, and varying the number of pieces each is cut into in order to vary the level of difficulty. Photocopy multiplication and division questions that you have made up, to prepare a sheet for each ability group, then photocopy, one per child. Do not include division questions that involve remainders.

LEARNING OUTCOMES

ORAL AND MENTAL STARTER
● **Know by heart multiplication facts for 2, 3, 4, 5 and 10 times tables**.
● Begin to know multiplication facts for 6, 7, 8 and 9 times tables.

MAIN TEACHING ACTIVITY
● Use the relationship between multiplication and division.
● Use closely related facts.
● Use doubling and halving, starting from known facts. For example: to multiply by 4, double, then double again; find the 8 times table facts by doubling the 4 times table.

VOCABULARY

Times; multiply; multiplied by; product; multiple; inverse; share; share equally; divide; divided by; divided into; divisible by.

ORAL AND MENTAL STARTER

TABLES BINGO: Repeat the activity from Lesson 2, Unit 8, Term 1, but for all the times tables.

MAIN TEACHING ACTIVITY

TIMES TABLES SQUARE: Display the blank times tables square and ask the children which columns will be easiest to fill in, such as 1s, 10s, 2s, 5s. Ask a child to come and fill in each of these columns and rows on the demonstration grid. Remind them that they can work out the 4s by doubling the 2s and then the 8s by doubling the 4s. Again, let a child come and complete these columns and rows.

Then ask them to work out the 3s, using a number line if necessary. Ask: *How could we use the 3s numbers to work out the 6s?* (Double them). Work out the remaining 9s by multiplying the number by 10 and then subtracting the number. They can fill in the remaining gaps in the 7s by counting on. Remove the completed grid from view. Children complete their own grids.

Then in pairs they take it in turns to roll the dice twice to generate a multiplication sum, such as 5 × 6. They then find the answer on their own grid and check with their partner. They should record any that they do not agree upon.

DIFFERENTIATION

More able: use dice to generate a two-digit and a single-digit number to multiply together. They should use any strategies they know (such as partitioning) to rearrange or simplify the question. They should record their calculations.
Less able: use a smaller grid, up to 6 × 6, and then use a 1–6 dice.

PLENARY

Using the large copy of the completed times table square check any answers that children did not agree on. Remind them that division is the inverse of multiplication and demonstrate how to use the square to work out division questions.

LESSON 2

Repeat the **Oral and mental starter** from Lesson 1. In the **Main teaching activity** children complete their times table jigsaw then use it to solve the prepared multiplication and division questions. **Differentiation** is achieved by the number of pieces that the jigsaw is cut into and by the level of questions you give the children. In the **Plenary** children explain how they worked out how to fit the times table square back together.

RESOURCES	Sets of cards with multiples of 10 from the range 10–500 and multiples of 100 from the range 100–5000, one set per group of three or four; pencils and paper.
LEARNING OUTCOMES	**ORAL AND MENTAL STARTER** ● Count on or back in repeated steps of 1, 10 or 100. **MAIN TEACHING ACTIVITY** ● Derive quickly: doubles of multiples of 10 to 500, and of 100 to 5000, and the corresponding halves. ● Use doubling and halving, starting from known facts. For example: double/halve two-digit numbers by doubling/halving the tens first.
ORAL AND MENTAL STARTER	NUMBER CHAINS: See Lesson 2, Unit 1, Term 2.
MAIN TEACHING ACTIVITY	DOUBLE MULTIPLES OF 10: Explain to the children how to work out doubles of multiples of 10 to 500: first double the significant digit and then adjust. For example, double 40 is double 4 = 8 then adjust the tens = 80. Tell them that they can use a similar method to double multiples of 100, eg for double 600 use double 6 giving 12, then adjust for hundreds to give 1200. Use the inverse operation to work out the corresponding halves. For example, for half of 620 use half of 62 giving 31 and then adjust for the tens to give 310. In groups of three or four, the children take turns to pick a card from the pile. They all then work out its double and its half, recording their agreed answer on a group record sheet.
DIFFERENTIATION	Vary the level of the activity by the range of cards you give each group.
PLENARY	Ask individual children quick-fire double and half questions, varying the difficulty level as appropriate, and involving all children.

RESOURCES

0–9 dice; 1–6 dice; sets of multiples cards; stop-watch; pencils and paper.

PREPARATION

Prepare cards with three each of ×2, ×4, ×5, ×8, ×10 and ×20, one set per group.

LEARNING OUTCOMES

ORAL AND MENTAL STARTER
● Derive quickly doubles of all whole numbers to 50 and the corresponding halves.

MAIN TEACHING ACTIVITY
● Use doubling and halving, starting from known facts. For example: double/halve two-digit numbers by doubling/halving the tens first; to multiply by 4, double, then double again; find the 8 times table facts by doubling the 4 times table; to multiply by 5, multiply by 10 then halve; to multiply by 20, multiply by 10 then halve.

ORAL AND MENTAL STARTER
DOUBLE/HALVE NUMBER CHAINS: See Lessons 6 and 7, Units 2–3, Term 2.

MAIN TEACHING ACTIVITY

CLEVER MULTIPLES: Remind the children of the strategy for doubling a two-digit number by first doubling the tens and then doubling the units and adding the two results. Similarly, for halving a number they halve the tens and then halve the units (including any remaining ten). Ask: *What if you want 4 times 28, how can you work it out?* Double 28 then double the result. Work through some examples. Repeat for dividing by 4, for example *What is a quarter of 96?* Half of 96, then half of 48 gives 24. Then ask: *How would you work out 8 × 46?* If they don't suggest the strategy themselves remind them that 8 is $2 \times 2 \times 2$, so they can double the number then double again and then once again. Write on the board: 8×46

> 8×46
> $8 \times 46 = 4 \times 92$
> $8 \times 46 = 2 \times 184$
> $8 \times 46 = 368$

Ask: *What is double 46? What is double 92? What is double 184?* Work through other examples. Then show the children how you can multiply by 5 by multiplying by 10 and halving the result (since 5 is half of 10), eg 5×77 = half of (10×77) = half of 770 = 385. Work through more examples. Then repeat for multiplying by 20 by multiplying by 10 and doubling the result.

In groups of four, children take turns to roll the dice twice to generate a two-digit number. A dealer then shuffles the multiples pack and deals one card to each player, face down. Each player then turns over their card and calculates that multiple of their two-digit number. The first person to call ready must turn their answer over for the rest of the group to check. If correct they win a point; if incorrect play starts again.

DIFFERENTIATION

More able: give them a time limit in which to answer, say, ten seconds; players taking turns to miss a round take charge of the stop-watch instead.

Less able: give them ×2, ×5 and ×10 cards only. You may also choose to restrict them to the 1–6 dice.

PLENARY

Recap on the different strategies used, going through some examples. Give some oral questions such as 5×72. Include division questions such as $98 \div 5$, $64 \div 16$.

RESOURCES

HTU number fans; prepared multiplication questions; practical base 10 apparatus; pencils and paper.

PREPARATION

Provide multiplication questions, such as 72×7, 58×3, 85×4, prepared yourself and written on the board.

LEARNING OUTCOMES

ORAL AND MENTAL STARTER
● Derive quickly doubles of all whole numbers to 50 and the corresponding halves.

MAIN TEACHING ACTIVITY
● Develop and refine written methods for TU × U.
● Approximate first. Use informal pencil and paper methods to support, record or explain multiplications and divisions.

<table>
<tr><td>

VOCABULARY

Times; multiply; multiplied by; digit; units; tens; hundreds; column; carry.

</td></tr>
</table>

ORAL AND MENTAL STARTER

DOUBLING AND HALVING: See Lesson 8, Units 4–6, Term 2.

MAIN TEACHING ACTIVITY

COLUMN MULTIPLICATION: Demonstrate the standard method for multiplication (using columns and partitioning, introduced in Lessons 6 and 7, Units 9–10, Term 2) by working through an example, such as 9×37.

Tell the children to approximate first, eg *10 × 37 is 370 so we know the answer is just less than 370.* Then set the sum out in vertical format and work through the method:

$$
\begin{array}{r}
37 \\
\times \quad 9 \\
\hline
\end{array}
$$

30 × 9:	270
7 × 9:	63
Add them together:	333

Go through several more examples with children demonstrating on the board. Explain that the calculation can be shortened by multiplying the least significant digit first and 'carrying the tens':

Say 7 × 9 is 63
Write the 3 units under the units and 'carry' the 6 tens.

$$
\begin{array}{r}
37 \\
\times \quad 9 \\
\hline
3 \\
\scriptstyle 6
\end{array}
$$

Then say 9 × 30 is 270
Add on the 60 or 6 tens that we carried to get 330
Add this to the 3 in the units column to give the answer:

$$
\begin{array}{r}
37 \\
\times \quad 9 \\
\hline
333
\end{array}
$$

Go through other examples in the same way. Children then practice the method working through your prepared examples. Tell them to approximate first.

DIFFERENTIATION

More able: encourage them to look at each question first and decide if they can find a better way of doing the calculation; this may be a mental or an informal method. For example, 37 × 9 could be calculated as (37 × 10) – 37. They should use 'their own' method and check the calculation using the standard method.
Less able: tell them to use the first of the standard methods, partitioning into units and tens. Encourage them to use practical apparatus if needed.

PLENARY

Ask children which methods they used for different questions. Let them explain their reasoning. Talk to children about the best method to choose. Encourage them not to rely on just one method.

RESOURCES

Prepared division questions for 2, 3, 4, 5 and 10 times tables with single-digit answers; sets of 0–9 digit cards (enough for 4 cards per child); prepared division questions (some including remainders); 0–9 dice; prepared six-sided dice marked 2, 3, 4, 5, 6 and 10; pencils and paper.

PREPARATION

Photocopy your prepared division questions, one per child and or write them on the board. Provide one 0–9 dice per pair. Prepare the six-sided dice with numbers listed above.

VOCABULARY

Times; multiply; multiplied by; divide; divided by; divided into; remainder; column; units; tens; hundreds; digit; inverse.

LEARNING OUTCOMES

ORAL AND MENTAL STARTER
● Derive quickly division facts corresponding to 2, 3, 4, 5 and 10 times tables.

MAIN TEACHING ACTIVITY
● Approximate first. Use informal pencil and paper methods to support, record or explain multiplications and divisions. Develop and refine written methods for TU × U and TU ÷ U.
● **Find remainders after division.**

ORAL AND MENTAL STARTER

DIVISION SNAP: See Lesson 5, Units 9–10, Term 2.

MAIN TEACHING ACTIVITY

COLUMN DIVISION: Tell the children that they are going to learn a standard written method for short division. Remind them that they should always approximate first and that when calculations are set out in columns it is important that units are placed under the units and tens under the tens. Write on the board $91 \div 7$. Ask for an approximate answer. Rounding both the 91 and the 7 to the nearest 10 gives $90 \div 10 = 9$ as an approximate answer. Then show them how this calculation can be written as: $7\overline{)91}$. Then show them the method for short division:

	$7\overline{)91}$	
We know that 10×7 is 70:	$-\ \underline{70}$	10×7
Take the 70 away from 91:	21	
We know that 3×7 is 21:	$-\ \underline{21}$	3×7
Take 21 away from 21:	0	
Answer:		$10 + 3 = 13$

Repeat for other examples such as $96 \div 6$, $72 \div 3$, $85 \div 5$, inviting children to demonstrate on the board. Stress the importance of positioning the digits carefully. Then go through an example with a remainder, eg $83 \div 3$. Set this out as follows:

	$3\overline{)83}$	
We know that 20×3 is 60:	$-\ \underline{60}$	20×3
Take 60 away from 83:	23	
We know that 7×3 is 21:	$-\ \underline{21}$	7×3
Take 21 away from 23:	2	
		$20 + 7 = 27$
Answer:		27 remainder 2

Invite children to go through some more examples on the board, such as $75 \div 6$, $61 \div 4$, $87 \div 6$. Children should then work on their own through your prepared examples.

DIFFERENTIATION

More able: check results using the inverse operation.
Less able: give them examples that involve dividing by 2, 3, 4, 5, 6 and 10.

PLENARY

Go through an example. Invite children to show some of their calculations and explain their reasoning.

LESSONS 7 AND 8

Repeat the **Oral and mental starter** from Lesson 6. In the **Main teaching activity** go through an example to remind children of the method. Then, in pairs, one child rolls the dice twice to generate a two-digit number, the other child rolls the dice once to give the divisor. They then calculate the division, recording their workings out and their results, noting which numbers divided exactly and which had remainders. In Lesson 8 they can repeat this or work through examples from published materials. For **Differentiation** encourage more able children to predict whether there is going to be a remainder. Less able children can use a six-sided dice marked 2, 3, 4, 5, 6 and 10. In the **Plenary** ask children to share calculations.

RESOURCES

0–50 number cards; packs of 2, 4, 5 and 10 digit cards; pencils and paper.

PREPARATION

Prepare 2, 4, 5 and 10 digit cards, at least five of each per pack. Provide one pack per group of three or four. Prepare packs of 0–50 cards, one pack per group of three or four.

LEARNING OUTCOMES

ORAL AND MENTAL STARTER
- **Know by heart multiplication facts for 2, 3, 4, 5 and 10 times tables**.
- Begin to know multiplication facts for 6, 7, 8 and 9 times tables.
- **Derive quickly division facts corresponding to 2, 3, 4, 5 and 10 times tables**.

MAIN TEACHING ACTIVITY
- **Find remainders after division.** Divide a whole number of pounds by 2, 4, 5 or 10 to give £.p.
- Approximate first. Develop and refine written methods for TU × U and TU ÷ U.

ORAL AND MENTAL STARTER

EQUATION GAME: Repeat the activity from Lesson 10, Units 2–3, Term 2, but this time for multiplication and division.

MAIN TEACHING ACTIVITY

DIVIDING MONEY: Remind the children that there are 100p in a £. Explain that if we divide whole numbers of pounds and there is a remainder we can then go on to change that to pence and divide the pence. Ask: *If we divide £1 (or 100p) by 2 what do we get?* 50p. Tell them that this can be written as £0.50 or 50p. Repeat for dividing £1 by 4, then by 5, then by 10, showing both ways to record the answer each time. Stress that they should use the £ sign with the decimal answer and the p sign when giving the answer in pence. Repeat for larger amounts, then include examples that do not involve whole number answers, such as £16 divided by 5 (£3 remainder £1). Explain that the remaining pound can be divided by 5, to give 20p or £0.20 so the answer is £3.20. Go through further examples. In small groups, the children each select one card from the shuffled 0–50 pack and one card from the 2, 4, 5 and 10 pack. The first card is the number of pounds and the second is the divisor. They each work out the calculation and record their answers showing pounds and pence. The first child to correctly complete their question wins a point.

DIFFERENTIATION

More able: use cards numbered up to 100.
Less able: limit cards to numbers less than 20 and the divisors to 2 and 10.

PLENARY

Ask questions of the type: *What is £2 divided by 4? ...half of £7? ...£1 divided by 5?* Invite children to explain their reasoning and discuss different methods of mental calculation.

LESSON 10

RESOURCES	Prepared bingo cards with corresponding questions; copies of photocopiable page 189 ('At the fair'), one per child; sets of coins; pencils.
LEARNING OUTCOMES	**ORAL AND MENTAL STARTER** ● **Know by heart multiplication facts for 2, 3, 4, 5 and 10 times tables.** ● Begin to know multiplication facts for 6, 7, 8 and 9 times tables. **MAIN TEACHING ACTIVITY** ● Use all four operations to solve word problems involving numbers in 'real life' and money, using one or more steps, including converting pounds to pence and vice versa.
ORAL AND MENTAL STARTER	TABLES BINGO: Repeat the activity from Lesson 2, Unit 8, Term 1, but for all the times tables.
MAIN TEACHING ACTIVITY	Give out the photocopiable sheets and talk through the first few questions. Remind the children to think about the operations they will need to use to solve the problems. They then work on the questions on their own.
DIFFERENTIATION	More able: make up their own similar questions for a partner to solve. Less able: use practical apparatus for support.
PLENARY	Go through the questions. Ask individual children to explain their methods and reasoning.

Name

At the fair

Simon, Ali, Satnam and Rachel went to the fair. They each had £5 to spend.

Satnam and Rachel wanted to go on the Merry-go-round. The two tickets cost £1 altogether. How much did they cost each?

Simon and Rachel went on the Dodgems. The ride cost 75p each. How much did they pay together?

Satnam bought the tickets for the Ghost Train. The four tickets cost £1.60. How much did each of the other three have to pay her for their ticket?

Ali and Simon had two tries each on the Coconut Shy at 45p a go. Simon paid for them both with a £2 coin. How much change was he given?

They all went on the Big Wheel, which cost 80p each. Ali paid for all the tickets with his £5 note. How much change did he get?

They each paid Ali for the Big Wheel ride. How much money has Ali got left now?

Ali paid Simon the money he owed him for the Coconut Shy with exactly three coins. What were they?

They all tried their luck on the Hoop-la stall. It cost 40p a go, but as Satnam won a prize she decided to have another go. How much did they spend on the Hoop-la altogether?

Hotdogs are 65p and burgers are £1; cans are 75p each. Rachel and Satnam each bought a burger and Ali and Simon each bought a hotdog. They each bought a can of drink. How much did they pay altogether?

Work out how much each of the friends spent at the fair and how much money they each have left.

UNIT 11

ORGANISATION (5 LESSONS)

LEARNING OUTCOMES		ORAL AND MENTAL STARTER	MAIN TEACHING ACTIVITY	PLENARY
LESSON 1 + 2	● Understand decimal notation and place value for tenths and hundredths, and use it in context. ● Recognise the equivalence between the decimal and fraction forms of one-half and one-quarter, and tenths such as 0.3.	DOUBLE MULTIPLES OF 10: Apply doubles knowledge to multiples of 10.	DECIMAL FRACTION MATCH: Match fractions with their decimal equivalent.	Chant decimal fractions in sequence. Given a decimal or fraction, say its equivalent.
LESSON 3 + 4	● Understand decimal notation and use it in context. For example, order amounts of money, convert a sum of money such as £13.25 to pence, or a length such as 125cm to metres, round a sum of money to the nearest pound.	EQUATION GAME: Give equivalent number facts.	POUNDS TO PENCE: Convert sums of money from decimal fractions to pence and vice versa. Convert decimal fractions including other metric units.	Convert decimal amounts of money to pence and visa versa. Share examples with class.
LESSON 5	● Begin to use ideas of simple proportion: for example 'one for every…' and 'one in every…'.	TABLES BINGO: Use knowledge of all times tables to play bingo.	WHAT PROPORTION?: Answer proportion questions.	Check answers and explain methods.

ORAL AND MENTAL SKILLS Derive quickly: division facts corresponding to 2, 3, 4, 5 and 10 times tables; doubles of multiples of 10 to 500; doubles of multiples of 100 to 5000 and the corresponding halves. **Know by heart multiplication facts for 2, 3, 4, 5 and 10 times tables.** Begin to know multiplication facts for 6, 7, 8 and 9 times tables.

Lessons 1 and 3 are shown in full. Lessons 2 and 4 are given as developments of the previous lessons. Lesson 5 is an extension of what has already been taught so is shown in outline.

RESOURCES

Number fans; prepared class number line and individual number lines from photocopiable resource sheet A ('Blank number lines'); decimal and fraction cards from photocopiable pages 194 and 195; prepared decimal and fraction dominoes; commercially produced decimal and fraction games; washing line; pegs; pencils and paper.

PREPARATION

Provide the number fans prepared for Lesson 1, Unit 1, Term 1. Use the blank number lines on resource sheet A to produce a class number line with divisions in tenths and a smaller version for each child:

Provide commercially produced fraction games. Prepare several sets of fraction cards and decimal cards by photocopying pages 194 and 195 onto thin card and cutting out. Use some of these sets to produce decimal and fraction dominoes. Allocate the games according to ability level.
For Lesson 2 hang the washing line across the classroom.

LEARNING OUTCOMES
ORAL AND MENTAL STARTER
● Derive quickly doubles of multiples of 10 to 500.

MAIN TEACHING ACTIVITY
● Understand decimal notation and place value for tenths and hundredths, and use it in context.
● Recognise the equivalence between the decimal and fraction forms of one-half and one-quarter, and tenths such as 0.3.

VOCABULARY
Decimal fraction; decimal; decimal point; decimal place.

ORAL AND MENTAL STARTER

DOUBLE MULTIPLES OF 10: Remind the children about doubling strategies, such as double 2 is 4 so double 20 is 40. Call out a multiple of 10 up to 500 for them to double, showing their answer on their number fans.

MAIN TEACHING ACTIVITY

DECIMAL FRACTION MATCH: Remind the children what they learned about equivalent fractions in the spring term (Lessons 1 and 2, Unit 11, Term 2). Tell them that now they are going to learn about decimal fractions. Write 0.5 on the board and explain that this is the same as a half or $^5/_{10}$. Remind them that this represents five parts of a whole that has been divided into ten equal parts. Write 0.2 on the board and ask if anyone can say how many tenths this is worth. Point out that 0.5 is $^5/_{10}$, so 0.2 is $^2/_{10}$. Go through other examples using tenths. Demonstrate on your blank number line. Write in 0, 1 and 2 and explain that each space represents 0.1. Ask children to find 0.5, 1.4, 2.3 and so on. Point out that 2.3 is equivalent to two whole ones and 3 tenths.

In pairs or small groups, children then play games which relate decimals to their fraction equivalent – such as fraction and decimal dominoes, fraction and decimal snap. For Snap, they deal out the cards among the players, then take turns to turn over their top card and place it face up on the central pile. If it matches the previous card on the pile the first player to shout 'Snap!' collects all the cards from the pile. The winner is the player who ends up with all the cards. Alternatively, children can select a card from a pack of decimal fraction cards and then write down an equivalent fraction. Let them use number lines to check equivalences.

DIFFERENTIATION

Choose games to match the ability of the children.

PLENARY

As a group, count in steps of 0.1 from 0 to 10, then in steps of 0.2 and 0.5 both forwards and backwards.

LESSON 2

Repeat the **Oral and mental starter** from Lesson 1 but go on to include multiples of 100. In the **Main teaching activity** remind the children that $0.5 = ^1/_2 = ^5/_{10} = ?/100$. Explain that it is the same as $^{50}/_{100}$. Give other examples showing fractions in hundredths. Point out that the first digit after the decimal point shows the tenths and the second digit shows the hundredths. Stress that zeros after the last number in the decimal fraction make no difference to the value (so 0.5 = 0.50 = 0.5000), but that if a zero after the decimal point is followed by another number, it *does* make a difference (so 15.705 is *not* equal to 15.75) – this is a subtle but important concept for the children to understand. Select some decimal fraction cards and write the values on the board, such as 0.2, 2.5, 1.7, 1.3. Discuss with the children which is the smallest and which is the largest. As they are identified, peg the cards on the number line, then add the other cards, placing them in order. Children then play different decimal and fraction games, as in Lesson 1. For **Differentiation** choose games to match the ability of the children. In the **Plenary** give a fraction for the children to give a decimal equivalent. For example, if you say $^4/_5$, they should reply with 0.8.

RESOURCES

0–9 dice; pencils and paper; £1 and 1p coins; metre rulers; prepared conversion questions.

PREPARATION

Provide enough 0–9 dice for one per child. Have available sets of coins for those children who need them. Provide conversion questions, £1 to pence and metre to cm, prepared yourself and copied, one per child.

LEARNING OUTCOMES

ORAL AND MENTAL STARTER
● **Know by heart multiplication facts for 2, 3, 4, 5 and 10 times tables.**
● Begin to know multiplication facts for 6, 7, 8 and 9 times tables.
● **Derive quickly division facts corresponding to 2, 3, 4, 5 and 10 times tables.**

MAIN TEACHING ACTIVITY
● Understand decimal notation and use it in context. For example, order amounts of money, convert a sum of money such as £13.25 to pence, or a length such as 125cm to metres. Round a sum of money to the nearest pound.

VOCABULARY
Decimal fraction; decimal; decimal point; decimal place.

ORAL AND MENTAL STARTER

EQUATION GAME: Repeat the activity from Lesson 10, Units 2–3, Term 2, but this time for times tables facts.

MAIN TEACHING ACTIVITY

POUNDS TO PENCE: Ask: *How many pence in a pound?* (100). Then ask: *How do we write one pound twenty five?* Accept £1.25 but not £1.25p. Explain that if we use the decimal point we are talking about decimal parts of a pound and this must be written with only the pound sign. Quote other examples such as £2.45, £1.40, also £0.25 and so on, for individual children to write on the board. Next ask: *How many pence in £2.45?* Explain that this would be written as 245p. Ask similar questions for children to answer. Organise the children in pairs. Ask them to each use their 0–9 dice to generate a three-digit number. They record this as pence and then write the equivalent decimal fraction in pounds: 287p = £2.87. They then ask each other to convert the decimal fraction back to pence.

DIFFERENTIATION

More able: generate larger amounts by creating four-digit numbers.
Less able: may need to use £1 and 1p coins for support.

PLENARY

Ask quick-fire questions that require the children to convert decimals amounts of money to pence and vice versa.

LESSON 4

Repeat the **Oral and mental starter** from Lesson 3. In the **Main teaching activity** introduce other decimal units such as length, perhaps converting 125cm to m. Children then use the dice to generate numbers to convert from cm to m. Alternatively, they can work through examples in commercially produced materials. For **Differentiation** again encourage the more able to work with four-digit numbers; let the less able use a metre ruler for support. In the **Plenary** ask individual children to give one of their numbers, in cms (or metres), for others to convert back to metres (or cm).

RESOURCES	Prepared bingo cards with numbers from the times tables, one per child; prepared bingo questions; practical apparatus such as Multilnk cubes and counters; prepared extension questions for the more able; pencils.
LEARNING OUTCOMES	**ORAL AND MENTAL STARTER** ● **Know by heart multiplication facts for 2, 3, 4 5 and 10 times tables.** ● Begin to know multiplication facts for 6, 7, 8 and 9 times tables. **MAIN TEACHING ACTIVITY** ● Begin to use ideas of simple proportion: for example 'one for every…' and 'one in every…'.
ORAL AND MENTAL STARTER	TABLES BINGO: Repeat the activity from Lesson 2, Unit 8, Term 1, but for all the times tables.
MAIN TEACHING ACTIVITY	WHAT PROPORTION?: Talk about simple proportion statements such as *Every week we have PE on 2 days out of 5, how many times do we have PE in 3 weeks?* Introduce 'Proportion' (page 196) and go through the questions. Children then work in pairs to complete the sheet. Tell them to discuss their ideas.
DIFFERENTIATION	More able: give them your prepared extension questions to complete. Less able: let them use practical apparatus to model the questions.
PLENARY	Go through the questions. Ask children to explain their work.

Fraction cards

$\dfrac{1}{10}$	$\dfrac{1}{5}$	$\dfrac{3}{10}$
$\dfrac{2}{5}$	$\dfrac{1}{2}$	$\dfrac{3}{5}$
$\dfrac{7}{10}$	$\dfrac{4}{5}$	$\dfrac{9}{10}$
$\dfrac{1}{10}$	$\dfrac{1}{5}$	$\dfrac{3}{10}$
$\dfrac{2}{5}$	$\dfrac{1}{2}$	$\dfrac{3}{5}$
$\dfrac{7}{10}$	$\dfrac{4}{5}$	$\dfrac{9}{10}$

Decimal fraction cards

0.1	0.2	0.3
0.4	0.5	0.6
0.7	0.8	0.9
1	1.1	1.2
1.3	1.4	1.5
1.6	1.7	1.8
1.9	2	2.1
2.2	2.3	2.4
2.5	2.6	2.7
2.8	2.9	3

Proportion

1. For every two bags of crisps that you buy you get a sticker. How many bags of crisps must you buy to get five stickers?

2. For every five eggs there is an extra one free. How many free eggs do I get if I buy 20 eggs?

3. We go to school on five days in every seven. How many days do we go to school in five weeks?

4. If you buy two bars of chocolate you get one more free. How many do I have to pay for if I want nine bars?

5. In Class 2 there are twice as many boys as girls. There are 33 children in the class. How many boys are there?

6. For every ten saving stamps there is one free bonus stamp. How many will I have altogether if I buy five saving stamps every week for six weeks?

7. One fruit gum in every five is red. If I buy a packet of 20 gums, how many red ones will I get?

8. For every ten snowdrops that I plant, I also plant two daffodils. If I plant 60 bulbs how many of them will be daffodils?

UNIT 12

ORGANISATION (5 LESSONS)

LEARNING OUTCOMES	ORAL AND MENTAL STARTER	MAIN TEACHING ACTIVITY	PLENARY
LESSON 1 +2 +3 ● **Develop and refine written methods for: column addition and subtraction of two whole numbers less than 1000, and addition of more than two such numbers;** for money calculations.	DOUBLING AND HALVING: Double and halve three-digit numbers. TABLES BINGO: Use knowledge of all times tables to play bingo.	MONEY CALCULATIONS: Use column addition and subtraction methods to answer money questions.	Recap on main teaching points. Children explain methods used. Answer quick-fire money questions.
LESSON 4 ● Use, read and write the vocabulary related to time. Read simple timetables and use this year's calendar. ● Use all four operations to solve word problems involving time.	EQUATION GAME: Give equivalent number facts.	CALENDARS: Use calendars to answer questions on time.	Put children's dates of birth in order.
LESSON 5 ● Estimate/check times using seconds, minutes, hours. Use am and pm. Read simple timetables and use this year's calendar. ● Use all four operations to solve word problems involving time.	DIVISION SNAP: Play snap for all times tables facts.	TIMETABLES: Use timetables to answer questions.	Children explain methods used.

ORAL AND MENTAL SKILLS **Know by heart multiplication facts for 2, 3, 4, 5 and 10 times tables.** Begin to know multiplication facts for 6, 7, 8 and 9 times tables. **Derive quickly: division facts corresponding to 2, 3, 4, 5 and 10 times tables**; doubles of multiples of 10 to 500; doubles of multiples of 100 to 5000, and the corresponding halves.

Lessons 1 and 4 are shown in full. Lessons 2 and 3 are given as developments of the previous lesson. Lesson 5 is an extension of what has already been taught so is shown in outline.

RESOURCES

Number fans; prepared money addition questions; coins; pencils and paper; bingo cards; prepared money subtraction questions.

PREPARATION

Provide money addition and subtraction questions, prepared yourself and copies, one per child. Vary the level of difficulty as appropriate for each ability group, so for subtractions give more able children calculations involving larger amounts and examples involving 'decomposition' such as £8 – £3.57, £6.25 – £5.88. Have sets of coins available for those children that require support. Prepare bingo cards with numbers from the times tables, one per child, and prepare corresponding questions.

LEARNING OUTCOMES

ORAL AND MENTAL STARTER

● Derive quickly: doubles of multiples of 10 to 500; doubles of multiples of 100 to 5000; and the corresponding halves.
● **Know by heart multiplication facts for 2, 3, 4, 5 and 10 times tables.**
● Begin to know multiplication facts for 6, 7, 8 and 9 times tables.

MAIN TEACHING ACTIVITY

● **Develop and refine written methods for: column addition and subtraction of two whole numbers less than 1000, and addition of more than two such numbers;** for money calculations.

VOCABULARY

Add; sum; total; amount; altogether; money; coin; penny; pence; pound; £; subtract; take away; minus; leave; column; digit; units; tens; hundreds; carry; inverse.

ORAL AND MENTAL STARTER

DOUBLING AND HALVING: See Lesson 8, Units 4–6, Term 2.

MAIN TEACHING ACTIVITY

MONEY CALCULATIONS: Tell the children that you want to add £3.55 to £5.63. Explain that you are going to set the calculation out in columns. Remind them of the importance of positioning the digits carefully. Write the sum on the board:

$$\begin{array}{r} £3.55 \\ + \ £5.63 \\ \hline \\ \hline \end{array}$$

Explain that it is important that the decimal points are written one below the other. Go through the calculation, adding the pence first: 55 plus 63 pence (£0.55 + £0.63). Ask the children for the total: 118 pence. Ask: *What is this in pounds?* £1.18. Say: *We can write the .18 under the pence and carry the £1.* Stress that the decimal point in the answer must be written immediately below the other decimal points.

$$\begin{array}{r} £3.55 \\ + \ £5.63 \\ \hline .18 \\ \hline {\scriptstyle 1} \end{array}$$

Now add the pounds. Say: *5 + 3 plus the 1 we carried gives how many pounds in total?* (9). Write this in the pounds column to give the answer: £9.18.

$$\begin{array}{r} £3.55 \\ + \ £5.63 \\ \hline £9.18 \\ \hline {\scriptstyle 1} \end{array}$$

Go through other examples such as £3.35 + £5.68, £7.53 + £4.27, £4.99 + £5.05. Children then work through your prepared questions. Explain that they should approximate first and then choose the method that they feel is most suited to the calculation.

DIFFERENTIATION

Defined by the level of difficulty of the questions you provide. Let the less able use coins to help with calculations.

PLENARY

Go over the main teaching points, stressing the position of the decimal points. Ask children to explain their methods and reasoning.

LESSON 2

In the **Oral and mental starter** repeat TABLES BINGO from Lesson 2, Unit 8, Term 1, but this time for all times tables. In the **Main teaching activity** repeat as for Lesson 1 but for money subtractions. For example, *Subtract £3.45 from £5.63.* Remind the children that they must write the bigger number on the top line. As before, when going through the calculation tell them to deal with the pence first: 63 pence minus 45 pence. Children should be able to use a variety of strategies to calculate this. Point out that 18 pence is £0.18 and write the 18 under the pence, after the decimal point. Then subtract the pounds to give the answer £2.18. Remind children that addition is the inverse of subtraction and check the result of the calculation by using addition: £2.18 + £3.45. Invite a child to do the calculation on the board. Go through other examples before the children work on their own to complete your prepared questions. Tell them to use the inverse operation to check their answers. **Differentiation** is achieved by grading the questions. In the **Plenary** ask children to explain their methods and reasoning.

LESSON 3

In the **Oral and mental starter** repeat TABLES BINGO from Lesson 2, Unit 8, Term 1, but this time for all times tables (as Lesson 2). In the **Main teaching activity** go through a money addition and a money subtraction example to recap on the two methods used in Lesson 1 and 2 respectively. Children then work through examples that include money addition and subtraction questions. As before, **Differentiation** is achieved by the level of difficulty of the questions you provide. In the **Plenary** ask children quick-fire money addition and subtraction questions that they can calculate mentally.

RESOURCES

Calendars; pencils and paper; calculators.

PREPARATION

Photocopy a current calendar, enough for one per pair.

LEARNING OUTCOMES

MENTAL AND ORAL STARTER
● **Know by heart multiplication facts for 2, 3, 4, 5 and 10 times tables.**

MAIN TEACHING ACTIVITY
● Use, read and write the vocabulary related to time. Read simple timetables and use this year's calendar.
● Use all four operations to solve word problems involving time.

VOCABULARY
Second; minute; hour; day; week; weekend; fortnight; month; year; leap year; century; millennium; calendar; date; date of birth.

ORAL AND MENTAL STARTER

EQUATION GAME: Repeat the activity from Lesson 10, Units 2–3, Term 20 but this time for multiplication and division.

MAIN TEACHING ACTIVITY

CALENDARS: Write on the board: second, minute, hour, day, week, month, year, century, millennium. Ask questions such as: *How many seconds in a minute? How many minutes in an hour? How many days in a month?* Remind the children of the rhyme '30 days hath September...'. Show them a current calendar. Remind them that there are 365 days in a year except in a leap year. Ask children how they know which years are leap years (the last two digits of the year must be multiples of 4 unless they are 00).

Point out that 1996 was a leap year, 96 divides exactly by 4. The year 2000 is a special year because it is the millennium as well as being a leap year. Give children a copy of a current calendar and ask them questions such as: *How many days in June and July? How many days in February this year? What day of the week will Christmas day fall on? How many Fridays are there in May?* Ask the children if they know what their date of birth is. Select a child and ask when his or her birthday is. Ask his age, then count back from the current year to work out his year of birth, taking account of whether he has had a birthday this year. Then record the complete date of birth. In pairs, ask the children to work out their own date of birth. Then, using the current year's calendar to help them, tell them to work out their exact age in years, days and months. Write some other 'challenges' on the board, such as: 'How many weeks to your next birthday? Can you work out whether you were born in a leap year? How many weeks until Christmas? How many days do we spend in school this term?' (Give the term dates).

DIFFERENTIATION

More able: use a calculator to calculate some big numbers such as how many days they have lived, how many hours in a week, a month, a year.
Less able: give them simpler questions such as: How many Saturdays in this month?

PLENARY

Ask for answers to particular questions, and for explanations of how they calculated them. Together rank the children in order of how old they say they are and see if these are then in date order.

LESSON 5

RESOURCES	Prepared division questions for all times tables with single-digit answers; sets of 0–9 digit cards (enough for four cards per child); copies of photocopiable page 201 ('Visit to the museum'), one per child; pencils.
LEARNING OUTCOMES	**ORAL AND MENTAL STARTER** ● **Derive quickly: division facts corresponding to 2, 3, 4, 5 and 10 times tables.** **MAIN TEACHING ACTIVITY** ● Estimate/check times using seconds, minutes, hours. Use am and pm. Read simple timetables and use this year's calendar. ● Use all four operations to solve word problems involving time.
ORAL AND MENTAL STARTER	DIVISION SNAP: See Lesson 5, Units 9–10, Term 2, but use all times tables.
MAIN TEACHING ACTIVITY	TIMETABLES: Talk to the children about timetables and when we use them. Explain am and pm. Remind them what they learned about digital time notation in Term 1. Give out the photocopiable sheets and go through some of the questions. Point out that when they are adding hours and minutes they should remember that there are 60 minutes in an hour. They then work on their own to complete 'Visit to the museum'.
DIFFERENTIATION	More able: make up similar questions based on the museum opening times for a partner to answer. Less able: may need adult support to help them get started.
PLENARY	Go through the questions asking individual children to give their answers and explain their reasoning.

Visit to the museum

Bus timetable

Uptown School	9.35		11.45	12.50
Post Office		11.00		
Church	10.15			
Museum				

A bus takes 20 minutes to travel between each stop.
Complete the timetable.

Which bus should they catch to get to the museum by 12 noon?

How long does it take to get from Uptown School to the Museum?

Museum opening times

Normal opening times: 9.30am to 6pm
January to March: Only open on weekends (1pm to 6pm)
April to June: Open on weekends, Mondays, Wednesdays and Fridays (9.30am to 6pm)
July to September: Open every day (9.30am to 6pm)
October to December: Only open on weekends (9.30am to 6pm)

How many months of the year is the museum open on Wednesdays?

In which months is the museum open on a Saturday morning?

Is the museum open on Tuesdays in May?

How many hours is the museum open on a Saturday in March?

What time does the museum close on 5 July?

What time does the museum open on 30 June?

Can I visit the museum on Thursday afternoon in December?

UNIT 13

ORGANISATION (5 LESSONS)

LEARNING OUTCOMES	ORAL AND MENTAL STARTER	MAIN TEACHING ACTIVITY	PLENARY
LESSON 1 + 2 ● Solve a problem by collecting quickly, organising and interpreting data in tables, charts, graphs and diagrams, for example: Carroll diagrams (two criteria).	NUMBER CHAINS: Count on and back in 6s, 7s, 8s and 9s.	FEATURE AND NUMBER SORT: Sort children by eye and hair colour onto Carroll diagrams and sort numbers onto a two-criteria Carroll diagram.	Discuss diagrams and interpret the data. Add numbers to class diagram.
LESSON 3 ● Solve a problem by collecting quickly, organising and interpreting data in tables, and diagrams, for example: Venn and Carroll diagrams (two criteria)	DIVISION SNAP: Play snap for all times tables facts.	NUMBER SORT: Sort numbers on to a two-criteria Venn diagram.	Compare Carroll and Venn diagrams.
LESSON 4 + 5 ● Solve a problem by collecting quickly, organising and interpreting data in tables, charts, graphs and diagrams, including those generated by a computer.	EQUATION GAME: Give equivalent number facts.	COMPUTER DETECTIVE: Create a questionnaire, collate data and use computer to interrogate results to solve a problem of their choice.	Report back on findings. Discuss results.

ORAL AND MENTAL SKILLS Know by heart multiplication facts for 2, 3, 4, 5 and 10 times tables. Begin to know multiplication facts for 6, 7, 8 and 9 times tables. **Derive quickly division facts corresponding to 2, 3, 4, 5 and 10 times tables.**

Lessons 1, 3 and 4 are shown in full. Lessons 2 and 5 are given as developments of the previous lessons.

RESOURCES

Prepared A3 and A4 copies of Carroll diagram with two criteria, (as shown on the right); pencils.

PREPARATION

Draw and label a Carroll diagram and enlarge it to A3 size, at least one per group of five or six. Provide the less able groups with a labelled copy of the diagram. For Lesson 2 you will need an enlarged version and at least one A4 copy per child/pair.

	Brown hair	Not brown hair
Brown eyes		
Not brown eyes		

LEARNING OUTCOMES

ORAL AND MENTAL STARTER
● Begin to know multiplication facts for 6, 7, 8 and 9 times tables.

MAIN TEACHING ACTIVITY
● Solve a problem by collecting quickly, organising and interpreting data in tables, charts, graphs and diagrams, for example: Carroll diagrams (two criteria).

ORAL AND MENTAL STARTER

NUMBER CHAINS: Repeat the activity from Lesson 2, Unit 1, Term 2, but this time count on or back in multiples of 6, 7, 8 and 9 within the range 0–100.

VOCABULARY

Data; sort; set; represent; range; chart; diagram; label; Carroll diagram; most/east common; most/least popular.

MAIN TEACHING ACTIVITY

FEATURE SORT: Explain to the children that they will be learning to use a sorting diagram called a Carroll diagram. Ask the children to put up their hands if they have brown hair, then ask the children to put up their hands if they *do not* have brown hair. Explain that everyone should have put up their hand once. Repeat for have brown eyes/*do not* have brown eyes. Display your prepared Carroll diagram then ask: *Who has brown hair?* Choose a child and ask if he or she has brown eyes? If the answer is yes write her name in the first 'box'. If the answer is no write her name in the second box. Ask: *Who does not have brown hair?* Choose a child and repeat the process. In groups of five or six the children then write the labels on to their Carroll diagram and complete it for their group, writing each child's name in the correct box. They then work with a second group and add the data about those children to their diagram. If time, they decide on their own criteria for a Carroll diagram, eg blue eyes, black hair etc.

DIFFERENTIATION

More able: include data from more than two groups. Devise other Carroll diagrams using different criteria.
Less able: may need adult help initially. Give them a labelled diagram to use.

PLENARY

Each group should present its diagram. Ask questions such as: *How many children have brown hair and brown eyes? How many children have brown hair and not brown eyes? Do we know how many children have brown hair and blue eyes?* (No). Compare the diagrams and discuss any differences.

LESSON 2

Repeat the **Oral and mental starter** from Lesson 1. In the **Main teaching activity** repeat the process from Lesson 1, but this time for NUMBER SORT, sorting numbers using the criteria 'even/not even' (odd numbers) and 'multiples of 3/not multiples of 3'. On their own or in pairs, children complete the diagram with numbers up to 20. For **Differentiation** more able children devise a second diagram and use it to sort a set of numbers using their own criteria. Less able children use the the criteria 'even/not even' and 'multiple of 5/not a multiple of 5'. In the **Plenary** the children tell you where to place each number to 20 on the class Carroll diagram. Discuss other diagrams that they have prepared. Ask where other numbers such as 60 or 123 would be placed on each diagram.

RESOURCES

Prepared division questions for all times tables with single-digit answers; sets of 0–9 digit cards (enough for four cards per child); Carroll diagram completed in previous lesson; copies of Venn diagram with two criteria as shown on the right; pencils.

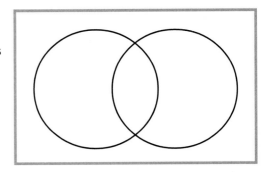

PREPARATION

Enlarge a simple Venn diagram (as shown) to A3 size for whole-class activity. Photocopy at least one A4 copy per child/pair.

LEARNING OUTCOMES

ORAL AND MENTAL STARTER
● **Derive quickly division facts corresponding to 2, 3, 4, 5 and 10 times tables.**

MAIN TEACHING ACTIVITY
● Solve a problem by collecting quickly, organising and interpreting data in tables, and diagrams, for example: Venn and Carroll diagrams (two criteria).

VOCABULARY

Data; sort; set; represent; list; chart; diagram; label; title; Carroll diagram; Venn diagram; criteria.

ORAL AND MENTAL STARTER

DIVISION SNAP: See Lesson 5, Units 9–10, Term 2, but use all times tables.

MAIN TEACHING ACTIVITY

NUMBER SORT: Tell the children that they will be showing the data that they prepared in the previous lesson on a different diagram: a two-way Venn diagram. Label one of the circles on the class Venn diagram 'even numbers' and the other 'multiples of 3'. Ask: *Where would we put the number 2?* (even number). *Where would we put the number 3?* (odd number). *What about number 6?* Explain that where the two circles overlap both criteria must apply. *What about number 1? Is it even?* No. *Is it a multiple of 3?* No. Explain that if a number does not fit the criteria of either circle it is placed outside the circles. Together position all the numbers up to 10. Tell the children to choose from the following criteria and sort the given set of numbers on their own Venn diagrams:

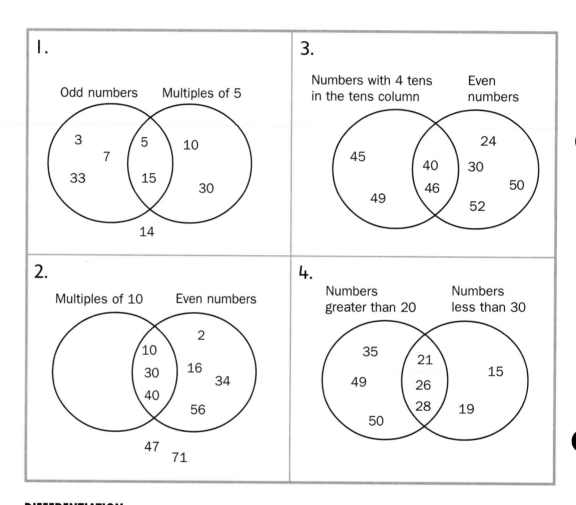

DIFFERENTIATION

The criteria are given in increasing order of difficulty. Less able children should start with the first. More able children should think of their own criteria, and in particular use < and >.

PLENARY

Children present their diagrams. Discuss the difference between a Venn diagram and a Carroll diagram, showing the Carroll diagram from the previous lesson.

LESSON 4 +5

RESOURCES

Prepared bingo cards; computer and suitable database software, such as *Pinpoint*; pencils and paper.

PREPARATION

Prepare different bingo cards with numbers from all the times tables, one per child, and write corresponding questions.

LEARNING OUTCOMES

ORAL AND MENTAL STARTER
● **Know by heart multiplication facts for 2, 3, 4, 5 and 10 times tables.**
● Begin to know multiplication facts for 6, 7, 8 and 9 times tables.

MAIN TEACHING ACTIVITY
● Solve a problem by collecting quickly, organising and interpreting data in tables, charts, graphs and diagrams, including those generated by a computer.

VOCABULARY

Vote, survey, questionnaire, data, count, tally, sort, set, represent, range, chart, diagram, label, most common, most popular, least common, least popular, axis, axes, title.

ORAL AND MENTAL STARTER

EQUATION GAME: Repeat the activity from Lesson 10, Units 2–3, Term 2, but this time for times tables facts, so if you say *6 × 4*, they should respond *3 × 8*.

MAIN TEACHING ACTIVITY

COMPUTER DETECTIVE: Tell the children that you want them to use the computer to help solve a problem. Explain that first they have to decide an issue they want to investigate. Give as an example, *How can we improve our playground?* Discuss how they could devise a questionnaire to collect the data they would need to solve this. Point out that they must have questions with alternative or multiple choice answers. Some possible questions, with their alternative responses, could be:
● Are you a boy or a girl?   Girl/Boy
● Do you prefer to play on the playground or on the grass?   Playground/Grass
● Do you think there should be football every day?   Yes/No
● Would you use games such as hopscotch marked on the playground?   Yes/No
   Then demonstrate how to design the questionnaire sheet on the computer, using a programme such as *Pinpoint*. In small groups, children decide on an issue to investigate, and put together ideas for their questionnaire. The groups take turns to design their questionnaires on the computer and then print them out. If time, they should begin to collect data by using their questionnaire on others in the class.

DIFFERENTIATION

Let the children work in mixed ability groups. Try to ensure that there are children in each group with knowledge of the software.

PLENARY

Groups show their questionnaires to the class and discuss any difficulties. Let the whole class complete one set of the questions ready for the next session.

LESSON 5

In the **Oral and mental starter** repeat TABLES BINGO from Lesson 2, Unit 8, Term 1, but for all the times tables. In the **Main teaching activity** demonstrate to the children how to enter the data into the computer and show how the results can be presented. The children then continue collecting their data. Groups take turns to enter the data on the computer. They then use the computer to interrogate the data, printing out the results of their surveys. Encourage the groups who use the computer first to write questions that can be answered by looking at their results. **Differentiation** is as in Lesson 4. In the **Plenary** session, groups report back their findings. Discuss the results. Let some groups ask the questions they have created for others to answer by looking at the printed results.

UNIT 14: Assess & Review

Choose from the following activities over the two lessons. During the group activities, some children can complete Assessment worksheets 6a and 6b, which assess their skills in: using all four operations to solve word problems; using decimal notation and knowing the equivalence between the decimal and fraction forms.

RESOURCES

Number fans; pencils and paper.

ORAL AND MENTAL STARTER

ASSESSMENT

● Do the children: **know by heart: multiplication facts for 2, 3, 4, 5 and 10 times tables**?
● Can the children: **derive quickly division facts corresponding to 2, 3, 4, 5 and 10 times tables**?

MULTIPLY: Ask quick-fire multiplication questions for the children to show an immediate answer on their number fans. Then direct questions at particular children in order to identify strengths and weaknesses.

DIVIDE: Ask quick-fire division questions for the children to show an immediate answer on their number fans. Read each question twice and allow five seconds for the children to decide on their answer, make the number on their number fans and hide their answer until you tell them all to show their fans at the same time.

NUMBER CHAINS: As a class, count in multiples of 6, 7, 8 and 9 with different multiples of the number as the starting point, for example, start at 14, count in 7s. Then give number chain instructions to different groups, to assess multiplication facts with particular groups.

GROUP ACTIVITIES

ASSESSMENT

● Can the children: solve mathematical problems or puzzles, recognise and explain patterns and relationships, generalise and predict; suggest extensions by asking 'What if..?'; **find remainders after division;** round up or down after division, depending on the context; use all four operations to solve word problems involving time?

PUZZLES: Write the following calculations on the board for the children to complete:
● Choose three digits from this set (3, 5, 8, 9) to fill in the three boxes to make this statement true: ?? – ? = 27.
● Find the missing digits: 3? + ?5 = 77   9? – ?3 = 48   3? × 3 = 105
REMAINDERS: Write on the board the following problems:
● I make 54 cakes. Each tin will hold 8. How many tins can I fill?
● Each taxi has 6 seats. How many taxis will we need for a group of 23 people?
● I have £58. Tickets for the concert cost £7 each. How many can I buy?
Ask the children to solve them and tell you whether they should be rounded up or down.
TIME CHECK: Write on the board these 'story' problems and ask the children to explain to you how they would solve them:
● Katie left home to go to the park at 2.25. She stayed there until 4 o'clock. It took her ten minutes to walk home. How long was she away from home?
● The football match started at 2.15pm. They played 45 minutes each way with a 10 minute break at half time. At what time did the match finish?

Assessment 3a

Write 489p in pounds: _____

Write £10.45 in pence: _____

Write in pounds the total of five £1 coins and six 1p coins:

_____

Draw in a line to match each fraction to its decimal equivalent:

$\frac{1}{4}$	0.3
$\frac{3}{4}$	0.5
$\frac{6}{10}$	0.7
$\frac{1}{2}$	0.75
$\frac{3}{10}$	0.25
$\frac{7}{10}$	0.6

Write the decimal fraction equivalent to:

forty-five and seven tenths _____

five tenths _____

Complete these calculations:

$4.9 - 4.7 = \boxed{}$ $9.3 + \boxed{} = 9.8$ $6.9 - 6 = \boxed{}$

Put these numbers in order of size, starting with the smallest:

4.5, 8.1, 0.9, 3.25, 6.1 _____

£5, 5p, 50p, £5.50, £0.55 _____

● Understand decimal notation and place value for tenths and hundredths, and use it in context.
● Recognise the equivalence between the decimal and fraction forms of one-half and one-quarter, and tenths such as 0.3.

Assessment 3b

Match the word problem to the correct calculation and then find the answer.

A card game costs £1.30 and a notebook 55p. How much more does the card game cost than the notebook?	55p × 3
Sam has £5. He spends £1.30. How much change will he have?	£1.30 – 0.55
Ali, Sita and Tanvir spend 55p each on a magazine. How much did they spend altogether?	£5 ÷ 4
Sita has 55p more than Tanvir. Tanvir has £1.30. How much has Sita?	£1.30 + 0.55
Sam, John, Ali and Raj earn £5 for doing some gardening. How much do they have each?	£5 – £1.30

Write a word problem to go with each of these calculations. Then work out the answers.

£1.25 + £2.50 _____

_____

£6 ÷ 4 _____

_____

75p × 6 _____

_____

● Use all four operations to solve word problems involving numbers in 'real life', money and measures, using one or more steps, including converting pounds to pence and vice versa.